YOUNG
STUDENTS
LEARNING LIBRARY ®

YOUNG STUDENTS LEARNING LIBRARY®

Science Yearbook

Margaret DiCanio, Ph.D., Editor

Teddi DiCanio, Photo Editor

FIELD PUBLICATIONS

MIDDLETOWN, CONNECTICUT

Young Students Learning Library Science Yearbook 1991

Young Students Learning Library is a federally registered trademark of Field Publications.

Special edition prepared for Field Publications by Facts On File, Inc.

ISBN: 0-8160-2599-1

Printed in the United States of America
10 9 8 7 6 5 4 3 2 1

Contents

PHOTO CREDITS

PART ONE

Life Science

Sarah East, wearing the Sabolich "Sense-of-Feel" System (patent pending) prosthesis. At age four Sarah, using the Sabolich Socket and the Oklahoma City running knee, was the world's first above-the-knee amputee to run "step over step."

EVENTS AND TRENDS IN LIFE SCIENCE

The population explosion continues to strain the resources of the earth, while scientists look for new ways to feed the burgeoning numbers. Despite great efforts to eradicate some diseases, some have reappeared, often as a consequence of changed social circumstances. The lure of doing science was made known in 1990 to the general public by Natalie Angier's book, *The Process of Scientific Inquiry*, about the search for the oncogene.

Animals and Plants

Millions of acres of land worldwide are unavailable for agricultural use because the soil, or the water available to irrigate it, is too salty. Yet the pressure brought by increasing population sizes in previously unproductive arid and semiarid lands, with a concomitant need for an increase in food, is turning attention to their potential use.

Over the last decade, agricultural scientists have domesticated halophytes, wild plants that thrive in salt water. Through crossbreeding, they have labored to make conventional plants more salt-tolerant, and to create hybrid species that not only serve as fodder for animals

but also have the capacity to replenish soils spoiled by salinization.

Farmers are growing grasses and food grains on the coastal dunes near Bhavnagar, India, lands once assumed to be too saltsoaked to support crops. In desert settlements in Egypt and Israel, farmers are using drip irrigation, a technique that keeps the roots of plants constantly watered rather than periodically wetting the whole field, which builds up salt. The result has been sweeter tomatoes and melons. In Pakistan, a grass called sordan (a hybrid of sorghum and Sudan grass) is not only serving as food for cattle, but also is improving land ruined by poor farming practices.

Although current research looks promising, the cost is high. A June 19, 1990, *New York Times* article entitled "Advances Raise Hope for Crops That Grow in Salty Conditions" reported that scientists are in disagreement about which areas of saline agriculture offer most hope for increasing the food supply of poor nations.

Scientists like Dr. James O'Leary, the director of the Environmental Laboratory at the University of Arizona in Tucson, believe that the most promise lies with domestication of especially salt-tolerant plants. Other

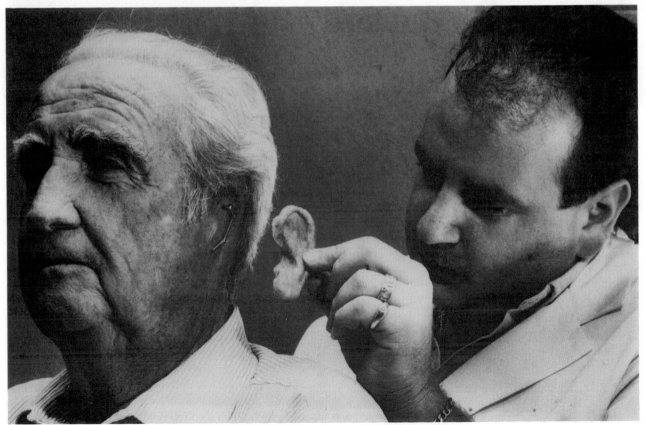

Maxillofacial specialists at the University of Florida sculpt facial prosthetics by hand. In the photograph above, Carl Smith is fitted with a silicone-rubber ear.

scientists, like Dr. Dov Pasternak, a professor at Ben Gurion University of the Negev in Israel, believe that making conventional crops more salt-tolerant will, in the long run, prove more useful.

A report published by the National Research Council in April 1990 listed hundreds of salt-tolerant plants that could be used for food, fiber, fuel and fodder. The report cited the needs of more than a billion people who rely on wood fuel, in an era of rapid deforestation, and identified a number of salt-tolerant shrubs and trees that can be grown on salty, marginal land. The management of such crops requires sophisticated and carefully planned irrigation, a cost not yet addressed. Dr. O'Leary believes that in ten years there will be either large-scale planting of halophytes, or they will have been tossed onto the scientific junk pile.

Health and Medicine

An absence of human body parts, whether through malformations at birth, accidental loss, or the ravages of disease, brings not only difficulties in daily living but also creates the social stigma of being different. Scientists are at work looking for solutions on both fronts.

An August 19, 1990, *New York Times* Sunday feature, Works in Progress, carried an item entitled "Steps in the Right Direction," about an effort to help amputees "feel the ground." John Sabolich, the president of Sabolich Prosthetic and Research Center in Oklahoma City, designed a prosthetic (substitute) foot with pressure-sensitive sensors. The sensors transmit impulses through a transformer to corresponding sensors placed in contact with the patient's skin in the socket of the prosthetic leg.

The designer described the function of the sensors by saying, "The foot can thus communicate with the socket and give the patient reliable information from the floor."

Sabolich explained that with continued use the patient's brain interprets the sensation in the thigh as if it were coming from the floor. In addition to helping amputees to walk, Sabolich hopes that the sensors will reduce "phantom pain," or the pain an amputee "feels" in the absent limb. Sabolich said, "Instead of trying to forget the foot, the patient will be learning to accept it."

Two maxillofacial specialists (who study the bones of the face) at the University of Florida's College of Dentistry fashion prostheses quite different from those made by Sabolich. Dr. Glenn Turner, a prosthodontist (a dentist who develops replacements for missing teeth), and Lee Mintz, a dental technologist, are working to create substitutes for missing facial parts. The June 1990 issue of *Today*, the University of Florida alumnae magazine, in an article entitled "Art Imitates Life," carried an account of their work. Each year, Turner and Mintz help 25 to 30 people feel more complete once again by devising realistic substitutes for ears, noses, cheeks and other facial parts lost to injuries

or disease too severe for reconstructive surgery, typically the consequences of cancer, gunshot wounds and automobile accidents.

When a Florida federal bankruptcy judge was faced with melanoma, a rapidly spreading cancer, that threatened to advance from his right ear across his face and beyond, his choice was amputation of the ear or eventual death. To replace the amputated ear, Turner and Mintz made the judge a silicone-rubber prosthesis. The hand-sculpted substitute, made by using the left ear as a model, is attached to the head with a latex medical adhesive.

Each prosthesis presents a new set of obstacles because each defect is unique and requires not only esthetic considerations, but also technical considerations, particularly in regard to the underlying surface where the prosthesis will be held in place.

Biology

During the 1980s, retinoic acid, a familiar derivative of vitamin A, gained widespread public attention as the active ingredient in Retin-A, an effective treatment for acne, and as a more debatable treatment for the feathery facial wrinkles of age. Retinoic acid appears to have a far more important role to play.

A March 20, 1990, *New York Times* article entitled "Biologists Identify 'Impresario' of Life in Vitamin A" reported that a flurry of papers published in *Nature, Cell,* and other scientific journals had identified retinoic acid as a determining factor in the development of the shape and pattern of a broad array of body organs, including the brain and spinal column, face, limbs, heart, skeleton, liver, and skin.

Although the studies of retinoic acid have been done largely on chicks and mice, researchers are convinced that they are likely to apply to humans as well. Gregor Eichele, a Harvard cellular physiologist and a leading researcher in retinoic acid, said in an interview with the *New York Times*, "It's a good bet that this is one of the body's master molecules." Lorraine Gudas, also at Harvard Medical School, concurred, "I think this is going to be one of the most exciting molecules in respect to embryogenesis [formation and development of the embryo] that exists. It's a master regulator that can send a very loud signal at critical points in development."

Not only is retinoic acid critical during development, Dr. Gudas and other investigators believe that it continues to be important in cell control throughout life, particularly in the orchestration of epithelial tissue. Epithelial tissue is a major component of the intestines, lining of the lungs, skin, breast and other organs. A better understanding of retinoic acid may enable researchers to explain why some cells proliferate into cancerous growths or shut down and die.

Current research indicates that retinoic acid is a morphogen, a molecule that helps cells to migrate and form patterns characteristic of mature organs. Scientists suspect that the amount of retinoic acid that reaches a given cell dictates, in part, the cell's ultimate fate.

This may help explain why taking some drugs, such as Acutane, has resulted in a harrowing array of birth defects, primarily in organs believed to be controlled by the body's own stores of retinoic acid during the early stages of embryogenesis, usually during the first month or two. Dr. Edward Lammer of the California Birth Defects Monitoring Project in Emeryville suspects that the intake of *additional* retinoic acid by women who did not yet know they were pregnant probably disrupted the biochemical precision necessary for normal cell growth.

Although research into retinoic acid is still in the early stages, scientists feel that findings are beginning to converge to provide a clearer picture.

The Changing Environment

One of the most deeply ingrained concepts of ecology, "the balance of nature," is being abandoned. In an interview for a July 31, 1990, *New York Times* article entitled "New Eye on Nature: The Real Constant Is Eternal Turmoil," Dr. Steward T.A. Pickett, a plant ecologist at the Institute of Ecosystem Studies of the New York Botanical Garden at Millbrook, New York, who co-organized a conference on the topic in Snowbird, Utah, said, "The balance-of-nature concept makes nice poetry, but it's not such great science."

A traditional assumption by ecologists has been that nature is normally in a state of equilibrium in which organisms compete and coexist in an ecological system that is essentially stable, that is, balanced. But an accumulation of evidence has led many ecologists to believe that nature is actually in a continuous state of disturbance and fluctuation. Change and turmoil, rather than constancy and balance, are the rule. While a coherent new theory has not yet emerged, leading ecologists predict that textbooks will have to be rewritten and strategies of conservation and resource management reconsidered and revised.

The change in concept has come about because scientists have recognized more recently that communities of plants and animals are inherently unstable due to idiosyncratic differences among communities and individuals in them. For example, a particularly aggressive wolfpack leader might upset an area's ecological balance by significantly increasing the pack's efficiency in hunting, or cause the pack to disperse by dying, also upsetting the area's ecological balance. Even when ecological communities display internal equilibrium, they are often affected by external disturbances, such as long-term climatic changes, year-to-year variations in weather, fires and disease.

Scientists are finding new evidence of constant change, from the glacial and global to the seasonal and local. Dr. George Jacobs, a paleoecologist at the University of Maine who studies ecological change as it is revealed in ancient sediment and rock, in an interview with the *New York Times*, said that while there might be a tendency toward a stable equilibrium, because of these mitigating internal and external factors, "it is never allowed to get there, so we might as well not expect it."

Within this developing new perspective, humans are emerging as a frequent disturber of ecological balance. Since humans have been disrupting ecological systems for a long time, such systems bear their indelible imprint. The question in need of an answer is which sorts of human interventions should be promoted and which opposed.

Archaeology and Anthropology

The new discipline of molecular paleontology may one day answer the prominent controversy of whether birds were once dinosaurs, as claimed by famed Colorado dinosaur paleontologist Robert Bakker, or whether birds were never dinosaurs and evolved from reptiles, as maintained by avian paleontologist Lawrence Martin of the University of Kansas. Gordon Curry, a molecular paleontologist at Glasgow University, believes that this problem might be solved by providing data on how quickly the animals changed per million years, thereby establishing the rate of evolution of dinosaurs.

An April 9, 1990, *Boston Globe* article entitled "Frozen Bone May Yield Dinosaur's Secrets," reported that in 1987 Curry received a package from a scientist friend who had recently returned from Alaska. Inside the package was a 65-million-year-old dinosaur fossil. Most animal fossils are as heavy as rocks, weighted by minerals that settle into spaces within the once spongy bone. Curry's fossil from Alaska was light in weight, indicating that it was in a rare state of preservation, having been locked since the animal's death in the Alaska ice.

Curry suspected that the fossil might retain many of the amino acids that had formed the bone when the dinosaur was alive. Nearly all the amino acids that make up proteins are present in every organism, often in similar ratios. What distinguishes one from another is the precise and infinitely varied sequence of amino acids within each protein. Analysis that took many months in his multimillion-dollar Glasgow University laboratory revealed that Curry's hunch was right.

With advances in the manipulation of antibodies, it became possible to unravel the exact sequence of amino acids in the fossil specimen. In the human body, and other organisms, antibodies are proteins that are formed in response to a target antigen, a substance foreign to the body, often a protein. A particular antibody responds only to a particular antigen, and the two fit together like a lock and key. The specific segment of protein that an antibody keys into is known as a determinant.

The locks, sometimes as small as four molecules in length, often survive intact in fossil specimens. Until scientists discovered how to mass-produce antibodies that would key into a single molecular sequence, it wasn't possible to screen a substance for a specific lock. The mass production was made possible during the 1980s when George Koehler of West Germany and Cesar Milstein of Argentina fused a single antibody-producing cell, or monoclonal antibody, into a fast-growing cancer cell.

Osteocalcin, an antibody manufactured using monoclonal technology and now widely used, reacts with known determinants found in fossils up to 70 million years old. Curry acknowledges that, in theory, once the full sequence of DNA (the carrier of genetic information) from a dinosaur's cells was known, cells could be cloned bearing the same DNA and grown to make the dinosaur itself. In reality, scientists have not yet cloned more than a portion of the genetic material of any organism, therefore the likelihood of accomplishing the feat for an entire long-extinct creature is remote.

Despite the remoteness of the possibility of growing a dinosaur, Canadian paleontologist Phillip Currie, who believes firmly that dinosaurs were the ancestors of birds, speculates that it may not be necessary to build on dinosaur DNA; living bird DNA could be manipulated to recreate dinosaur ancestors. By contrast, the more cautious Gordon Curry only reluctantly acknowledges that it may one day be possible to make a very small part of a dinosaur.

1

Animals and Plants

BEES

They Travel, They Work and They Dance

Worldwide, there are 30,000 species of bees. For many kinds of scientists, bees have long been a source of fascination. Agricultural entomologists have a particular interest in them as a key factor in commercial agriculture. Other scientists, including entomologists, long to discover how they communicate.

Migrant Pollinators

In the United States, approximately 1,600 commercial beekeepers and 200,000 hobbyists maintain an estimated 3.5 million colonies of European honeybees (*Apis melifera*). Each colony contains approximately 50,000 bees. European honeybees annually pollinate U.S. crops variously estimated to be worth between $9 billion and $20 billion and produce about $109 million worth of honey and beeswax.

A number of northern commercial beekeepers take their bees south in the winter to pollinate crops, such as bell peppers, watermelons and some citrus fruits. The hives are moved from crop to crop like migrant workers. Bees are not only hauled north and south, they traverse the country. Each year, tens of thousands of bee colonies are transported throughout the nation to pollinate such crops as almonds in California, apples in New York, blueberries in Maine and cranberries in Massachusetts. U.S. farmers pay beekeepers more than $30 million annually for the use of their hives to pollinate crops.

U.S. honeybees have faced three major threats in recent years, two from mites and one from African bees.

The Asian Mite

An invasion of Asian mites leads to a decline in pollination activities and honey production. The Asian mite was first detected in the United States in September 1987. In response to the discovery, the United States Department of Agriculture (USDA) conducted a survey, which was completed in January 1988. As a result of their research, scientists concluded that if the mite were left unchecked, it could infect 90% of the nation's honeybee hives within nine years, thereby wiping out the honeybees and the industry they support.

Roger Morse, the chairman of Cornell University's department of entomology and a bee expert, described the Asian mite as the world's leading pest problem among honeybees. During an interview for a January 26, 1988, *New York Times* article entitled "Mite from Asia Poses Big Threat to Honeybees and U.S. Crops," Dr. Morse estimated that before an invasion of mites in Europe during the early 1980s was brought under control there was a drop of as much as 50% in European honey production and a significant reduction in the pollination of crops.

The mite, *Varroa jacobsoni*, is about the size of a pinhead, has eight legs, a hairy shell and a sharp,

To attract pollinating insects, flowers secrete nectar. Honeybees collect the nectar and convert it into honey. Honey is simple to store, free of microorganisms that could cause spoilage and easily digested by bees, animals and humans.

two-pronged tongue. The mites are a threat to both adult bees and bees' larvae (offspring at an early stage). Female mites attach themselves to adult bees to suck their blood. The adult bees are weakened, made vulnerable to secondary infections and often die. Research at Cornell University has determined that an attack by even a single mite can cut an adult bee's life span in half.

Typically when female mites finish dining on an adult bee, they follow a scent that leads them to a nursery cell that houses bee larvae. (The honey bee nest is made up of small cells, some hold honey, some hold pollen and others are nurseries.) In the nursery cell, the female mites find male mites with whom they mate. The male mites spend their entire lives in the brood cells. Following mating, the female lays her eggs. Within five to eight days, adult mites emerge from the eggs to feed on the bee pupae (the developmental stage between larva and adulthood) and on the pupae's food. The adult mites and their offspring sometimes suck the bee larvae dry of body fluids.

If a bee larva survives a mite attack in the brood cell and emerges as an adult, it usually carries a female mite attached to its body, hidden between segments of the abdomen.

Those bees that are not killed by the mite in the brood cell grow into malformed adults. A typical malformation is withered wings. Healthier hivemates are apt to evict a deformed bee, thereby condemning it to death.

The Asian mite was first discovered in Indonesia in 1904. From there, the mite has spread to almost all parts of the world. Indonesian bees and bees from a number of other regions have developed some resistance to the mites. However, American honeybees, which are mainly descended from European bees, have had no previous encounters with the mite and thus have built up no resistance.

The first discovery of the mite in the United States was made in Saukville, Wisconsin, at Gary Oreskovic's apiary. (An apiary is a place where several beehives are tended for their honey). At the time, Oreskovic had 1,800 hives, each containing about 50,000 bees. He immediately destroyed 19 infested hives.

Authorities are not sure how the mites entered the United States. Some believe that the source of the mite is Asian bees, who are immune to the mite. Asian bees carrying the mite were brought to Paraguay in the late 1960s by a

Japanese company that was producing honey. Experts agree that mite-infested bees could not have flown on their own to the United States from contaminated areas in South America. They suspect that the mites came to Florida by boat or in the pocket of a beekeeper who illegally brought a queen bee in from another country. A Cornell bee expert, Dr. Richard Nowogrodzki, attributes the global spread of the mite to beekeepers who have carried bees from one place to another.

Despite the extensive damage done by the mite in Europe, by late summer of 1989—almost two years after its discovery in the United States—the mite had not yet caused significant harm. Only about 30 to 35% of beekeepers had reported the presence of mites in their hives. Scientists suspected that the beekeepers might be using some unregulated chemicals to deal with the mites. They worried about the mite's potential to develop resistance to the toxic chemicals.

The most effective, regulated chemical in use in 1990 was a plastic strip saturated with fluralinate. After the bees walk on the strip, they distribute the toxin around the hive.

Food is a major American export. A sharp decrease in the number of pollinating bees would affect the world's food supply and America's trade balance.

In response to the chemical, the mites fall off the bees and starve to death.

Research in France suggested a better method to eradicate mites than the use of pesticides. Since the female mite, after a meal on an adult bee, routinely heads for a brood cell housing a bee larva, preferably a drone (male), French scientists made extracts of whole drone and worker larvae and identified 10 possible chemical attractants in them. Drones are male bees that fertilize the egg-laying queens. Workers build and repair the nest, feed the larvae and look after the queen.

To test the power of the attractants, the scientists set up an X-shaped chamber and placed the female mites in the center. Each arm of the chamber wafted either plain air or one of three types of fragrance: live drone larvae, larval extracts, or versions of the 10 attractants. Each mite was tested individually and the chamber arm that the mite entered was recorded. The mites showed no interest in the plain air or in seven of the attractants. Many mites homed in on the live drone larvae and its extracts, preferring drone over worker extract. However, the winner was an attractant called methyl palmitate.

Guy Ourisson of the Institut de Chimie des Substances Naturelles, a coauthor of a paper describing the study that appeared in the August 11, 1989, issue of *Science*, reported that a piece of blotting paper saturated with methyl palmitate could be simply placed at the bottom of a hive to attract the mites, where they could be collected and killed.

Trachael Mites

Even before the Asian mite made its appearance, USDA scientists were worried about another invader, the tracheal mite, which, as its name implies, takes up residence in the trachea (windpipe). The tracheal mite was first detected in Weslaco, Texas, in 1984 and has been a problem ever since.

Like the Asian mite, the tracheal mite sucks its host's blood and probably also blocks the trachea. The mite reduces the adult bee's life span significantly. Within three to five years, tracheal mites can kill an entire colony.

In severely contaminated hives, beekeepers are likely to find the honey intact, but only a handful of bees left alive. The keepers kill the bees in the severely contaminated hives and treat only large colonies with low-level contaminations.

The problem has become widespread. With the exception of a few beekeepers who don't migrate with their bees, most American beekeepers have had to cope with tracheal mites. In an August 1990 telephone interview, James Bach of the USDA and president of the Apiary Inspectors of America estimated that beekeepers during the 1988–89 winter season had suffered 40% more than their normal loss of bees. For the 1989–90 season, Bach expected the loss to be between 25% and 40%.

Menthol has been found to be an effective remedy for tracheal mites. Menthol crystals about the size of a lentil are packed in plastic bags and placed in the hive. The crystals are only effective at temperatures about 80 degrees Fahrenheit or above. The remedy developed in Texas works well in the Southwest. Unfortunately, in order not to interfere with the bees' activity the beekeepers have to wait until the bees finish collecting in the fall before they can use the treatment; therefore, scientists question how effective it will be in northern states.

Scientists expect a chemical called Miticur, made by NOR-AM Chemical Company, to become available soon. As with fluralinate, a plastic strip saturated with Miticur is placed in the hive. Bees walk around on the strip and then distribute the chemical through the hive.

African Bees

Known in the popular press as "killer bees," African bees (also referred to as Africanized bees) have been a source of anxiety for the agricultural departments of the United States and Mexico for three decades. The African bees were imported to Brazil from South Africa and Tanzania in 1957 by Dr. Warwick Kent, a scientist at the University of Sao Paulo, for the purpose of breeding a hardier bee. A visiting beekeeper inadvertently allowed 26 swarms to escape. (A swarm is a large body of bees led by a queen that leave together from a hive to seek another.) By the late 1980s, the 26 swarms had grown to an estimated 2 million colonies.

The African bee colonies have moved toward North America at a rate of about 200 to 300 miles per year. Scientists' hopes that the African traits would be diluted as African bees interbred with European and wild bees have been slow to materialize, partly because the African bees breed so quickly and set up far more new colonies than European bees. Moreover, when they interbreed with other bees, their African traits predominate in the offspring.

There are several reasons why African bees are viewed as a threat to the U.S. and Mexican beekeeping industries. African bees are much more aggressive about defending their hives than are European bees and will pursue an intruder for longer distances than their European counterparts. Although an individual African bee's venom is not any stronger than that of a European honeybee, African bees sting in such massive numbers that they often cause serious injury and even death to people, poultry and cattle.

African bees have been erroneously reported to produce less honey than European honeybees. In reality, they produce more honey; however they constantly feed it to the enormous quantities of young they produce, so there is little stored for a beekeeper to collect. While the European bees are busy storing honey all spring and summer, the African bees are busy raising their young. A charge that African bees do not pollinate as much as European bees is also wrong. They pollinate extensively, but their choice of crops seldom coincides with what farmers have in mind.

One factor that makes the African bees particularly undesirable for beekeepers who use their bees as migrant laborers is that African bees don't like being moved. If their hive is moved, the next time they leave the hive, they are apt not to return.

If African bees took over the hives in North America, many beekeepers would probably suffer losses in honey production and would be faced with increased costs. With European bees, beekeepers wear little in the way of

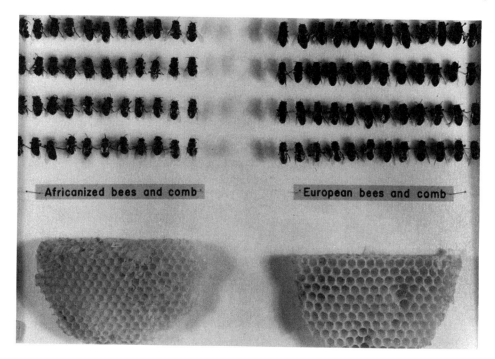

European honeybees and Africanized bees are not easily distinguishable.

Africanized bees and comb   European bees and comb

Nectar is mostly water and sucrose, a sugar with 12 carbon atoms. The bees secrete an enzyme called invertase, to convert the sucrose into six-carbon sugars, glucose and fructose. With a second enzyme, glucose oxidase, the bees transform a tiny fraction of the glucose into gluconic acid. This acidity protects the honey against bacteria. To further reduce the presence of microorganisms and to save storage space, the bees reduce the water content of the honey by spreading droplets of honey throughout the hive then fanning it with their wings.

The honey produced by European bees is fairly easy to collect because of the bees' docility. Below, as an entomologist slips a translucent cover over the hive, he wears no protective clothing. The cover will provide solar heat as well as retain heat generated from the bees.

protective clothing. With African bees, keepers would need complete protective attire. Moreover, colonies of African bees would require isolation of hives from animals and people. The difficulty in handling the bees would inevitably lead to a rise in insurance costs. As a consequence of increased beekeeper expense, growers would have to pay more to have their crops pollinated and the price of produce would increase.

Efforts to Stop the African Bees

Amid a scientific debate about the odds for success, the U.S. and Mexican Departments of Agriculture began a counteroffensive in September 1987. With the aid of an array of biological, chemical, mechanical and social weapons, the two departments set up a program on the narrow Isthmus of Tehuantepec in southern Mexico. The plan called for an expenditure of $1.7 million the first year and $3 million each year thereafter through 1990.

By 1990, the program had been moved further northeast; however, the plan and techniques remained essentially the same. Several methods of attack were put into practice, among them the use of baited traps. An orientation pheromone (a chemical substance that stimulates physiological or social responses) was used to signal to African bees that the trap would be a good place for a nest.

The lures were placed in cardboard boxes about the size of a photocopy paper box, with a tiny hole for a hook at the top to hang the trap. Although bees constantly go in and out of their hives, they don't like drafts; therefore, the researchers put only one small entrance-exit hole at the bottom where they placed the bait.

Traps in south Texas and northern Mexico baited with pheromone were checked every two to three weeks. The checkers could wait that long because normally the bees are unlikely to leave a new nest before three weeks. When the traps were found to contain African bees, they were destroyed.

The goal of the program was to overwhelm the African bees by substantially increasing the number of European bees, rather than by trying to destroy the African bees entirely. To gain control of the genetic makeup of North American bee colonies, European honeybee drones were detained inside specially constructed hives for several days, during which time African drones were hunted down and killed. Once the African drones were disposed of, the European drones were released to mate with queens, who typically lay eggs for two or three years. Hives were carefully monitored and African queen bees were replaced.

Another way that scientists hoped to outnumber the African bees was by producing more European drones, thereby increasing the number available to mate with European queens. Queens lay their eggs on a sheet of wax called a drone foundation. Some cells in the wax are for honey and some are for larvae. The size of the nursery cell differs by sex, with drones having a larger size. The queen lays her eggs in accordance with the size of the cell. By increasing the number of drone-sized cells, the scientists manipulated the queen into producing more drones.

Socially oriented aspects of the planned program were not neglected. Bounties were offered to program personnel for finding and bringing in African bee colonies to be destroyed. Moreover, intensive quarantine efforts were also made to keep African bees off trucks and trains heading north. A cornerstone of the program was a comprehensive survey and collection program, during which bees were collected off flowers and identified on the spot using new rapid identification methods developed by USDA scientists.

Differences of Opinion

Many entomologists were confident that the counter-offensive against the African bees could succeed. But other entomologists, including Dr. Orley Taylor, Jr. of the University of Kansas, disagreed. In an interview for a June 14, 1988, *Christian Science Monitor* article entitled "Taking the Agricultural Sting Out of 'Killer' Bees," Taylor criticized the joint U.S.–Mexican effort by saying, "In order to make anything like this work, first of all you've got to have the technology, second, you've got to have the money, thirdly you've got to have the personnel, and fourthly you've got to have the infrastructure . . . They don't have anything."

While being interviewed for the *New York Times*, Taylor pointed out that no one had come to grips with the incredible migratory ability of the African bee. "We have seen evidence," he said, "that some of the swarms are able to

One of the traps used to track the progress of the Africanized bees through Mexico.

move hundreds of miles from the time they issue from their colony to the time they build a new nest."

Taylor was of the opinion that an effort to Europeanize the African bees would be more successful in the Rio Grande Valley of Texas, where the population density of African bees would be lower and the African bees would be

Without knowing whether he is dealing with European honeybees or with Africanized bees, this USDA worker does not risk handling this honeycomb without full protective gear.

approaching their limit in ability to adapt to the climate. The mountains on two sides, in Taylor's opinion, would serve as natural barriers to further migration.

Not everyone agreed with Dr. Taylor's belief that climate would stop the spread of the African bee. Dr. Thomas Rinderer, research leader of USDA's honeybee breeding, genetics and physiology laboratory, during an interview for the *New York Times*, noted that the African bee had been found at 40 degrees south latitude in Argentina, a latitude in North America equivalent to New York City. He believes that the African bees, which were able to adapt to unpredictable climate conditions in Africa, have the capacity to colonize in colder temperate zones.

Evidence to support Rinderer's opinion was presented at the 1988 annual meeting of the American Association for the Advancement of Science, where scientists reported that African bees could survive for six months at 0 degrees centigrade (32 degrees Fahrenheit).

Despite their critics' gloomy predictions, by late summer of 1990, USDA scientists felt that their counteroffensive had been successful enough to begin winding down the program. By then it was located on the eastern coast of Mexico in La Pesca, Tamaulipas, the most northeastern state in Mexico.

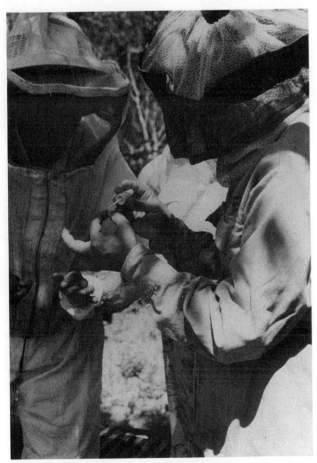

Using white typewriter correction fluid, agricultural workers learn how to mark queen bees by practicing on drones.

Scientists were encouraged because the African bees' movement toward the United States had been slowed for 18 months and been almost stationary for about a year. USDA scientists credited the counteroffensive, but they acknowledged that hurricanes had played a part in slowing down the bees' movement. However, scientists still expected the African bees to reach the United States some time in late 1990 or early 1991. Their predictions were borne out. On October 15, 1990, the first identified swarm of African bees was trapped near Hidalgo, just north of the Mexican border.

The African bees' movement has been much slower up the west coast of Mexico toward the United States than the east coast for several reasons. The center of Mexico is mostly mountains. The bees don't go over mountains; they go around them. And, because they need water, they tend to follow waterways and the coast. Perhaps the most significant reason is that Mexico's west coast is 1,100 miles long compared to the east coast, which is only 200 miles long.

In addition to trying to outnumber the African bees or destroy them, USDA scientists have been exploring new techniques to help beekeepers manage the bees once they arrive. These techniques include new methods for opening the hives and harvesting the honey more often to prevent the bees from using it up.

A High-Tech Approach to African Bee Recognition

Scientists other than entomologists have also been studying the African bee. In 1988, engineers who are instrumentation specialists with the Martin Marietta Corporation, based in Bethesda, Maryland, while working at the Oak Ridge, Tennessee, National Laboratory, developed a solar-powered semiconductor chip that could be glued to the thorax of a captured bee. The 35-milligram prototype chip transmits infrared signals to receivers up to a mile away. The chips would permit the study of the African bees' mating and foraging habits.

In 1989, Howard Kerr and Michael Buchanan, engineers at the Oak Ridge Laboratory, and Kenneth Valentine, a former researcher at the lab, developed a portable device to monitor the sound made by the movement of bees' wings. Kerr is an amateur beekeeper whose work on safety controls for nuclear reactors provided the technology for the detection device.

After a visiting scientist from Venezuela mentioned that the African bees made a distinguishably different buzz than European bees, the three men began considering some type of noise analysis technique for monitoring the insects. By recording colonies of African bees in Venezuela and colonies of European bees in the United States, using acoustic signal processing methods employed to detect nuclear reactor malfunctions, the engineers discovered that the two types of bees move their wings at different frequencies. The detector device the team developed can be worn on a belt and flashes red in the vicinity of the sound of African bees and green in the presence of the sound of European bees and could serve as a cost-efficient method of detecting the presence of African bees within a colony.

Honeybees' Waggle Dance

Scientists who study aspects of bee behavior unrelated to their ability to make honey and pollinate have frequently made discoveries that, in the long run, may prove equally useful to beekeepers and farmers. In 1921, German researcher Karl von Frisch documented that honeybees perform a waggle dance to communicate to one another the direction, distance and quality of food sources. His work and that of his students led scientists to yearn to create a mechanical bee that might be able to imitate the insect's choreography. A contemporary of von Frisch, the naturalist J. B. S. Haldane, predicted that fruit growers might someday use mechanical model bees to tell hivemates the location of trees in need of pollination.

Most scientists' attempts to introduce a mechanical bee into a hive simply angered hive residents, who attacked the intruder. However, success was finally reported in the June 1989 issue of the German journal *Naturwissenshaften.* Led by bioacoustics researcher Axel Michelsen of Denmark's Odense University and entomologist Martin Lindauer of West Germany's Wurzburg University, a research team was able to make a computerized bee that performed dance steps well enough to convince its fellow hivemates to act on its message.

When the scientists programmed the model (a brass pellet coated in beeswax) to dance a message about food that was 1,000 meters (3,281 feet) to the southwest, hivemates flew to the exact location. Reprogramming the bee to deliver a different signal sent new recruits to a new destination. In the October 28, 1989, issue of *Science News*, Gene Robinson, a bee specialist at the University of Illinois at Urbana Champaign, said about the new waggle dance research, "This is the kind of thing where a technical advance is going to open up a whole lot of biological avenues."

Scientists' interest in a mechanical bee dancer is not so much for its potential impact on agriculture as it is to help them to understand the bee's complex language, considered to be one of the most sophisticated systems of communication in the animal kingdom.

By programming the model to perform various dances and observing the effect on the audience of bees, researchers hope that robot bees will serve as a key to unlocking the honeybee language. Although scientists have learned a great deal while simply observing bees, they have found it difficult to discern which particular aspects of the dance convey information. By mixing and matching elements of different bee dances, the researchers can create new dances to see how the bees respond.

Von Frisch's initial discovery of a dance language was received with great skepticism but years of experiments by von Frisch and his students confirmed his original findings and earned him a Nobel Prize. The experiments documented that there were specific details in the dance: number of waggles, distance danced and the direction and intensity of the movements. Moreover, the scientists found that the smell of the food source on the dancer and regurgitated food provided by the dancer to begging bees helped to convince hivemates of the accuracy of the message. Despite an accumulation of knowledge, some elements of the dance remained unclear.

Since the dance is performed inside a dark hive, most researchers assumed that observer bees obtained their information through touch. A remarkable series of experiments done by William Towne of Kutztown University in Pennsylvania and Wolfgang Kirchner of Wurzberg University in Germany in the spring of 1989 established that touch was not necessary. The bees' acoustic sense is sensitive enough to allow them to detect the movement of air particles within several millimeters of a sound-emitting dancer. Thus, Towne and Kirchner established that sound was an element scientists had overlooked.

To make use of this new knowledge, Lindauer, Michelsen and their students built a new robot bee model that included a piece of stainless steel razor blade on the model's back to simulate wings. The blade vibrates at a frequency of 280 hertz, a frequency comparable to a live dancer's wing movements. The scientists developed a computer program to make the robot bee perform a classic figure-eight dance pattern documented by von Frisch.

While the robot bee dances, an electromagnetic driver vibrates the model's steel stainless steel wing. At the same time, a step motor, connected to a minuscule syringe, pumps scented water through a soft tube to the front of the model as "food" for the begging hivemates.

Every 10 minutes, the computer adjusts the robot bee's orientation to follow the changing angle of the sun, which is a reference point bees use to convert dance directions into geographic bearings. The dancing model's actions and the reactions of the hivemates are recorded using videocameras and oscilloscopes (fluorescent screens that display variations).

The robot bee is inherently clumsier than a live bee. Sometimes it sprays food on bees who haven't asked to be fed. Or, lacking in sense organs, it may run over bees in its way, at which point it is likely to be attacked. Michelsen expects that it will take years for scientists to decipher all the dance's components and their significance.

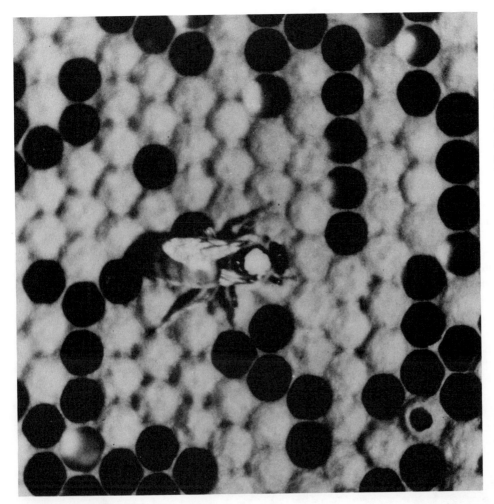

Queen with irregular brood pattern.One method honeybees use for communication is via a glandular substance, produced by the queen, called honeybee queen mandibular complex (HQMC). HQMC elicits a "retinue response," which includes licking, touching with antenna and other behavioral actions that signal that the bees are in the presence of a dominant, reproductive queen.

At the Third Chemical Congress of North America, Canadian researcher Keith Slessor, of Simon Fraser University, reported that he and his colleagues had identified five chemicals that could be blended together to elicit retinue response. The discovery could be used to stimulate the bees to increase crop yields and might prove helpful in countering the spread of Africanized bees.

Cornell entomologist Richard Nowogrodzki described the work by saying, "It's very exciting. All the more so because it is very much in the tradition of von Frisch, with Lindauer [von Frisch's student] and now Lindauer's students doing much of the work. These experiments have required tremendous care in their design, tremendously precise observations and tremendous patience. It's very elegant and satisfying research."

Much Remains to Be Done

Although a great deal has been learned about the honeybee, many mysteries remain. If the European honeybee in North America is to be protected, much more needs to be learned. Research continues in a variety of disciplines, among them entomology, acoustics, engineering and chemistry. The waggle dance may ultimately prove of significance for more than just honeybees.

BIRD MIGRATION

Many Questions Remain Unanswered

Interest in bird migration is not new. The Bible mentions bird migration, as do the Greek philosophers, among them Aristotle. But not much actually has been known about this phenomenon until technology recently made it easier to at least learn the *where* of migration. The why and the how remain less certain.

Billions of birds, 5 billion in North America alone, move north out of the tropics into temperate and arctic zones every spring. One reason ornithologists believe that birds head north in the summer is that the larger territory offers the greater food supply needed to raise their families.

Almost nothing is known about the origin of that annual trek, because few fossils are left behind by fragile-boned birds, and each bird group has evolved in its own way.

Aristotle thought that redstarts, summer songbirds in Greece, turned into robins in winter. Old World redstarts and robins are both thrushes and they look similar. Therefore, when robins from farther north replaced redstarts who had left for Africa, it was reasonable to assume that they were the same bird.

At one time, it was thought that all North American summer songbirds began migrating south when the glacial advance of the Pleistocene Era (from 2 million to 100,000 years ago) forced them south. Recent behavioral studies by ornithologists of migratory songbirds in the tropics have indicated that, while some species may have migrated south because of the ice, most of the summer songbirds are neotropical birds that have always had a well-integrated part to play in the structure and functioning of tropical communities.

The number of birds in transit, and the speed with which they travel, is almost too extravagant to comprehend. Aldo Leopold, the father of the wilderness movement, who was quoted in a fall 1990 *Wilderness* article entitled "Avian Nations: The Patterns and Problems of Migrating Birds," by David Rains Wallace, commented on the disappearance of the passenger pigeon. He said, "Yearly the feathered tempest roared up, down, and across the continent, sucking up the laden fruits of forest and prairie, burning them in a travelling blast of life." When the passenger pigeon became extinct, many observers initially assumed that they had simply raced off somewhere else.

The question of how birds migrate would appear to be amenable to scientific research; however, the results of

Most birds migrate at night, though some migrate by day. Snow geese travel by day and night.

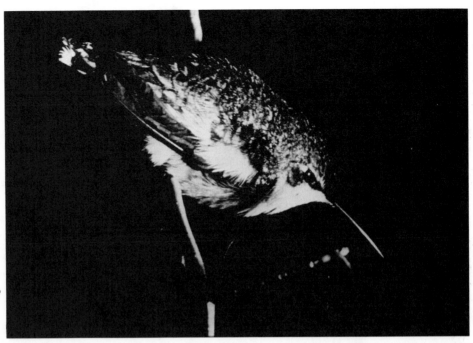

Of the species of hummingbirds that are found in the United States, many have a relatively short migration path and do not travel past the Mexican border states. Only one of the species, the ruby-throated hummingbird, shown at right, lives east of the Mississippi River. This songbird breeds form Florida to Labrador and winters from southern Florida to Central America. There is strong evidence in weather radar images taken 20 years apart, examined by ornithologist Sidney A. Gauthreaux, that the ruby-throated hummingbird, along with other migrating songbirds, has experienced a serious decline in numbers. The data show that the number of birds flying across the Gulf of Mexico has dropped by half.

research have been complex and bewildering. Wallace's article reported some of the research efforts to learn more about bird migration. One such project involved the U.S. Fish and Wildlife Service (WSFWS), which put radio-transmitters on white-fronted geese in northern California and followed them north to their Yukon Delta breeding grounds and then south to their wintering grounds in northwest Mexico.

Techniques for the Trip

Day-flying birds may steer by the sun or on cloudy days use polarized light (electromagnetic radiation whose frequency is in the optical range). Night-flying birds possibly use the stars as guides. Pigeons carry tiny magnetic crystals lodged in their heads that permit them to orient themselves by the magnetic field of the earth. Social birds, such as geese and cranes, follow habitual routes, which they pass on to their young. Some fledglings make their first southward trip independently of their parents, raising the possibility that a genetic program tells them to fly in the proper direction for the proper length of time.

Occasionally birds fly in the wrong direction, though for the normal distance and time, a factor that helps to explain the appearance of Old World birds in the New World and New World birds in the Old. Some observers believe that birds hear low-frequency sounds such as surf over long distances, a factor that could help them to follow coastlines or to make landfalls while flying, as many do, at heights of 20,000 feet.

Impetus to Gather Information

Birds were in great abundance in 17th-century America. However, with the arrival of Europeans in the New World, hunting and encroachment on avian territories consistently took their toll. Migrants, such as pigeons and parakeets, that nested and wintered in human settlements were the first to disappear. By the end of the 19th century, commercial hunters were killing entire flocks with batteries of guns.

A plunge in the waterfowl numbers in the late 1920s was so stark that it forced recognition in 1929 that precise information about flock size and migratory patterns was needed to develop effective conservation and management strategies. The task fell to Frederick Lincoln, a former curator of the Colorado Museum of Natural History, who had been directing a bird-banding program for the U.S. Biological Survey. (The Survey, an agency of the Department of Agriculture, was a predecessor of the current Fish and Wildlife Service.)

In the course of accumulating vast records for the Survey from across the nation on the banding and recovery of birds, Lincoln had been struck by the consistency with which ducks and geese returned to the regions where they had been banded. Among pintails and widgeons banded at Lake Merritt in Oakland, California, between 1926 and the mid-1930s, almost 97% of the band recoveries were found west of the Rockies. During the winter of 1933–34, more than half of the ducks trapped on Lake Merritt bore bands from previous years.

Lincoln arranged to have ducks that were caught at Avery Island in Louisiana transported to the Atlantic and Pacific coasts and then released. Many returned to Avery Island the following winter.

Most migratory paths run roughly north and south. But a few species like to travel east and west. The redheaded ducks from America's prairie states fly to the East Coast and back.

Flyways: Routes of Travel

Lincoln's data suggested to him the existence within North America of a kind of avian nation in which the lanes of travel (the migration routes) from a particular breeding ground to the winter quarters of the birds that used them were "associated and blended within a definite geographical region." Lincoln called such geographical regions "flyways."

Lincoln identified four flyways in North America and delineated them in a USDA circular issued in 1935 and in his 1939 book, *The Migration of North American Birds*. The flyways in the 48 contiguous U.S. states were: the Atlantic Flyway, which extended from the East Coast to the Appalachians; the Mississippi Flyway, from the Appalachians to the eastern edge of the Great Plains; the Central Flyway, from the Great Plains to the Rocky Mountains; and the Pacific Flyway, from the Rockies to the Pacific Coast.

Lincoln conceived of the flyways as funnel-shaped, wider in the areas of the far north where the birds nested and narrower along the migration routes south through Canada and the Lower 48 states down into Mexico, Central America and South America. Lincoln acknowledged that there was a considerable amount of crossover from one flyway to another. Some birds flew south in one flyway and returned home in another. "Except along the coasts," Lincoln wrote, "the flyway boundaries are not always sharply defined."

Despite some imprecision, Lincoln's concept of flyways was widely accepted. After World War II, the newly formed Fish and Wildlife Service in 1948 made them the basic administrative units for hunting regulations and refuge management. Lincoln's concept made it possible for Flyway Councils to shut down the hunting season on a species in a flyway where the population was declining, while leaving it open in a flyway where the population was stable.

In addition to banding birds along migration routes, Lincoln introduced the technique of counting birds from an airplane. Although the technique missed a lot of ducks and had to be supplemented by ground counts, aerial surveys remain a major way of counting migratory waterfowl, and Lincoln's work significantly contributed to their conservation.

After Lincoln's death in 1960, ornithologists began to discount the notion of fixed flyways, while recognizing their value as administrative tools for counting and managing species, such as geese and ducks, that follow established, traditional routes from breeding to wintering grounds.

Nonetheless, the numbers of North American duck breeding populations fell from 45 million in 1956 to 35 million in 1988, demonstrating, if nothing else, the complexities of managing migratory wildlife.

Travel Routes: Migration Corridors

In his influential book *Ducks, Geese, and the Swans of North America*, Frank Bellrose characterized Lincoln's flyways as covering too broad an area and failing to delineate lateral movements from the north-south direction. He proposed that waterfowl move in what he called "migration corridors."

Bellrose developed his own concept, after watching migration tracks on films of radarscopes at U.S. Weather Service stations. He said, "I was struck by the rather consistent directional flow of waterfowl migrants night after night at the same locations. The passage of the migrants was seldom north-south, and at several sites there was a pronounced easterly component to the courses followed . . . Migration routes are at most ten miles wide and are only apparent when river valleys, seacoasts, and other significant landscape features are visible . . . Most waterfowl migrate at night. My radar observations indicate that nocturnally migrating waterfowl cover a broad front, with little suggestion that routes per se are followed."

Military Need to Know

The need for additional information about bird migration patterns is mostly aimed at reversing rapid losses of bird species. However, a December 13, 1988, *Christian Science Monitor* article entitled "Israeli Air Force 'Drafts' Bird Watchers," by Abraham Rabinovich, described a different concern behind Israel's bird-monitoring program.

During the 1973 Arab-Israeli war, the Israeli Air Force lost one-quarter of its planes to encounters with birds. Between 1972 and 1982, there were hundreds of such collisions.

Israel is the locale of the second-densest bird migratory corridor in the world. The skies above Israel become a narrow choke point in the migration routes followed by flocks of birds on their way to winter in Africa. The flocks emanate from a vast area bounded by Germany and Afghanistan. When winter is over, the bird migration traffic reverses itself, and the birds head back to their summer homes.

Only in Panama, in Central America, is the migratory flow heavier than in Israel. However, unlike Panama, Israel is the site of intensive aircraft activity and a training ground for one of the largest and busiest air forces in the world.

Although the dense bird migration over Israel has been known since biblical times, the extent and exact character of the migration essentially remained a mystery. The Air Force sought help from the Society for the Protection of Nature in Israel (SPNI). In 1980, the Air Force agreed to fund a survey, and SPNI established a string of ground observer stations to monitor the migrants.

Ornithologist Yossi Leshem attempted to supplement the ground observations by following the migrants in a light plane. When the plane's speed proved to be too great to keep pace with the flocks, a motorized sports glider was substituted.

Barn swallows may fly from North America as far south as Brazil to spend the winter. From a family of birds known for their skill at flight, the barn swallows are particularly adept at making abrupt, yet graceful changes of direction.

Lifting off in the morning with the travelers, after their night's rest, Leshem and the glider pilot accompanied eagles, storks, pelicans, and other flocks in their passage over Israel. During an interview with the *Christian Science Monitor*, Leshem said, "They just seemed to regard us as a big bird." He went on to say about his research, "We discovered that there was a certain regularity in the time of the migration, in the times when the large flocks appeared and also in the route and height they flew. The results of these findings have been beyond anything we could have expected." The migrating birds, originally thought to number in the hundreds of thousands, are now calculated in the tens of millions.

The researchers found that songbirds and other small birds take a direct route south, crossing the Mediterranean overnight. Given their weight, large birds don't have the energy to flap their wings that far. They ride rising currents of air known as thermals that develop when the ground is warmed by the sun. Gliding from the top of one thermal to the bottom of another, the birds spiral upward on their extended wings. In that manner, they can migrate thousands of miles to their African wintering ground, covering 200 to 300 miles a day. Since thermals require the heat of the sun on land, they are not available to birds at night or over water.

SPNI's data on altitude, direction and times of flights were used by the Air Force to form "bird hit areas," where pilots were forbidden to fly during migratory seasons. The program virtually eliminated bird-plane encounters.

Military actions are likely to have contributed to other bird losses. Ignorance of migratory patterns has made it difficult to pinpoint why the numbers of rare Siberian cranes are dwindling. The cranes, which breed along the Ob River in the Soviet Union, have for centuries made an 1,800-mile journey through Afghanistan and Pakistan to winter in India.

The whooping crane population, nearly hunted to extinction, has grown from 16 in 1941 to over 200 by 1988, but loss of habitat may bar increased growth. Each year the remaining whooping cranes migrate from swampy, conifer country, in the Canadian interior, to winter in protected marshes along the Gulf Coast of Texas.

The range of the common or Atlantic puffin extends from the islands of the North Atlantic south to the state of Maine. Since it winters in or near its breeding range, the puffin is sometimes termed non-migratory. In stark contrast, the Arctic tern and the American golden plover travel from the Arctic to the Antarctic and the pampas of Argentina, respectively.

During an interview for a May 16, 1989, *New York Times* article entitled "Flock of Rare Siberian Cranes Is Dwindling in War-Torn Region," ornithologists at India's Bharatpur bird sanctuary reported that only 23 cranes were counted in their winter census, down from at least 100 in the 1960s and 200 or more a century ago. The crane's migratory path passes through an area where guerrilla armies and refugees have been based. In addition to having their feeding and rest stops disrupted by guerrilla warfare and Soviet bombardment, the birds have also been at risk of being shot for food.

Indian ornithologists hope to eventually go to the Soviet Union to track the birds from there. They think there is some possibility that the cranes are not dwindling, but instead are migrating to parts of India where there is no monitoring. Ornithologists in India need a strategy to protect the Siberian crane, but first they need to know whether the species is on the verge of extinction or has simply relocated its winter home.

Tourist Bird Watchers

As a consequence of the bird survey in Israel, hundreds of foreign bird watchers stream into Israel each migratory season. A similar trend can be found in the United States in the rising number of packaged "bird-watching vacations for backyard naturalists." An April 23, 1989, *Boston Globe* article entitled "In Belize, Bird Watching Is Definitely In," discussed the trend. Two popular bird watching destinations are Costa Rica and Belize. The Massachusetts Audubon Society sponsors several tours a year to Belize, as part of an effort to raise money to endow a 152,000 acre sanctuary in Belize. Many New England birds spend their winters in Belize. A loss of habitat due to deforestation in Belize would decrease the New England bird populations.

As with many other threats to the earth's ecological system, the loss of bird species races ahead of the knowledge of actions needed to prevent further devastation.

2

Health and Medicine

ALLERGIES AND ASTHMA

Ailments That Lend Themselves to Self-Management

Asthma and allergies are the most common chronic diseases in the United States and cause the greatest number of lost school and workdays. An estimated 24 to 52 million Americans, approximately 9% to 20% of the population, have an allergic disease. But many cases of allergy go unrecorded because people confuse allergy symptoms with colds, and estimates of allergy's toll are, at best, educated guesses. On the high end of the scale of estimates, the U.S. National Institutes of Health (NIH) proposes that 35 to 40 million people suffer from rhinitis (hay fever) from wind-borne pollens and that another 12 million people have allergies unrelated to pollen. On the low end of the scale of estimates, the American Academy of Allergy and Immunology claims that 24 million Americans suffer from hay fever, asthma or both.

Canadian estimates indicate that about 3,750,000 Canadians receive medical care for allergies and that another 6,250,000 Canadians may suffer from less severe allergies. The Canadian estimates suggest that as many as 40% of the population may have some kind of allergy, and the incidence is said to be rising.

In the United States, over $1 billion is spent annually by those suffering from asthma on hospital care, medications and visits to physicians. Asthma results in 90 million days of restricted activity each year, 35,000 of which are spent in bed. On allergy medications alone, upward of $600 million is spent each year, including $140 million for over-the-counter remedies.

According to the Asthma and Allergy Foundation of America, 2,598 Americans died of asthma in 1979 and by 1990 the numbers had risen to almost 4,000. A 1987 report released by a task force of specialists blamed the rise in deaths on the failure of patients and their physicians to take asthma seriously. One study found that 88 of 90 asthma deaths could have been prevented with proper treatment.

Despite the size of the U.S. population affected by allergies and asthma, in the view of Dr. Michael Kaliner, the head of the National Institute of Allergy and Infectious Diseases, the average family physician is unlikely to be able to provide his or her patients with accurate or current information regarding allergies or asthma.

Because allergies and asthma are seldom life threatening, medical schools give little attention to them during a physician's training. Even if a physician received adequate training during medical school, there has been an explosion of information about allergic diseases in the last twenty years, making it virtually impossible for the average physician to keep up to date.

Genetic Responsibility

While sensitivity to allergens appears to be genetic, sensitivity to a specific allergen is not inherited. A mother might be allergic to ragweed, a father to cats and their offspring to mold. If one parent has an allergy, the chances

COMMON QUESTIONS ABOUT
ASTHMA

What is asthma?

Asthma is a condition in which there is difficulty moving air in and out of the lungs, because:

Muscles around tubes to the lungs squeeze shut.

Mucus in the airways increases.

The walls of the airways swell.

How do you know when your child has asthma?

When the air has a hard time getting through, your child may:

Wheeze.

Have shortness of breath.

Cough.

How did your child get asthma?

Some people are born with the possibility of developing asthma.

Of these people:

Some develop it.

Others do not.

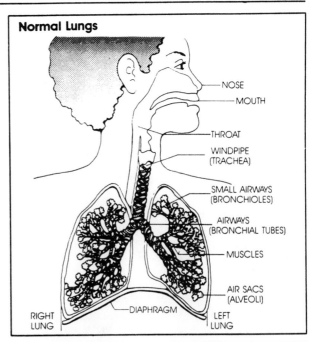

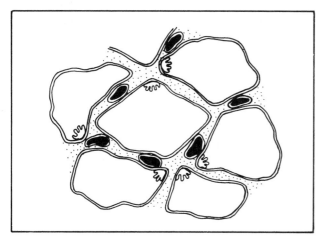

Three hundred million air sacs make up the final branching of the airways. Above is a cross section of a cluster of air sacs showing the blood vessels running through the space between their walls. Inhaled oxygen flows from the air sacs into the capillaries. Carbon dioxide flows from the blood to the air sacs to be exhaled.

are 25% to 40% that the child will have allergies. If both parents have allergies, the chances that the child will have allergies rise to 30% to 60%.

Asthma

Physicians differ widely in their views on what role allergies play in asthma. A study reported in the February 1989 *New England Journal of Medicine* took the position that virtually all asthma is rooted in allergy. Many physicians believe allergies are responsible for asthma in about half of the adults with the condition and in about 90% of the children. At the opposite extreme, in Thomas Plaut, M.D.'s 1988 book, *Children with Asthma: A Manual for Parents*, Dr. Emlen Jones, writing on allergy and allergy shots, claims that allergy plays a role in only 5% to 10% of children's asthma.

Physicians are in general agreement that patients and their families have a significant role to play in handling the disease. In his book *Asthma: The Complete Guide to Self-Management of Asthma and Allergies for Patients and Their Families*, Allen Weinstein, M.D., says, "Asthma cannot be cured, but it can be well managed."

The Mechanism of Asthma

Dr. Weinstein describes asthma as an obstruction or blockage of the airways (breathing tubes) that is reversible, either spontaneously or with proper medication. As the airways narrow, breathing becomes more difficult and a wheezing sound or cough occurs, the result of trying to force air through blocked tubes.

During normal breathing, air is breathed through the trachea (windpipe). The air is funneled into two large bronchi (air tubes) that separate into branches that are in turn divided into bronchioles (small air tubes) that lead to alveoli (air sacs). During an asthma flare, three factors can lead to narrowing and blockage of the breathing tubes. Those factors are:(1) constriction of the muscles surrounding the air tubes; (2) inflammation and swelling of the lining of the air tubes; and (3) increased mucus production that clogs the air tubes.

The air tubes are made up of several layers. The outer layer is muscle that controls the size of the air tube's opening by tightening and relaxing. In the same way that blinking is automatic, contraction of the muscle surrounding the air tubes is outside of conscious control. In the asthma patient, the airways are over-reactive. Dr. Weinstein characterizes them as "twitchy."

The over-responsive airways in someone with asthma react to allergen triggers, such as cat dander (small scales from the skin, hair or feathers of animals) and ragweed, and to many other factors, such as changes in atmospheric pressure, exercise, cold air, viral infections and cigarette smoke.

Asthma is not simply a problem of muscular constriction. Equally important is inflammation of the lining of the airways. Dr. Weinstein compares the process of inflammation to the events that follow scraping a knee. The scraped area becomes swollen and oozes with a fluid that contains many kinds of cells, including some to fight potential infection. The oozing fluid contributes to the swelling. During an asthma episode, the innermost lining of the airways is filled with cells and fluid that are a product of the inflammatory response. Like the scraped knee, the airways become swollen with cells and fluid, narrowing the space for the passage of air.

In addition to the contributions of the muscular constriction and the swelling, a third factor, mucus, worsens the blockage. During an asthma flare, mucus that normally serves as a lubricant increases in amount and, in time, becomes a sticky plug to clog the airways, particularly the smaller ones.

Asthma is often compared to a cocked gun. An episode can be triggered at any time by a wide variety of familiar and unfamiliar precipitating factors, and symptoms can be varied. They may be a tickle in the throat or a dry cough unaccompanied by wheezing. More typically, persons with asthma cough to clear the mucus in their airways. Laughing is apt to trigger a spell of coughing.

An asthma attack can be as brief as several minutes or as lengthy as hours or days. Some asthma patients can be symptom-free between attacks. Others have symptoms continuously. Some have subtle asthma symptoms, such as a hacking cough or chest tightness. The onset of symptoms may come at any age and they may subside at any age.

For most people with asthma, the symptoms follow a customary pattern typical for them. For example, those with

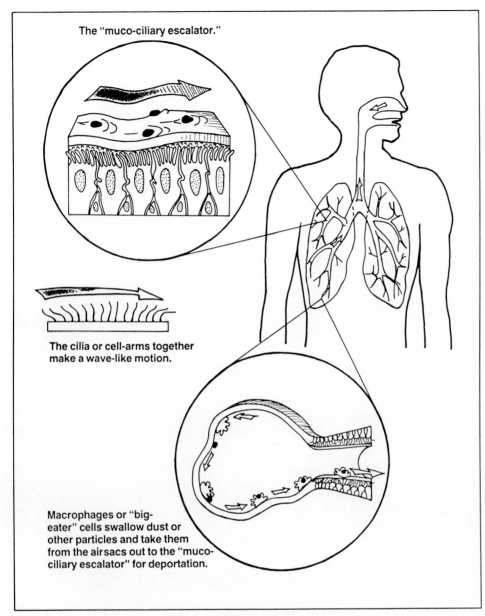

The "muco-ciliary escalator."

The cilia or cell-arms together make a wave-like motion.

Macrophages or "big-eater" cells swallow dust or other particles and take them from the airsacs out to the "muco-ciliary escalator" for deportation.

Lungs have several means of defense. Coughing and sneezing expel dirt, germs or other irritants that have been inhaled. The lungs also have a series of traps and filters. Nose hairs act as a sieve. When irritated, muscles that wrap the airways clamp down, slowing an irritant and blocking its journey. Sticky mucus lines the back of the nose and the airways, trapping dust and germs. Special skin cells that line the airways have tiny arms that stick up into the mucus layer and act like a conveyor belt, pushing the mucus and trapped dirt down from the nose to the mouth or up from the lungs to the mouth to be spit out or swallowed. Macrophage action can be seen in the illustration to the left. Some materials, which can neither be digested nor expelled, are sometimes walled off from the healthy parts of the lung by scar tissue.

Deep defenses of the lung.

an allergy to tree or grass pollen are likely to have their symptoms worsen in the spring when the pollen count is high. (The pollen count refers to the amount of pollen transported through the air by winds.) When the count is high, it becomes virtually impossible for those who are allergic to tree or grass pollen to avoid breathing in pollen.

During a serious asthma attack, muscular constriction, inflammation and swelling of the lining, together with excessive mucus secretion, result in a severe blockage of the airways. Little or no air is able to move beyond the obstruction. The person having the asthma attack is unable to exhale all the air in his or her lungs. The air that has been breathed in that cannot be breathed out has given up its oxygen to be transported from the air sacs into the

bloodstream. Because the trapped, carbon dioxide-ladened air cannot be exchanged for fresh oxygen, carbon dioxide begins to build in the bloodstream, while the oxygen content drops. Without intervention to restore free breathing, the skewed oxygen-carbon dioxide balance can become life threatening. To monitor the carbon dioxide-oxygen balance, blood is drawn from an artery.

Typically, the asthma symptoms are treated with medications called bronchodilators to expand the airways. When symptoms are severe, steroids are used to reduce inflammation. Because asthma can be triggered by so many things and because the level of severity is dependent on a patient's state of health, treatment is tailored to the individual. The effectiveness of each unique treatment plan requires a high level of patient knowledge and cooperation.

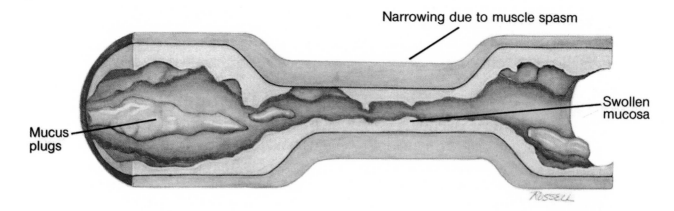

Narrowing due to muscle spasm

Swollen mucosa

Mucus plugs

During an asthmatic attack, the smooth muscles enveloping the airways tighten. Swelling of the mucus membrane and excess production of mucus can make the bronchus undergoing muscle spasms even narrower.

For those with asthma who have symptom-free periods, a spirometry (a breathing test that is used to determine whether a person has asthma) may be normal between attacks. Spirometry compares the breathing ability of a person diagnosed with asthma with people of the same age and height who don't have asthma. If the test reveals a below average ability to breath out, the patient is given two puffs of an asthma inhaler. Inhalers deliver medication aimed through the mouth at the throat and taken in on an inhaled breath. If the airways open even partially, then a diagnosis of asthma seems reasonable, because asthma is defined as a *reversible* obstructive airway disease. (Emphysema is distinguished from asthma in that the damage with emphysema is irreversible. The walls between the air sacs have permanently broken down. The primary cause of emphysema is smoking.)

Children with Asthma

About 7% of all American children have asthma. It is most common among male, black and urban youngsters. During the 1970s, according to the National Center for Health Statistics, asthma cases among 6 to 11-year-olds increased by 58%.

A book intended to help parents of asthma sufferers entitled *Children with Asthma: A Manual for Parents* (an edition available from Pedipress, Inc. of Amherst Massachusetts) by Dr. Thomas Plaut has been given high praise by the *Journal of the American College of Chest Physicians*. Dr. Plaut writes that children are particularly vulnerable to asthma because their airways are smaller than those of adults. Moreover, they are more susceptible to viral infections (to which adults have already developed immunity) that trigger attacks.

In the preface to the second edition to his book (1988), Dr. Plaut says, "Asthma care which was good enough in 1983 when *Children with Asthma* was first published is not good enough today. You and your doctor can now do a much more effective job in preventing and treating asthma episodes."

Some parents fail to recognize the seriousness of their child's illness. A comment often heard in the waiting rooms

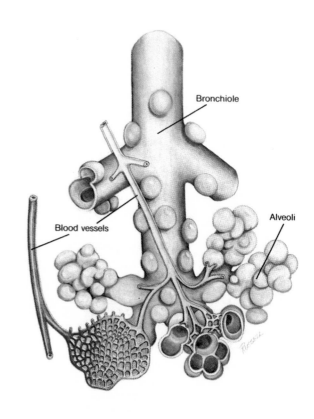

Bronchiole

Alveoli

Blood vessels

The bronchioles open into balloon-like sacs called alveoli, which are separated by a thin membrane from the blood vessels of the lung. Across this membrane inhaled oxygen and carbon dioxide to be exhaled are exchanged. Asthmatics have problems with this gas-exchange process.

of allergy specialists is, "I don't mind the extra house cleaning, but I'm not giving up my wall-to-wall carpeting." The things the parent doesn't mind and the things the parent won't give up vary with the individual. A listener might conclude that the carpeting is more important than the child. In reality, the comment probably means that the parent can't believe that the carpet could make that much difference in the well-being of his or her child.

Many more parents who do understand the severity of their child's illness have difficulty in coping with the child's asthma because they don't know enough about it. In Plaut's view, parents left in ignorance by their children's physicians can only lead to a worsening of the child's condition. The Amherst pediatric group in which Plaut practices cares for more than 400 children with asthma and strongly believes that parents can become expert in the treatment of their child's asthma.

Plaut says, "As in the case of every chronic illness, we believe the parents should take on the role of the physician and the physician should serve as their consultant. The parents should observe the child's symptoms and physical state and make management decisions within limits set by their physician consultant . . . Parents grow in their ability to care for the child with asthma as they learn more about it . . . Within a few months they begin to say, 'Asthma is a nuisance, not a tragedy.'"

When asthma is well controlled, the child or adult with asthma can lead a normal life. When physicians, parents and patients are not well informed and asthma is not well controlled, the toll is severe, and children seem to suffer more than adults.

The September 4, 1989, issue of *Newsweek* carried an article entitled "Getting a Grasp on Asthma's Grip." The article described the "Asthma Report," the results of a survey done by Research & Forecasts, a public-opinion consulting company. The survey, the largest of its kind, included 500 adults with asthma, 250 parents of children with asthma, 100 school nurses, 109 pediatricians and 204 other physicians, including allergists and lung specialists. The survey found that physicians reported seeing a dramatic increase in the number of patients with asthma. The reason most often cited by the physicians for the increase in asthma was air pollution.

Researchers emphasize that asthma is not *caused* by emotional problems. Child psychologist Lee Salk was quoted in *Newsweek* as saying, "There is a great deal of folklore about asthma being psychological in origin because the symptoms are so responsive to the patient's emotional state. It is definitely and clearly a physiological problem with many psychosocial implications."

Despite the fact that asthma is not an emotional disease, having asthma has emotional consequences. Parents reported that 41% of the children expressed fears and anxieties. Almost half of the children felt socially restricted, perceived themselves as "different" from other youngsters,

felt more self-conscious and were embarrassed at having to take medication. Asthma frequently strikes at night, and those children who had nocturnal attacks seemed to be more adversely affected.

Depression has been implicated in deaths of children who have asthma. A study reported in a May 30, 1989, *New York Times* article entitled "New Research Links Depression with Asthma Deaths in Children," indicated that children with asthma who experience loss through divorce, abandonment or death, or who are raised in conflict-ridden families, may be more prone to sudden death than other children with asthma. Although all children who have serious asthma are subject to periods of depression, the study concluded that children who felt hopeless about their personal lives might be at a greater risk of a fatal asthma attack. The researchers suspected that depression and a sense of hopelessness could also be factors in the deaths of adults with asthma.

Although unable to explain why depression might trigger attacks, the researchers had two theories. One theory proposed by Dr. Robert Strunk, a pediatric allergist at Washington University in St. Louis, suggested that many children with asthma get depressed because they have a chronic, incurable disease. The depression may lead them to skip medications. The other theory, proposed by Dr. Bruce Miller, a psychiatrist at the National Jewish Center for Immunology and Respiratory Medicine in Denver, suggested that depression might foster a chemical imbalance in the nervous system that aggravated the asthma symptoms.

Exercise and Asthma

According to Dr. Plaut, exercise is the most common trigger of asthma. Some researchers believe that exercise triggers asthma by lowering the temperature of the bronchioles, as air is exchanged rapidly. Eighty percent of the people with asthma experience some degree of chest tightness, cough or wheeze when they exercise. Dr. Plaut believes that the symptoms brought on by exercise signify that the person's treatment plan is not adequate to control the symptoms and needs revision.

Except in the midst of an attack, in Dr. Plaut's view, asthma should not limit the activity of any child, and he or she should be back to normal activity within a week after an attack. The children with asthma in Plaut's practice compete in hockey, soccer, cross-country running, basketball and tennis. He points out that Bill Koch, who won an Olympic silver medal in cross-country skiing, has asthma and is able to compete by using adequate medication to guard against the dual triggers of exercise and cold air. Another highly successful Olympic medalist with asthma is track star Jackie Joyner-Kersee.

Doctors often recommend swimming as the proper sport for children with asthma. Swimming involves exertion of short duration and it takes place at a temperature and humidity unlikely to trigger an asthma episode. Plaut believes that children with asthma can participate in many other sports as well. In his opinion, the athlete and not the physician should pick the sport, provided that the physician and the athlete have worked out a good treatment plan.

Circadian Rhythms of Lung Function

Circadian rhythms refer to the waxing and waning of bodily functions that take place during approximately 24-hour intervals. Circadian rhythms are seldom raised in discussions of asthma. Yet, according to Dr. Richard Martin, the director of the sleep laboratory at the National Jewish Center for Immunology and Respiratory Medicine in Denver, Colorado, the circadian rhythms of lung function change greatly from day to night.

As many as 75% of the 12 million people with asthma in the United States experience increased symptoms at night. Their lung functioning may decrease as much as 60%. Moreover, the time of day that a person with asthma may encounter an attack-provoking allergen can greatly influence the reaction. The reaction is apt to be stronger and long-lasting at night. Knowing that timing has a significant effect on the control of symptoms should greatly improve patients' ability to handle their asthma.

Allergies

A simple definition of an allergy might be an overly sensitive reaction to substances that under ordinary circumstances would not produce such a reaction in most people. Routinely, people take into their bodies substances that are foreign to their own chemical makeup: food, drink, drugs, and substances that are inhaled, touched or injected. Normally, the body either excretes matter taken in as unusable or breaks it down in order to assimilate it. In an allergic person, it attempts to fight off the foreign substances as if they were invaders such as viruses or bacteria.

Antibodies are generally thought of as the body's defense system for fighting infections. (Antibodies are molecules made by lymph tissue to defend the body against bacteria, viruses or other foreign bodies.) In a person with allergies, the body's defense system reacts to substances in the

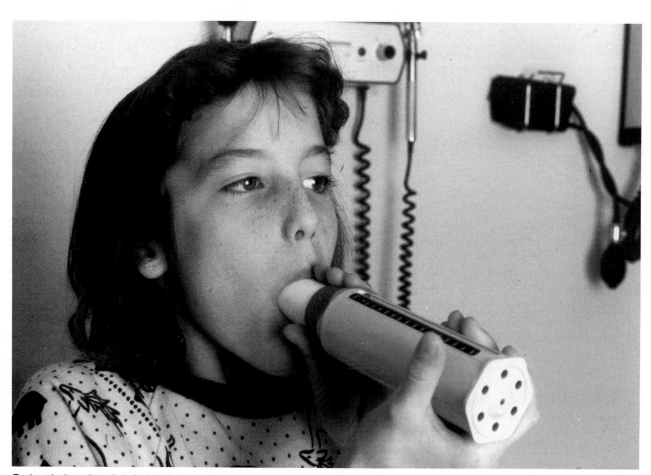

Patient being given inhalation therapy.

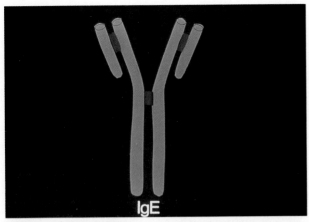

Diagram of IgE formation.

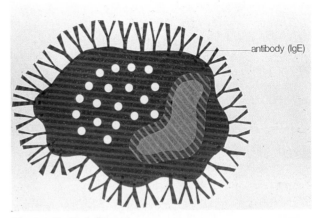

Mast cell with IgE.

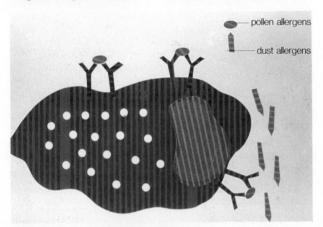

pollen allergens

dust allergens

Pollen joining IgE on a mast cell.

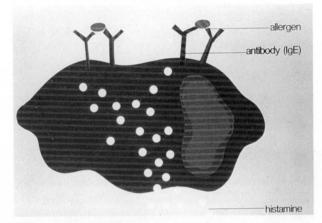

allergen

antibody (IgE)

histamine

Mast cell degranulating.

The body becomes allergic to a substance, referred to as an allergen, by producing a blood protein known as IgE antibody. Each antibody is specific for and will react with only one allergen. Up to 500,000 IgE antibodies can attach themselves to mast cells, awaiting an encounter with an allergen. When an encounter takes place, the antibodies signal the mast cells to release irritating chemicals, such as histamine. These chemicals cause the symptoms that allergy sufferers experience.

environment, referred to as allergens, such as dust, pollen or animal dander, as if they were a serious infectious threat.

A chain of events happens when an allergy-prone person is first exposed to an allergen. Cells called mast cells are found throughout the body but tend to be concentrated in the nose, eyes, lungs, skin and intestines. In people who have allergies, attached to each mast cell is an antibody, a class of proteins called immunoglobulin E or IgE. The initial encounter with an allergen normally elicits no noticeable symptoms. However, after additional exposures, the immune system reacts by flooding into the bloodstream an enormous amount of IgEs custom fit, like a lock to a key, that attach to the provoking substance. The exact form of reaction depends on how the allergen enters the body and the degree of sensitivity. In the most typical reaction the antibodies arrange themselves on the outer surface of mast cells that line the nose, throat and lungs. When the allergen touches those tissues, the IgE antibodies catch the allergen and signal the mast cells to release histamine (a compound found in all cells) and other chemical substances. The

released chemicals dilate blood vessels, making tissues swell and leak fluid. Sneezing and runny eyes, the classic allergy response, are the most common result.

Inhaled Allergen

The most common cause of allergy-related problems is inhaled substances. The best known is hay fever, or rhinitis, which is not caused by hay and does not produce a fever. Hay fever affects the nose, eyes and throat, and produces an excess of mucus. Wind-borne pollens, usually from trees, grasses and weeds, particularly ragweed, are a frequent source.

Rhinitis can be caused by other airborne allergens as well. Mold, a common culprit, grows in damp leaves and grass, soil, damp basements, books, potted plants, carpets and inside air conditioners and humidifiers, to mention only a few. Most mold originates outdoors and is apt to be in the air from the time the snow leaves the ground until it returns

Skin tests can be administered to try to determine if and to what a patient might be allergic. Substances are injected beneath the skin and observed for a reaction.

with the first substantial fall of the year. Mowing the lawn stirs up molds and makes them become airborne.

Another frequent source of inhalant allergen is any animal with fur or feathers. Until recently, the problem was thought to stem from the fur or feathers alone, but recent research has established that the animal's saliva and skin shed dander, small scales that trigger an allergic reaction; even dogs without hair are sources of dander.

Another very common inhaled allergen is house dust. House dust is made up of a number of components, but the main allergenic component is the excretions of dust mites. Excretions from cockroaches can also make dust allergenic.

Allergy Testing

Despite enormous advances in recent years, allergists still lack a single, simple test that will pinpoint the substances to which an individual is allergic. An allergy first is investigated by compiling a detailed family history, an environmental assessment and laboratory studies that include a blood count and measurement of IgE. Under specific circumstances, a variety of other tests may be performed.

Finally, skin tests are conducted. Inhalant allergens can be relatively accurately identified through skin tests involving small amounts of suspected allergens that are either pricked, scratched on or injected into the skin. Typically, at sites where a substance introduced is an allergen, the site soon thereafter becomes reddened and swollen to varying degrees.

The tests are not foolproof, however. A swollen, red, itchy spot indicates sensitivity and irritation of the skin but not necessarily allergy, and the nose, throat and lungs may be unaffected. Dr. Harold Nelson of the National Jewish Center for Immunology and Respiratory Medicine and his colleagues tested 100 allergy-free volunteers. Forty reacted to one or more skin tests. As a consequence, Dr. Nelson said, "A skin test is a useful lab test, but that's all." Therefore, when the test contradicts the patient's history of symptoms, the test should be ignored.

Allergies That Affect the Skin

Skin allergies are less common and less understood than those of the nose and lungs. There are three typical skin problems triggered by allergies: hives, eczema and contact allergy.

Hives (urticaria) are itchy bumps that come and go. The individual hives are red, swollen blotches that generally last only hours. They spread more when they are scratched. Giant hives can be blotches the size of dinner plates. Although they are very uncomfortable, hives are only dangerous when they occur internally, as they sometimes do with a severe food allergy. Although hives usually last for only a short time, on rare occasions they last for months or years.

Eczema typically develops in childhood. The skin becomes extremely itchy and the person afflicted is apt to scratch until the skin bleeds. The areas most affected are the folds of the skin, particularly the bend on the inside of the elbow and the bend on the back of the knee. Food allergens often trigger hives or eczema. Eczema in infants is often associated with an allergy to food, including milk.

Contact dermatitis is the term used for skin allergies caused by the touch of substances such as poison ivy, poison oak and poison sumac; certain chemicals and metals such as the nickel often found in earrings; and by various drugs and cosmetics. With this type of allergy, white blood cells become sensitized to do battle with substances perceived as threatening and disrupt the functioning of the skin, resulting in an itch and/or rash.

Food Allergens

Food allergens are probably the most individual and controversial of allergens. The most frequent allergens are related to the most common foods in North American diets: wheat, milk, eggs and corn. Because such foods are ingredients in many other products, avoidance of these foods is difficult. For example, an allergy to milk not only means avoidance of dairy products, it means avoidance of such products as lunch meat, hot dogs, salad dressing and cream soups or gravies.

Food allergies generally cause gastrointestinal (stomach and bowel) symptoms, including: pain, nausea, bloating, vomiting, diarrhea and/or constipation. Food allergies have also been implicated in skin reactions, and allergy sufferers often find that food reactions trigger their asthma or rhinitis.

Some physicians who call themselves clinical ecologists claim that as many as half of the American population are allergic to one or more foods. These allergies they say can be blamed for a range of complaints from intermittent fatigue and bloating to chronic migraine headaches and arthritis. In a national survey, 43% of 3,300 adults queried reported that they experienced adverse reactions to foods.

Traditional allergists insist that only 2% to 5% of children and fewer than 1 in 100 adults are truly allergic to foods. Moreover, they claim that in the rare cases of allergy, fewer than a dozen foods are the culprits. Mainstream allergists and immunologists maintain that people who are truly allergic to a food substance experience allergic responses similar to those of a person allergic to ragweed or animal dander. The immune system reacts, usually within an hour, with an increase in blood levels of IgE and the onset of typical symptoms—runny nose, hives or, in the extreme, anaphylaxis (life-threatening allergic shock).

Clinical ecologists, in contrast to the allergists, believe that thousands of chemicals in the environment, ranging from those found in many foods to others found in polluted air and water, are frequent sources of reactions they consider to be allergic. They claim that adverse reactions to food may not occur until hours or even days after eating the substance. Nor, in their view, does the reaction have to fit the pattern of hives or wheezing. Moreover, they believe that chronic fatigue and stomach cramps may represent allergic reactions to food.

Traditional allergists acknowledge that in rare cases some people are "sensitive" to various foods for reasons that have nothing to do with allergy. For example, between 5% and 10% of children lack the enzyme needed to digest the sugar in cow's milk, therefore milk causes those children to have gas, stomach upset and diarrhea. The debate is likely to continue until definitive studies offer proof to support one view or the other.

The person with gastrointestinal problems in search of help is unlikely to care about the distinctions between allergy and sensitivity. Numerous reports published in European and Israeli journals seem to support the clinical ecologists' contentions; however, American studies have not supported them.

Exercise as an Allergen

The existence of exercise-related allergies was first reported in a published study in 1980, in which Dr. Albert Sheffer, the director of the allergy clinic at Brigham and Women's Hospital in Boston, and his colleague, Dr. K. Frank Austen, chief of rheumatology and immunology at Brigham and Women's, concluded that 10 of Sheffer's patients were allergic to exercise.

Sheffer's interest began in 1969 when one of his patients told him that he broke out in hives and developed a nose drip only when he exercised. Over the next 10 years, 15 people reported similar symptoms. Sheffer ruled out asthma because there was no evidence of disturbed pulmonary (lung) function or bronchial spasms.

In a study published in 1989, Sheffer, together with Dr. Mathew Liang of Brigham and Women's Hospital and Dr. John Wade of Vancouver General Hospital in Canada, reported that the researchers had found 700 people in the United States and Canada who reported exercise-related symptoms to allergists. Of those cases, 199 had been confirmed by other researchers. Almost everyone known to be allergic to exercise is an active athlete. Dedicated athletes typically wait until allergy attack subsides and resume exercising. Perhaps if they had an attack every time they exercised, they would stop.

Proving the existence of the exercise-allergy link took years because of the intermittent nature of the severe reactions. To prove the allergy was real, Sheffer set up a treadmill experiment in 1982 with seven patients dressed in plastic suits to retain body heat. Blood samples taken before the patients began running showed no histamines present. During the exertion, four of the seven developed hives, and blood samples taken after the exercise showed the presence of significant amounts of histamines. Another experiment two years later led to a similar finding.

The question of why the allergy reaction does not appear every time the athlete exerts himself or herself remains unanswered. Sheffer, Austen and others suspect that food may be a co-conspirator. Eating certain foods before exercise—celery, cabbage and shellfish, for example— seemed to set off attacks. A survey of 199 people who experience exercise-related allergy reactions found that a warm environment and a recent meal were typical factors. Anti-inflammatory drugs, such as aspirin, also seemed to set off a reaction.

A factor that complicates tracking down the source of an allergic reaction or a "sensitivity" is the cumulative impact of allergy reactions. A person may be mildly allergic to a pollen, and mildly allergic to mold, and mildly allergic to a food substance. Individually, he or she might be able to handle the allergens with relatively little discomfort. Put them all together and he or she is apt to feel miserable.

Indoor Pollution as a Source of Allergic Reactions

Another factor that complicates tracking down the source of an allergy or a sensitivity is the presence of indoor pollutants at home and in the workplace. Indoor environmental factors that can cause burning eyes, runny nose, aching throat, headaches, dizziness and fatigue include radon gas leaking into basements; formaldehyde slowly escaping from new walls, floors and furniture; and an array of chemicals seeping out of cleaning solvents, insecticides, paints, perfumes and other household items in the garage, under the sink or in the bathroom cabinet or bedroom dresser. Smoking is an indoor pollutant not to be underestimated. The estimated 5,000 nonsmokers who die each year from breathing the smoke from others' cigarettes, cigars and pipes probably experienced sore eyes, noses and throats prior to developing cancer.

A clue that there are indoor toxins at work or at home is that the individual's symptoms improve when he or she is away from the setting. Many people subjected to toxins at work find that they feel better on the weekends.

Linda Mason Hunter's book *The Healthy Home* (1989) describes many of the routine toxins to which individuals are exposed daily in typical homes and suggests substitutes for a number of them. Reducing toxins in the workplace is apt to be a bit more difficult than it is in the home. Sometimes a change of job is the only remedy.

Allergies to animals are common. Yet giving up a furry member of the family is not the emotional equivalent of avoiding ragweed or keeping the home well dusted, and removal of the animal from the house may not eliminate the presence of the allergen because numerous traces of fur, dander and particularly saliva are apt to linger. By minimizing their exposure to other allergens, some people try to keep their pets and still remain well. To do so, many train the animal to stay out of the bedroom. Recent studies show that cat allergen levels can be reduced by use of a tannic acid solution. Cat owners can make their pets' presence more tolerable by washing them regularly.

Skin allergies arise from contact with substances such as poison ivy (seen above), certain cosmetics, fabrics and a variety of cleaners and other chemicals.

Anaphylaxis

The most frightening allergic reaction is anaphylaxis (also known as allergic shock), a life-threatening syndrome that, if not treated promptly, can result in death. Translated into English from Greek, anaphylaxis literally means "backward protection."

A July 2, 1990, "Body and Mind" column from the *New York Times* entitled "Backward Protection" by physician Elisabeth Rosenthal provides a brief description of this phenomenon. Rosenthal says, "The antibodies [IgE], in effect, take a biochemical 'mug shot' of the invader and remember it indefinitely. At the time of the next exposure, the foreign invader, or allergen, is 'caught' by this vigilant immunologic patrol squad. Then for reasons that are not fully understood, the patrol squad gets mightily carried away, setting in motion the release of chemical weapons—notably histamine and leukotrienes—that attack the lungs, blood vessels, intestine and skin . . . the misguided immune system attempts to keep out the foreigner by burning down the house."

The attack may occur within seconds to two hours after exposure to the allergen. The reaction typically begins with itching and flushing, hives or a lump in the throat. Even in the early stages, victims may sense that something unusually severe is happening. Their fear often seems wildly out of proportion to their symptoms.

Any of a combination of symptoms can indicate the possible onset of anaphylaxis. The list includes: flushing, dizziness, weakness, wheezing, diarrhea, hives, itchy eyes, nasal obstruction, tingling lips, itchy skin, constricted throat, shortness of breath, vomiting, shock, total respiratory failure, a drop in blood pressure and loss of consciousness. Severe anaphylaxis may combine these several symptoms.

The causes of anaphylaxis are limited. The usual culprits are: nuts (especially peanuts), shellfish, eggs, fish, sulfites (preservatives often used on salads), penicillin, aspirin and insect stings. While anaphylactic reactions to other substances are rare, they have occurred with substances as seemingly innocuous as celery. Those at risk usually carry an adrenaline kit, because adrenaline administered promptly will keep the symptoms under control until medical care can be obtained.

Fortunately, anaphylaxis is relatively rare. Nevertheless, New York Hospital allergy specialist Dr. Gillian Shepherd has an average of two cases referred to him each week. It is virtually impossible to predict who will have a first anaphylactic attack. People with mild allergies are no more likely than the general population. Two factors, alcohol and exercise, seem to enhance otherwise slight or unrecognized silent allergies, perhaps by increasing the uptake from the stomach. Moreover, the increased release of histamine due to alcohol intensifies any allergic reaction to foods or other substances that are already occurring.

The dose of the allergen is also important. In Dr. Shepherd's words, "The best time for an anaphylactic reaction is at the end of a wedding. People drink too much. They dance. And they are exposed to all sorts of foods that they usually eat in small quantities."

Several hundred otherwise healthy people die each year in the United States after reactions to penicillin alone. The incidence of nonfatal reactions is much higher. The march of fire ants across the South after their accidental importation into the United States in the early 1950s has intensified interest in the prevention and treatment of anaphylaxis. Up to 2% of fire-ant bites may have caused anaphylaxis.

Chocolate, a relatively common source of allergy reactions. Easy to detect and avoid, cocoa (above) can be eliminated from the diet. But not every substance is easy to avoid. Milk and nuts are often hidden ingredients in other products.

Advances

During the last decade several new drugs have become available that individually or in combination make it possible to control asthma and allergy and thereby permit individuals who have these conditions to live normal lives. In January 1989, NIH researchers announced that they had unraveled the gene for the key protein that anchors the IgE molecules to the mast cell. With this information, the scientists could next look for ways to prevent the IgE from attaching itself and thus stop the allergic reaction. Some scientists believe that a cure for allergies can be expected by the year 2000.

Current information about asthma and allergies is available from a number of organizations. Below are four:

Asthma and Allergy Foundation of America
1717 Massachusetts Avenue N.W., Suite 305
Washington, D.C. 20036
(202) 265-0265

American Academy of Allergy and
 Immunology
611 East Wells St.
Milwaukee, WI 53202
(414) 272-6071

Allergy Information Association
65 Tromley Drive
Suite 10
Islington, Ontario M9B 547
(416) 244-9312

National Jewish Center for Immunology and
 Respiratory Disease
1400 Jackson St.
Denver, CO 80206
1-800-222-LUNG

ALL BUT FORGOTTEN DISEASES ARE MAKING A COMEBACK

Some Never Went Away

Scientific breakthroughs, such as vaccines, and diligent actions by public health officials have made many once familiar diseases fade from public consciousness. But while unfamiliarity has made many people unaware of how dangerous most of the once common diseases can be, many of them have not disappeared altogether and several are on the rise.

Measles

When Hartford, Connecticut, officials banned spectators from attending the North Atlantic Conference basketball tournament in March 1989 to prevent an outbreak of measles, the ban provided a resounding reminder that the viral disease, the common nine-day measles (also known as rubeola), failed to disappear as predicted almost a decade ago.

Despite massive efforts to eliminate measles, scattered outbreaks are reported each year across the United States. They represent a fraction of the half a million cases that annually struck Americans before a vaccine became available.

Within four years after the measles vaccine was licensed in 1963, the number of annual cases dropped from roughly a reported 500,000 cases to 63,000. By 1976, the number of cases was down to 27,000 per year. A more stable vaccine was introduced in 1980 and the reported cases fell to a low of 1,500. The totals rose back to between 3,000 and 4,000, where they have remained most years.

The closing years of the 1980s brought a dramatic change. The annual count of measles cases tabulated by the federal Centers for Disease Control (CDC) during 1989 amounted to 11,258 cases. CDC's year-to-date count of measles cases during 1990 was 18,991 on August 25, 1990, a substantial rise over the total number of cases in all of 1989.

Outside of the United States, among the global population of children, measles is the second most prevalent cause of disease after diarrheal disease. In recent years in the United States, scattered local outbursts of measles have been sufficiently large that Lisa Belkin, the author of a February 26, 1989, *New York Times* article entitled "Measles, Not a Thing of the Past, Threatens a Vast Resurgence in '89," made the comment, "Every year at least one American city finds itself overwhelmed by measles, a disease many people thought had gone away."

An August 20, 1990, *U.S. News and World Report* article entitled "Return of a Childhood Killer" pointed out that besides Houston, three other cities, Dallas, Los Angeles and Chicago, had suffered measles epidemics in 1989. Houston had 1,000 cases and public health officials suspected that as many as 3,000 cases might have been unreported.

Cases go unreported when the child is not taken to a health care provider. Dr. Rob Lincoln of CDC's Division of Immunization said in a telephone interview on September 10, 1990, that measles is a disease with clearly recognizable symptoms and tends to get reported accurately if it is seen by a health care provider.

The disease is spread by droplets from the nose, throat or mouth during a period from two to four days before a rash appears, until two to five days after the rash's onset. The incubation period (the time elapsed between the infection and the appearance of symptoms) is 7 to 14 days. Vaccination early in the incubation period can offer protection. The capacity of the virus to spread through the air can result in a susceptible child becoming infected in a physician's office an hour after a patient with measles has left.

In describing how quickly someone with the disease can spread it, Lisa Belkin quoted Dr. Jeffrey Starke, a Baylor College of Medicine specialist in pediatric infectious diseases, who said, "If you put 100 non-immune people in an auditorium and then brought in a kid and had him stand in the front of the room and just breathe for 20 or 30 minutes, then 99 of the people in the room would get the measles."

Measles is not a benign disease. Even in the United States, children sometimes die from its complications; most who die are under the age of two. Measles can cause hearing loss and encephalitis (inflammation of the brain). An example of the seriousness of measles was demonstrated in the Samoan community of Los Angeles in early 1989. Sixty unvaccinated children contracted the disease. Six of those children, 10% of the total, died of complications, mainly pneumonia.

Seventy percent of 1990's cases that had been counted by late summer were among unvaccinated infants and preschoolers, a group that as a whole has the opportunity to rapidly spread the virus through day care centers, shopping malls and hospital waiting rooms. Nationwide, by the time they enter school, 98% of all children are vaccinated. However, federal health officials estimate that fewer than half of the nation's preschoolers are vaccinated before school requirements demand it.

Infants and preschoolers, mainly in the inner cities and in rural areas, and young people in their late teens through early thirties who never had measles, mainly those in high school through college, are those most likely to get the disease.

Babies are particularly vulnerable. Provided a child's mother has had measles or has been vaccinated, the child is protected during the first 15 months of life. Vaccinations before the age of 15 months leave a child at risk of contracting the disease, because the mother's measles antibodies (a molecule that defends against bacteria, viruses and other invaders) can block the vaccine's ability to confer full immunity (resistance to disease). Nevertheless, when an outbreak strikes a community, physicians recommend that even those under 15 months should get a shot and, if they do not get measles, they should be revaccinated at 15 months.

Among those born after 1956 and before 1980 when a more stable vaccine was introduced, a small percentage received ineffective doses, because the vaccine during that period was less stable and weakened in the presence of light and heat. The CDC assumes that most Americans born before 1957 have had the disease and thus gained immunity. Those born between 1956 and 1963 when the vaccine was licensed may or may not have had the disease before they were vaccinated.

Because the shots fail to protect in 5 to 8 out of 100 cases, CDC recommends that everyone who is in a vulnerable age group should get two shots. The American Academy of Pediatricians recommends that the second shot should be given before junior high school; the CDC recommends it at age five, just before starting school, which is likely to become the more common practice. Those age 33 and under who have never had measles should also get two shots, the second one month after the first. Virtually everyone who gets a second shot is assured immunity.

Although CDC has not specifically recommended canceling high school and college gatherings, such as sporting events, local health officials are apt to adopt such measures in some locales, as soon as one or two cases have been reported. Because the spread of measles has been documented at such events, local officials theorize that measles will spread rapidly in the confines of an indoor arena or auditorium.

Buoyed by their success in eradicating smallpox, CDC launched a program in 1978 to eradicate measles by 1982. The eradication plan was based on a theory known as the "herd effect," which assumes that the spread of a disease can be halted if a sufficiently large number of susceptible people can be immunized.

Eradicating the disease turned out to be more difficult than had been predicted. Scientists discovered that a larger proportion of the population needed to be immunized against measles than they had originally thought. The high cost of vaccine and gaps in the health care system had continued to leave many unprotected. Moreover, the disease proved to be more contagious than they had believed. On a contagiousness scale of 1 to 10, experts rate measles as almost 10.

Containing an outbreak of measles is not easy either. The virus can be spread in the few days before someone becomes ill, as well as up to five days after the rash appears. Moreover, not everyone develops the classic measles symptoms; therefore, some children may be diagnosed by parents or caretakers as having some minor childhood ailment not worthy of a visit to a health care provider. These factors make it difficult for health officials to pinpoint the source of most outbreaks.

The first symptoms of measles are usually fever, runny nose, hacking cough, inflammation and discharge of the eyes, with sensitivity to light, and usually mild itching. Two to four days after the onset of the first symptoms, Koplik's spots (small irregular bright red spots with minute specks in the center) appear on the inside of the mouth on the cheeks. One to two days after the Koplik's spots, the typical rash of brownish-pink spots and bumps begins on the face and neck, spreads to the trunk and limbs, and lasts four to seven days. Diarrhea is common. Half of all patients develop secondary bacterial infections that carry substantial risks, such as pneumonia, brain damage and impaired hearing. Deaths from measles are usually the result of lung infections.

CDC officials admit that measles eradication remains a long way off. They hope to prevent large outbreaks and to change parents' blase attitude toward the disease. A wave of children entering the country from Central America, where measles is rampant and vaccinations are rare, could complicate their efforts.

The epidemic in 1989 was no different than other years. The combination of vulnerable preschoolers, at-risk young adults and immigrant children contributed to the spread of measles.

Tuberculosis

After decades of decline, tuberculosis (TB), once the leading killer in the United States, began making a slow comeback in 1979. Data released by CDC in January 1988 revealed that for the first time, the incidence of TB has increased significantly. Hardest hit have been those with AIDS, the homeless, the drug-addicted and those whom poverty or prison force to live in crowded, unsanitary conditions.

In an interview for a February 6, 1988, *Science News* article entitled "TB Troubles: Tuberculosis Is on the Rise Again," the chief of CDC's Division of Tuberculosis Control, Dixie Snider, said, "Most people who are infected with the tubercle bacillus [the source of the disease] have a latent or subclinical infection [one without obvious symptoms], and most of them will not develop the disease

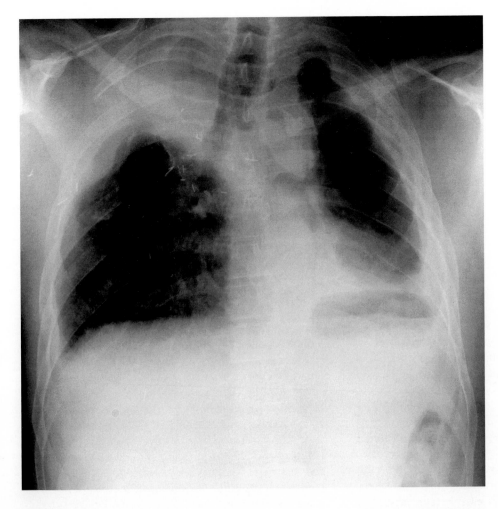

This chest x ray of tubercular lungs shows the characteristic cavities where the disease has "eaten" away lung tissue. TB patients who are diagnosed early and respond to drugs pose little threat to public health. However, the disease remains a threat. Outbreaks of drug-resistant TB have occurred in 10 states.

unless something stresses their immune system—something like AIDS. There is tremendous potential for TB to reemerge as a much larger problem than it is now."

The tubercle bacillus usually prefers the top of the lungs, where it may eat away and leave large holes. Its victims die painful deaths, after prolonged bouts of fever and pneumonia. Tuberculosis most commonly affects the respiratory system, but other parts of the body may become infected.

Tuberculosis was the leading cause of death in America during the 19th century. TB was so widespread that it was called the "white plague." In 1918, according to the National Center for Health Statistics, 118,000 people in the United States died of TB. As late as the 1950s, 100,000 new cases and 40,000 deaths were annually attributed to the disease.

In a June 1990 *Discover* article entitled "The Return of Consumption," the physician-author, Elisabeth Rosenthal, described why TB can catch physicians and patients unaware. She said, "Some patients develop obvious tuberculosis symptoms when they are first infected. But on the whole, this is a stealthy disease. The initial infection is rarely recognized for what it is and can remain dormant in the body for decades, kept in check by the immune system. Even when TB becomes active—usually as the result of a

faltering immune system—it tends to waste its victims slowly. Gradually the patient loses weight, spirit, and energy, until he finally fades away. Nineteenth century doctors called the deadly disease consumption, for the way it ate away at its victims."

If left untreated, active tuberculosis kills two-thirds of its victims within two to three years. However, medical advances in the 1940s and early 1950s brought forth three drugs effective against TB: isoniazid, streptomycin and paraminosalicylic acid. Used alone or in combination, the drugs were often able to effect a complete cure. Isoniazid, a synthetic chemical compound that inhibits the growth of the tubercle bacilli, was particularly effective. Drug therapy caused TB cases to plunge from 84,000 cases in 1953, when a national reporting system was instituted, to 23,000 in 1988, a 78% decrease.

A continuing decline in the incidence of TB, in conjunction with the availability of effective drug strategies and general improvements in health and nutrition, prompted many public health officials to believe that the battle against TB had been essentially won. But some public health experts suspect that physicians became complacent about the disease and often failed to recognize it. CDC data support that view. Records for 1987 indicated that many cases of TB in the elderly were diagnosed only on autopsy, which means that the TB victims probably had ample opportunity to infect others.

Despite the missed cases the incidence of TB did drop steadily. With the exception of 1980, following an influx of South Asian refugees, there was an average annual decline of 5.9%. But in 1986, there was an increase of 2.6%. The 1986 data revealed some striking parallels between the epidemiology (the tracking of the cause and control of epidemic diseases) of TB and that of AIDS.

Public health experts suspect that the resurgence of TB is linked to two factors. One factor is a rising number of immigrants from Southeast Asia and Central America, regions where TB is widespread. A second factor is a pool of people infected with AIDS, who, because of their compromised immune systems, are particularly susceptible to TB. They serve as a reservoir for the infection, with the potential to infect others.

A healthy person can be infected with tuberculosis if he or she spends considerable time with a person with tuberculosis. The risk is not to passersby but to health care workers and family members who spend lengthy periods of time with the TB-infected person. When droplets of bacteria-ladened moisture are coughed into the air, non-infected persons may breathe in the particles of bacteria.

CDC found the largest increases in the number of TB cases occurred among blacks and Hispanics in the 25 to 44-year age group, and the increase was greatest in New York. The number of TB cases among children declined.

Because children would be getting TB for the first time, a rise in the number of cases due to increased transmission would be reflected by a rise in the number of children's cases. Since children's cases declined, the new cases were apparently due to the activation of already existing latent TB infections.

Based on the data, authorities inferred that the resurgence of TB might be due, at least in part, to immune suppression (the failure of the immune system to control the latent TB). Theories about the role of immune suppression TB led some local health departments to compare names on citywide registries of TB and AIDS patients. They found that as many as 42% of the TB patients' names appeared on the AIDS registries as well. Overlap was especially high in New York City and Dade County, Florida.

An estimated 10 to 15 million people in the United States harbor the TB bacillus, and an estimated 1.5 million people in the United States are infected with the AIDS virus. Since many of the same people in the United States who have AIDS also have TB, it would not be unreasonable to suspect that among the 1 billion people worldwide who harbor the bacillus, a portion will be rendered more susceptible to their latent TB by AIDS.

Crowded conditions also foster the transmission of TB. A CDC study released in January 1988 reported that in Folsom Prison, California's largest maximum-security prison, nine cases of TB had been reported over a six-month period, compared with one case for the entire previous year. Because AIDS compromises the immune system and because sexual behavior is difficult to control even under

TB can infect animals as well as people. If it has not been pasturized, milk can be a source of infection.

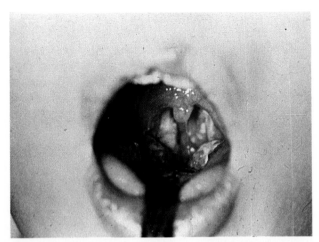

A view of a strep-infected throat, i.e., pharyngitis caused by Group A streptococci. Untreated strep infections can lead to complications such as rheumatic fever. A child with a sore throat may need a throat culture taken to determine if he or she is harboring a streptococcus infection.

normal conditions, crowding increases the potential for an increase in TB. Barry Dorfman, chief of the California State Department of Health Services' TB control unit in Sacramento, said in an interview with *Science News*, "Who goes to prison? Poor people and disproportionately minority groups that have a higher prevalence of tuberculosis. And then if you put them all together, crowd them together, and then you stress them out—stress is definitely a risk factor—you shouldn't be surprised that you get TB."

Not all new cases of TB can be traced to AIDS. In some states only a small percentage of those with TB also have AIDS. Public health officials are concerned that no matter what the underlying reason for the resurgence of TB the growing number of TB-infected people will infect others. In most parts of the country, those with TB are minority groups, the poor, immigrants from Central America, Haiti, Portugal and Indochina, and the homeless. For most of these groups, compliance with taking the medication regularly, which is the only way to defeat the TB bacillus, is difficult.

Public health officials would like to see TB eradicated, a goal they know would not be realistic. To eliminate the pool of latent tubercle bacilli in people who have no overt symptoms would require each of those people to be treated for a full year with isoniazid, a potent drug that can have serious side effects, including fatal hepatitis. The most difficult part would be getting people who felt well to take a pill for a year.

Before the era of effective treatments, those with TB were isolated in sanitariums until their disease was arrested or they died. Once it became possible to treat patients at home, most of the sanitariums were closed or converted into other kinds of health care facilities. If the trend in cases of TB continues to rise, some sanitariums may have to be reopened to care for those who can't comply with taking medications on their own.

Rheumatic Fever

Rheumatic fever (sometimes referred to as acute rheumatic fever or ARF) is not itself a disease. It is a complication following an untreated throat infection of streptococcus bacteria, Group A, or so-called strep throat.

During the 1940s, rheumatic fever was one of the most common diseases in America. The rheumatic fever rate reached 388 per 100,000 in some Army camps during World War II. A decline in the incidence of the disease began soon thereafter for no obvious reason. By the mid-1960s the disease affected only about 30 per 100,000 schoolchildren in mid-sized cities and subsequently dropped to 1 per 100,000. A similar decline took place in Canada and Europe. But in some parts of the world, the disease persisted. In India, the Middle East and Africa, rheumatic fever remains the leading cause of death from heart disease.

In July 1988, a four-year-old girl was admitted to Baystate Medical Center in Springfield, Massachusetts. She had been sick for four days and her condition was worsening rapidly. When she died within hours, the results of an autopsy on the child stunned physicians. She had died of rheumatic fever. Her heart revealed damage typical of the disease and blood tests demonstrated evidence of a recent streptococcus infection.

In scattered outbreaks around the country, rheumatic fever appeared to be back. Doctors who hadn't seen a case in years began seeing children and adults with the telltale signs.

According to a scheme known as the Jones criteria, there are five major and three minor indicators of rheumatic fever. The major ones are: inflammation of the heart; arthritis; a syndrome of several symptoms, including jerky movements, halting, slurred speech, and facial grimaces (known as chorea); a rash that does not itch; and bumps under the skin. The minor indicators are fever; joint pains; and a history of previous attacks of rheumatic fever. The presence of two major indicators, or one major and two minor manifestations, signals a substantial likelihood of rheumatic fever.

The acute attacks of rheumatic fever occur one to four weeks after the strep throat. Researchers know that the streptococci do not migrate in the body to cause the attack, but they don't know how the bacteria set off the inflammatory reaction.

Except for the heart damage, the symptoms, thought to be a side effect of fighting off the strep bacteria, dissipate. However, after the initial heart inflammation disappears, it may leave behind scarred, damaged valves that leak or obstruct blood flow.

The condition normally strikes children 5 to 15. Once a child has had an attack, he or she is prone to subsequent attacks, increasing the risk of permanent, progressive, sometimes fatal heart damage. For those who have had rheumatic fever, physicians are apt to prescribe long-term, sometimes life-long, treatment with penicillin.

Rheumatic fever was already on the wane in the United States when research in the 1950s established that treatment with antibiotics prevented rheumatic fever from developing. A 10-day antibiotic treatment regimen became the standard technique to kill strep bacteria. The initiation of Medicaid in 1965 made treatment with antibiotics available to poor children, and rheumatic fever all but vanished until the early 1980s.

Unlike many diseases, the reappearance of rheumatic fever has occurred mostly among middle-class children, who have access to physicians. In some cases, the sore throat that preceded the rheumatic fever was not severe enough to warrant a trip to the doctor. In other cases, the child did not take the prescribed antibiotics for the full 10 days.

There is no absence of theories to explain the reappearance of rheumatic fever, from a change in the virulence of streptococci to shifts in living standards. In an interview for a March 22, 1988, *New York Times* article entitled "Rheumatic Fever Cases Posing Many Puzzles as Comeback Is Feared," Dr. Alan Bisno of the University of Miami and the Miami Veterans Administration Medical Center, reported that there was no convincing evidence of a decline in streptococcal sore throats to parallel the decline in rheumatic fever.

A common theory among researchers is that particular strains of streptococci are responsible for rheumatic fever. But the question remains as to why such strains come and go.

Pneumonia

The death on May 16, 1990, of Jim Henson, the creator of the Muppets, from pneumonia shocked many Americans who mistakenly believed that after the introduction of antibiotics pneumonia had ceased to be a major killer. Yet pneumonia remains the most common cause of death from infections and the sixth leading cause of death among Americans, killing about 65,000 people a year, according to the National Center for Health Statistics.

Human beings live in a sea of bacteria, fungi and viruses invisible to the naked eye. Many of the microbes are harmless, some are essential to life, and some are dangerous. Among an estimated 500 infectious diseases, no effective treatment exists for about 200.

The relationship between humans and microorganisms that cause disease (microbes) has many unexplained puzzles. One puzzle is why one person may be overwhelmed by dangerous microbes while another becomes a carrier for them but remains symptom-free. The onset of an infection is unclear. The microbes that cause pneumonia, like other infections, are everywhere and are constantly spread. There is no explanation for why someone suddenly becomes ill.

Normally, the body neutralizes the host of invaders that enter through the mouth and nose to attack the lungs. But in individuals whose immune systems have been compromised, the microbes infect the air sacs of the lung. Usually only one lung is infected. (When both are involved, the patient is said to have "double pneumonia.")

Cross section of a heart damaged by acute rheumatic fever (ARF). Recently there has been a resurgence of ARF after decades of decline. A couple of explanations have been proposed: that the medical profession may have become lax in culturing for streptococcal infection and that there may be new, more virulent strains of the bacteria. One episode leaves a patient susceptible to additional attacks and more heart damage with any additional strep infection.

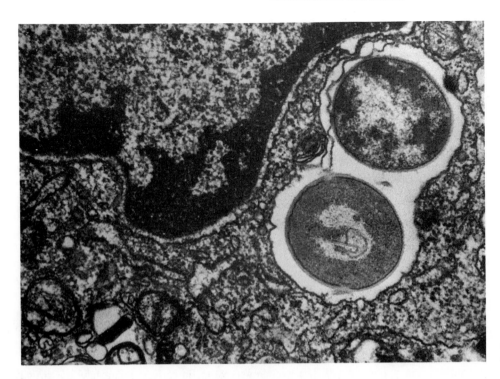

Strep ingested by white blood cells.

In a January 29, 1989, *Boston Globe* "Health" column called "The Peril of Pneumonia," author Madeline Drexler described various types of common pneumonia. Viral pneumonia is typically sudden, mild and accompanied by fever, malaise and a dry cough. Bacterial pneumonia may cause shaking chills, a sudden high fever and stomach problems. "Walking" pneumonia refers to the infection of young healthy people who go on with their daily routine in spite of their illness from a bacteria-like organism called a mycoplasma, and they generally have a dry cough, a headache and unusual fatigue. Legionnaires' disease, linked to the bacterium *Legionella pneumophila*, is usually accompanied by general muscle pain, abdominal disorders, sore throat and occasionally a headache and confusion. The deadly "opportunistic" (meaning that it takes advantage of a compromised immune system) infection pneumocystis carinii pneumonia (PCP) is the most common cause of death in AIDS patients. PCP is characterized by progressively more severe coughing and shortness of breath and set off by one-celled protozoa, which are the lowest form of animal life and are more complex then bacteria, the lowest form of plant life. About 60% of pneumonias are brought on by bacteria usually of the pneumococcal type.

There are striking differences among various pneumonias. Streptococcus usually leaves little lung damage, while other types result in substantial scarring in the lungs.

A danger with any infection is that it may erode local tissue and then spread through the body, a condition called septicemia or blood poisoning. Septicemia risks depend upon where the microbes lodge. If they collect in the kidneys, they can result in a buildup of toxic wastes leading to death.

Jim Henson's infection spread so fast that if he had come to the hospital even a few hours earlier, he might have been saved with antibiotics. Henson died from toxic shock syndrome due to streptococcal bacteria, Group A. His condition resembled the staphlococcal infections that killed women who used a certain type of tampon during the early 1980s. Streptococci, Group A also causes rheumatic fever and scarlet fever.

There is no treatment for the viral type of pneumonia except bed rest and fluids. Antibiotics are used to treat bacterial pneumonia.

Most bacterial pneumonias can be warded off by a pneumonia vaccine that guards against 23 strains of bacteria. Viral pneumonia, particularly the type brought on by the influenza virus, can be prevented with an annual flu vaccine at the start of winter, when the risk of contracting

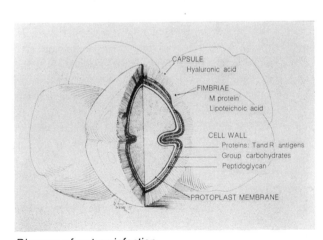

Diagram of a strep infection.

pneumonia is greatest. In the view of Dr. Jeffrey Drazen, chief of the pulmonary division of Beth Israel Hospital in Boston, the two vaccines in concert could lower the annual pneumonia death rate by 30% to 50%.

Unfortunately, fewer than 10% of the population at risk, those over 65, and those with a compromised immune system from such conditions as chronic lung disease, cancer or sickle-cell anemia, receive the pneumonia vaccine and fewer than 20% have an annual flu inoculation.

After AIDS patients and the elderly, children under two are the most susceptible to pneumonia. Streptococcus pneumonia is the leading cause of middle-ear infections among children, which can cause deafness. The current vaccine is not effective in very young children.

The 23-strain pneumonia vaccine is not fully effective in adults either. One reason that the vaccine is effective in only 60% of the people vaccinated is that there are more than 90 known stains of rare pneumonias not included in the vaccine. Moreover, scientists estimate that only 50% of the microorganisms that cause pneumonia have been isolated. Many seriously ill people in hospitals are vulnerable to hardy, antibiotic-resistant strains of pneumonia that flourish there. Much research about pneumonias has yet to be conducted.

Chicken Pox

Chicken pox can spread faster than any of the more serious childhood infections. A child with chicken pox in a waiting room can infect every other child in the room who hasn't had the disease. Chicken pox is about the only routine childhood illness in the United States that almost every child contracts in the first decade of life.

An acute viral disease, chicken pox is easily recognized. Symptoms include a mild headache, fever and malaise (a vague feeling of illness or depression), followed by characteristic skin eruptions.

The rash begins as flat red spots, develops in a day or two to raised bumps, and finally leads to blisters surrounding a reddened base and containing clear fluid. The blisters soon turn cloudy, are easily broken, and become encrusted. The rash erupts in crops so that all three stages are present at the same time. The rash first appears on the back and chest, then spreads to the face, neck and limbs. Swollen glands and extreme irritation from the itching are frequent symptoms.

The disease, caused by a herpes virus, varicella zoster virus (VZV), is transmitted by direct contact with the blisters and by droplets carried on the breath of infected persons, usually in the early stages of the disease. The fluid and scabs of the blisters are infectious until they are entirely dry. The incubation period for chicken pox averages two to three weeks. The symptoms last from a few days to two weeks.

After the varicella virus precipitates the chicken pox, it infects certain target cells in which it settles for a latent period. In many people, it never flares up again. In those whose immune systems are compromised and in the elderly, it may cause a painful skin eruption called zoster, or shingles.

In earlier decades, parents gathered children together for chicken-pox parties on the theory that they might as well get the disease over with. Few pediatricians actually suggest this procedure, but in a December 25, 1988, *New York Times* "Body and Mind" column, pediatric resident Perri Klass implied that it might make sense. She said, "Parents go on year after year waiting for each child to get it. And there's no prize for evading the disease as a child; you only become more vulnerable later." Adults are more likely than children to have severe cases and to suffer with complications, including pneumonia and hepatitis.

"So why," Dr. Klass expains, "in the hospital, are we so paranoid about varicella zoster . . . Well, certain patients don't do so well. We are especially concerned about children whose immune systems are weak for one reason or another . . . Those kids are susceptible to a far more serious form of chicken pox, disseminated varicella, one that has a mortality rate of 20%. Newborn babies are vulnerable . . . If a woman gets varicella early in pregnancy, the virus is known in rare cases to cause malformations in the fetus; if she gets it a few days before delivery, the baby can contract a dangerous dose then as well."

It is possible to contract a mild enough case of chicken pox to not know that one has had it. Health care workers and pregnant women with older children should be tested for the presence of antibodies, which the body manufactures upon exposure to the virus. For those at special risk, there is a preparation of immunoglobulin (one of five classes of antibodies) called Varicella Zoster Immune Globulin (VZIG) that contains antibodies to the varicella virus. There is also an antiviral drug, acyclovir, which has been used to treat chicken pox in patients with leukemia and cystic fibrosis.

A vaccine for chicken pox has been slow in coming. During a September 7, 1990, telephone interview, CDC official Roy Scrikas wondered at the wisdom of using a vaccine since chicken pox is such a mild, childhood disease. However, he felt an argument could be made for administering the vaccine to those who work in the health care field and to children with compromised immune systems, such as children with cancer.

Scrikas reported that a chicken pox vaccine has been tested for five years on thousands of Americans and was to be approved some time ago. It is now expected to be available in 1991. The virus strain comes from Japan, where Scrikas thought that it had been used quite often. He foresaw a problem in widespread use, because of the fact that the vaccine might require two doses.

In addition to the low mortality rate in children, another factor that may have slowed the development of a vaccine, some authorities believe, was the fear that it might give only

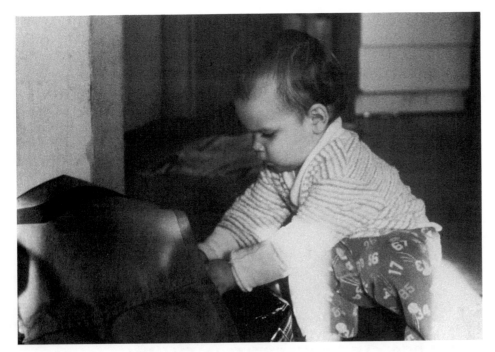

If a baby receives a measles vaccine before 15 months, chances are that the vaccine will be ineffective. Antibodies inherited from the mother, via the placenta, may prevent the mild infection that triggers the baby's own immune system to produce its own antibodies. However, if this inherited natural immunity should wear off early, the baby is vulnerable to a disease that can be fatal.

temporary immunity, resulting in many adults becoming seriously ill as adults.

Once a chicken pox vaccine is available, there are bound to be two opinions regarding its use. One camp will call for incorporating the vaccine into the regular schedule of childhood immunizations to wipe out the disease. The other side will question exposing millions to unknown side effects, when the risks of chicken pox are minimal.

Complacency Is Dangerous

The resurgence of several diseases once thought to have been conquered are reminders of how much there is yet to be learned about the paths these diseases take. Preventive measures, such as vaccinations, must be taken, conditions that foster the communication of diseases improved and policy decisions made about current and future research.

3

Biology

THE PROCESS OF SCIENTIFIC INQUIRY

Natalie Angier's Account of the Search for the Oncogene by Some of the Nation's Best Scientists in Two of the Most Prominent Labs

In her book *Natural Obsession*, science writer Natalie Angier documents how science gets done in two premier molecular biology laboratories. Her investigation was conducted in Robert Weinberg's lab at the Whitehead Institute of Biomedical Research in Cambridge, Massachusetts, and in Michael Wigler's lab at the Cold Spring Harbor Laboratory in New York.

In a forward to Angier's book, the scientist and author Lewis Thomas said about "doing science," "Surprise is what scientists live for, and the ability to capitalize on moments of surprise, plus the gift, amounting to something rather like good taste, of distinguishing an important surprise from a trivial one, are the marks of a good investigator."

Molecular biologists who study the physical and chemical properties of the molecules of cells, spend 7 to 12 years in training and the rest of their lives racing to stay abreast of the field. Over a period of a year and a half, for a total of six or seven months, Angier trailed molecular biologists through their lengthy days and nights in the lab. She tagged along to whatever activities they engaged in: conferences, seminars, meetings, beer hours, picnics, dog races, jogging and meals, which she said young scientists tend to turn into events.

Throughout the effort, she tried to see the problems from the scientist's point of view. She deliberately narrowed the scope of the book and considered problems in small steps to sharpen the focus.

To explain her approach, Angier said,

> I realized that I couldn't possibly draw the paradigm [model] of a Scientist or of a Laboratory. The best I could do was convey the concerns of a limited group of people: Bob Weinberg himself; the researchers who helped lift Weinberg from his early obscurity to the first stages of his fame; and the researchers I watched in action at the Whitehead Institute, who labor under the burden of Weinberg's now enormous reputation and yet who, miraculously, continue to push the field forward. I attempted to put the concerns of the Weinberg scientists in perspective, both by spending time at the competing Wigler lab and by interviewing scores of molecular biologists around the country. Nevertheless, what emerged is a nonfiction version of a drawing room novel. I have written on a small scale, and from a very personal perspective, about a small segment of a very big chase. I don't pretend to have limned [drawn] any universals. In writing a story scaled to the drawing room, I've placed no more emphasis on the celebrated scientists who run the labs than on their uncelebrated proteges . . . senior and junior alike know that great ideas bubble up from below as often as they trickle down from above.

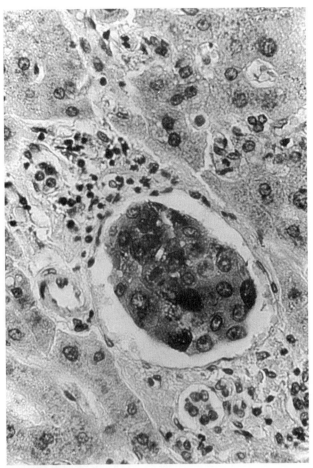

Breast cancer cell.

Motivation to Work with Oncogenes

Scientists who study oncogenes (genes that induce cancerous growth) participate in one of the most densely populated specialties in molecular biology. Despite the fact that they have chosen to look for the genes that may be the key to human tumors, molecular biologists who work with oncogenes seldom discuss cures for cancer.

Their reluctance to talk about cures is complicated and mostly justified. The possibility of raising false hope is ever present. Globally, an estimated 5.9 million people contract cancer annually. Scientists confronted with the question, "When are you going to cure cancer?" sense an unspoken question, "Why are you taking so long and why should taxpayers keep giving you research dollars?"

The scientists point out that only a third of the projects that peer review committees deem worthy are actually awarded government grants. Angier counters their argument by pointing out that during an era of slashed budgets, the National Institutes of Health (NIH) awarded $1.4 billion to cancer-related research in 1987, an increase of 42% over 1983 allocations. By contrast, social sciences suffered slashes of 75% of their funding between 1981 and 1987.

During 1987, the same year that NIH was giving out substantial funding, the General Accounting Office (GAO), the investigative agency for the Congress, severely criticized the National Cancer Institute (a division of NIH) for exaggerating progress in cancer treatments. The GAO charged that increased survival rates (years lived after diagnosis) are often simply a matter of an improved ability to diagnose earlier.

Even though basic researchers do not work directly on the treatment of human cancer, they cannot help but be chastened by the persistence of the disease. However, in Angier's opinion, the real reason that basic researchers don't discuss cures is that medical problems are not what motivate them. If they were, they would have become physicians. Motivation for doing science varies, but the reason most often stated is an enjoyment of solving puzzles. For molecular biologists, the living cell is the most challenging puzzle available. And cancer is an intrinsic problem to the cell.

Looking for a Place to Start

A way to understand a cell's normal processes is to look at how they can go wrong. If cancer is cells gone awry, oncogenes are genes gone awry. When they study malignancy (diseased tissue), molecular biologists are grappling with such things as biochemical pathways, the interplay of proteins, the cycle of DNA division, and the structure of the plasma membrane. Reducing the problem into smaller components is the only way to get anything done.

In the pursuit of components, biologists often focus on one isolated enzyme (a protein that speeds up or causes chemical reactions) from a fraction of a patient's cancerous tissue. In order to work with the enzyme, they select a biological "system" that can be worked within a laboratory, however different that organism may seem from humans. They might set up and vary conditions using yeast cells, nematodes, fruit flies, rats or mice. They point to such basic research, familiar to only a few, as the soundest investment society can make.

The examples of basic research that have had ultimate use in the treatment of human disease are legion. Everything known about DNA (the basic material of the cell nucleus) and the genetic code (information carried by the DNA molecules that determine physical traits) is traceable to work done on an obscure, insignificant virus that infects bacteria. The mechanisms of the AIDS virus could be quickly understood because similar pathogens (disease-causing organisms) have been under study since 1910, when biologist Peyton Rous speculated that chicken tumors might reveal something about human disease.

Bob Weinberg shares his peers' interest in the puzzle. He told Angier,

My central passion, which I realize more and more is consistent with my life, is to look at the complex, multifactorial, muddled system and try to extract out of it a small number of truths. I'm really interested in how one can explain the actions of a small number of genes in creating the complexity of a cancer cell. What excites me are those moments when I'm able to see, quite clearly and quite suddenly, how two apparently unrelated cellular events may be intimately intertwined . . . I believe that someone whose stated goal is to cure cancer will never have a chance to do so. You have to approach it as a desire to understand how cells work.

Unlike many of his colleagues, Weinberg doesn't talk about how formidable the enigma of cancer is. He talks about it as if it has neared solution. He believes that by 1990, molecular biologists will understand what goes wrong metabolically (processing of nutrients) with cells and that the lab findings will have a direct, clinical significance for treating cancer. Many molecular biologists share Weinberg's feeling that an understanding of the metabolic basis of cancer is close, but they are not so sure that it will translate into a cure.

Despite the seeming distance between the lab and the cancer patient's bedside, work that has emerged from Weinberg's lab has already directed attention to potential treatments. His group helped to discover an oncogene that seems to be a primary factor in colon cancer, one of the three leading lethal cancers. The gene may serve as a marker (warning signal) permitting physicians to begin treatment at an early stage. Another oncogene studied in his lab is extremely overactive in certain breast cancers; this knowledge can again lead to an early diagnosis and treatment. A third oncogene cloned by Weinberg's lab appears to be critical to the development of eye and bone cancer. The protein produced by the oncogene may lead to preventive drug therapy.

Angier raised the argument that oncogene analysis might be no more effective than current standard radiation and chemotherapy. Both work by attacking all growing cells in the body, both healthy and cancerous. If oncogenes are as fundamental to cells as molecular biologists claim, how could their actions be counteracted without rendering normal cells ineffective as well? Weinberg responded by saying that there are subtle molecular differences between normal genes and oncogenes that have mutated (changed abnormally) to cause cancer. Drugs could be designed to attack only mutant forms of the gene.

The Allocation of the Director's Effort

Weinberg is a typical director of a typical academic lab. He does not spend his time in a lab doing "benchwork," which requires concentration and continuity. This daily experimental work is left to subordinates. Weinberg lives on the phone and on the road. About a quarter of Weinberg's

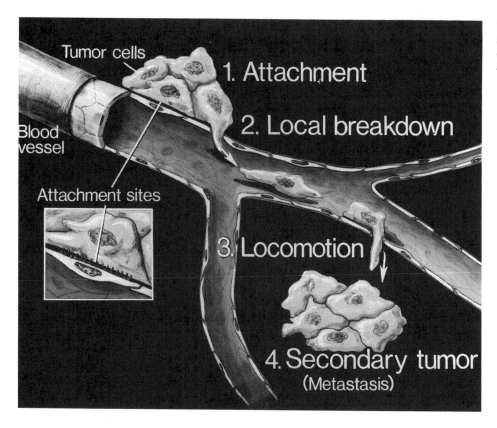

Diagram of the process of mestastisis, the spread of cancer from one part of the body to another.

time is spent traveling, attending meetings and seminars, giving or hearing lectures, and "schmoozing" (chatting with colleagues). Scientists get most of their ideas from other scientists.

If scientists are not gregarious by nature, they must learn to be. Angier explains by saying, "Only rarely does science lurch forward by nocturnal eurekas. A scientist hears what somebody else is doing, relates that information to a recent report in a scientific journal, blends in a few personal ideas, and decides to do an experiment that is not radically different from the work that antedated it . . . refinements on past results can have profound implications. And, the more disparate [unlike] bits of data that scientists can synthesize [combine], the more likely they are to be the ones that push barriers forward."

Weinberg returns from meetings with spiral notebooks filled with the details of the seminars he attended and the conversations exchanged with a vast network of friends and friendly competitors. The notes are legible and organized to be accessible to his scientists.

Another sizable chunk of Weinberg's time is spent writing grant proposals to raise money for his lab. Gossiping, synthesizing and fund-raising would be irrelevant talents if Weinberg did not have a superb lab. He prides himself on his ability to put together an extraordinary team.

Postdoctoral Fellows

Turnover in an academic lab is constant. Once a graduate student receives a Ph.D., he or she must move on to continue his or her training elsewhere as a postdoctoral fellow (known as a postdoc). Weinberg receives about 75 to 100 letters each year from potential postdocs. Because he is famous, the quality of applicants is high.

Early in the evolution of his lab, Weinberg accepted the fact that the constant turnover built into the scientific system of a university-affiliated lab might not be a bad thing. Upon visiting a colleague in Berlin, he was horrified to find that the colleague's staff had all been with him for 10 or 15 years. He described the lab as a stagnant pond.

With substantial scrutiny and a good deal of intuition, Weinberg's postdocs are chosen not only for their ability to generate ideas, but also on the basis of how well they will work in the lab populated with other scientists. Someone, for example, who monopolizes a centrifuge and thereby denies access to others can be disruptive of a lab's functioning and destructive to the mental well-being of colleagues.

An academic lab is quite different than a lab in a research corporation. The major portion of an academic lab's labor is either free or inexpensive. Generally, postdocs bring with them their own income secured through grants from the government or a charitable organization.

Not only are the young scientists in the lab financially independent, they are professionally autonomous. Once Weinberg has agreed to take on a graduate student or a postdoctoral fellow, he must keep them until they finish their schooling or their fellowship. Nor can he tell them what they are to work on, beyond making suggestions. Postdocs can dress as they please and come to work when they please. Because they are trained to be skeptical, they are apt to say whatever pops into their head, however cruel or tactless. Their time is their own. Demands and threats would be contrary to the norm of academic freedom and, in the long run, undermine the lab.

On the other hand, a postdoctoral fellowship is the most critical and intense period of a scientist's career. Postdocs must constantly assess their progress and weigh the riskiness of a project against its potential payoff. The Nobel Prize–winning, Brazilian-born British biologist Sir Peter Medawar said in his book *Advice to a Young Scientist,* "It can be said with complete confidence that any scientist of any age who wants to make important discoveries must study important problems."

Young scientists must publish. A small paper on a small result is better than no paper on a cosmic effort. Moreover, at a trendsetting lab, such as the Whitehead Institute, postdocs must do something to set themselves apart. They have to do something original, a project with the capacity to evolve into an effort capable of sustaining a whole lab. A great experiment carries a potential for future work. Timid experiments may have acceptable outcomes, but they don't help build paradigms. When prestigious universities select new faculty, they look for paradigm builders.

Although the innovations of recombinant DNA technology of the early 1970s transformed molecular biology into a high-tech field, it nevertheless has remained essentially an old-fashioned, labor-intensive industry. The scientists use much of the same equipment that they have used for decades. Much benchwork is routine, but it requires highly skilled performers, and some scientists find it exciting. Others find it boring and wonder why, after a long and expensive education, they spend most of their time looking for equipment or labeling tubes.

Even biologists who enjoy benchwork agree that the high points are at the beginning and end of an experiment. There is joy at the outset in designing an experiment and setting its parameters (conditions). The end of an experiment is less predictable. Getting expected results is great fun. Having disastrous results is sad and frustrating. The most common outcome is ambiguity, that is, the results differ from the scientist's prediction. At that point, the skill of puzzle-solving, the task scientists enjoy most, comes into play.

The Whitehead Institute

Although the Whitehead Institute is a center for advanced research, it is also as an affiliate of the Massachusetts Institute of Technology (MIT) and thus exists in a university setting. Weinberg considers himself to be a teacher as well as a scientist; he teaches those who work for him how to do and think about science, and each year he teaches one or two graduate-level courses at MIT.

The Whitehead Institute was the gift of Edwin (Jack) Whitehead, who had earned a fortune as co-founder and president of Technicon, a medical instruments firm. Advised by his accountants to set up a tax shelter, Whitehead approached Nobel Prize–winning MIT biologist David Baltimore to head up an independent biomedical research institute, associated with a university to lend it prestige.

In the spring of 1981, Whitehead and Baltimore presented a proposal to the MIT corporation, the university's governing body. The terms of the proposal were clear. Whitehead would spend $120 million to construct and endow the institute. In addition, he would pay the salaries of the 15 to 20 faculty members who worked there, on the condition that the faculty would be joint professors at the Whitehead Institute and MIT. Moreover, Whitehead would give $7.5 million to MIT to spend on biomedical research interests of the institute.

Many MIT faculty were bitterly opposed to the stipulations in the contract, to the unorthodox nature of the affiliation between the Whitehead Institute and MIT Institute, and to the fact that Baltimore would have control of 20 faculty slots of the Biology Department. The dispute bubbled for months until it was voted on by the faculty in November 1981. The pro-Whitehead forces prevailed. The MIT faculty could not justify turning down so much money in an era of tight funding.

The new institute, in a new building, was dedicated in December 1984. The major area of research at the institute is developmental biology—the study of how a single fertilized egg becomes a multicellular animal—a broad enough rubric to permit great latitude.

David Baltimore's Influence over the Institute

Most university labs look like basements, no matter what floor they are on. Angier quotes a postdoc who assessed a typical lab by saying, "Peeling paint and UV light are considered good for the soul." Whitehead Institute labs are an exception.

In accordance with David Baltimore's philosophy, the Whitehead Institute has high ceilings, contemplative colors, carpets, inspiring artwork, lots of windows, wide workbenches, computer rooms, an auditorium and lots of equipment. Angier describes it as "a gilded cage," and goes on to say, "Less obvious but every bit as palpable, David Baltimore gave the institute David Baltimore."

Although he is elegant and sophisticated, Baltimore is first and last a brilliant scientist, who has a ferocious capacity for work. Angier says, "Baltimore's dark impatience and competitiveness float freely through the Whitehead corridors, setting the tone and pace. MIT has one of the best and most difficult biology departments in the world; the Whitehead Institute is MIT on an imploded [more compacted] scale. Baltimore expects more than hard work of his scientists. He expects their lives."

Angier quotes Baltimore as saying, "If there's one thing that I believe that all great scientists share, it's an obsession with science. There's no getting around it. You have to be obsessed."

Young scientists at Whitehead are expected to produce. Every week, the individual senior scientists hold two-hour group meetings with the members of their own lab. During the meetings, several scientists must discuss their work in progress.

Baltimore demands more. Each week, at a designated time, three or more labs gather in the institute's auditorium. A designated speaker from each of the labs presents a talk for 20 minutes, complete with slides and diagrams. The senior scientists gather in the front row and offer pointed criticisms of the presentation. One Weinberg postdoc told Angier, "I hate the way they do that. They remind me of the gorilla judges on *Planet of the Apes*."

Postdoctoral fellows and graduate students at the Whitehead Institute have a better chance of succeeding than do young researchers at other, less-prestigious universities. They are likely to publish more first-author papers in the best journals and they will get more job interviews and at better universities. However, their models of success are also larger, and thus their opportunities for failure on a relative scale may be greater. One graduate student said to Angier, "How many of us are going to win a Nobel Prize? All of us, of course. Well, maybe only a couple of us. Well, maybe none of us."

Whitehead Institute can be one of the worst places to be when a researcher is floundering—when experiments fail to work, results can't be reproduced, and there are no publications in the offing. Angier describes the unique drawbacks of being at Whitehead by saying, "Worst because it's easy enough to feel dimwitted there under the happiest of circumstances. Worst because everybody works so hard, and few things are more painful than working hard when nothing is working. Worst because the rest of the scientific community is watching."

Most of science is a story of failure; however, it is during periods of failure that a scientist's reasons for being in science are clearest. Angier explains the defining quality of failure by saying,

Normal and Cancer Cells
Structure

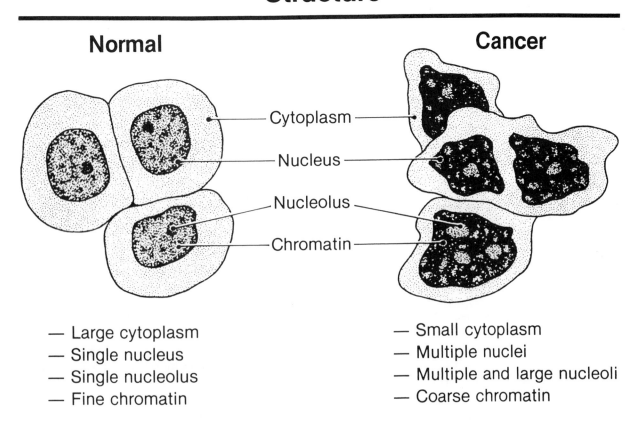

Normal

Cancer

— Large cytoplasm
— Single nucleus
— Single nucleolus
— Fine chromatin

— Small cytoplasm
— Multiple nuclei
— Multiple and large nucleoli
— Coarse chromatin

Anybody can understand the why of doing science in the wake of a big discovery. What's harder to fathom is why anybody would be in such a risky, low-paying, spine-breaking business when so many years can pass with nothing to show for them. And not only do people continue to slog away at their experiments; most retain a love of science. They continue to be obsessed. At that point, the point of failure, motivations other than simple competitiveness—the drive to be first and best—come into play . . . It is the stress of failure that lends scientists their character, their humanity. Failure makes them interesting.

The Multiple Personalities of Genes

In their search for the genetic cause of cancer, Weinberg's scientists look at oncogenes from every possible angle. A gene is both a collection of its parts and more than just its parts.

Genes are coded instructions, which the cell decodes to use as a recipe in order to reproduce itself. DNA is the critical chemical of genes. It supplies the blueprint of heredity. DNA is a molecule of deoxyribonucleic acid that exists in every living cell and has the ability to "create self from self." Resembling a spiral staircase, DNA's steps each consist of a pair of chemicals called nucleotide bases (the structural unit of a nucleic acid, a chainlike molecule), which lock onto one another. The exact sequence of nucleotides determines the gene. The possible sequences of nucleotides run in the millions.

DNA consists of four alternating subunits of nucleotide bases, adenine, thymine, crytosine and guanine (called A, T, C and G) that are held together by a firm spine of sugar and phospate. One twisting strand of sugar and nucleotides faces a complementary strand of sugar and nucleotides, a form referred to as a double helix. The nucleic acid units of the opposing strands are joined in their middles by hydrogen bonds. When the double helix needs to separate, either to replicate itself in preparation to synthesize a new cell, or to expose a portion of itself for the propagation of a protein, the hydrogen bonds are easily dissolved in water.

During routine genetic functioning, the sequence of replication goes from DNA, the substance of the genes, to RNA (ribonucleic acid), which has a number of roles in the manufacture of the live cell's products. By itself, DNA simply rests in the nucleus of the cell curled up into chromosomes. Before it can do anything, it must first be transcribed (translated) into RNA. An RNA transcript is a working copy of the gene ready for circulation and execution.

The transcription, a mirror image of the DNA template, once complete, peels away leaving the exposed DNA to rebond with its facing strand of the double helix. Much of RNA's exact duplication goes to waste. Through a mechanism still not understood, sections of the RNA transcript loop until they look like a bow on a gift package. Proteins snip off the bows, destroy them and splice the unlooped RNA transcript together.

The snipped off bows are called introns and the spliced transcripts are called exons. In human cells, about 90% or more of newly transcribed RNA transcript is thrown away almost immediately as introns. The remaining spliced RNA transcript, known as messenger RNA, is ready to travel out of the nucleus to become protein.

When the RNA moves out of the nucleus, it is immediately clasped by a ribosome (proteins that synthesize proteins), which reads the message by reacting to arrangements of three nucleotides. Each triplet nucleotide combination, called a codon, is a code for an amino acid, one of the twenty substances that the cell uses to make protein.

The ribosomes pile one amino acid on top of another, until the end of the message is reached. At that point, some of the bent and pleated proteins pull free, others are further modified with extra side chains. The new protein eventually migrates to its proper position in the cell or is transported outside to perform its task.

Everything that can be said about a healthy gene can be applied to its malignant counterparts. Oncogenes are genes that have been mutagenically skewed (suddenly altered), but like normal genes, oncogenes must proceed stepwise from DNA to RNA to protein. Therefore, researchers must consider oncogenes in the same piecemeal manner that they use to analyze normal genes.

Like a normal cell, a cancer cell possesses 50,000 genes; however, most biologists believe that only several are responsible for the malignant power of the cells. Researchers struggle to distinguish between the genes responsible for malignancy and the bulk of the innocent genes.

They examine the DNA sequence of oncogenes, looking for signs of mutations. They analyze an oncogene's RNA production and ask if RNA synthesized at the wrong moment during replication of the cell. They wonder if there is a failure to shut down the oncogene. They check to see if the initial transcript of the gene is being cut and pasted in the wrong place.

The most difficult challenge for scientists is to analyze the activity of the protein within the cell. It is proteins that distort a cell into a cancer cell. They track the mosaic of biochemical pathways that link the protein to a hundred or a thousand protein neighbors.

They check whether the protein is the proper size and shape, and whether a side chain might be missing or whether one may be present that is not supposed to be there. They look to see if the cancer protein stimulates the same enzyme that a comparable healthy protein stimulates or stimulates proteins that ought to be ignored. They wonder if the protein migrates to its proper location in the cell or strays to off-limits territory.

When researchers run out of questions, they head off to the library, get on the phone, travel to see colleagues or nod off to sleep in search of inspiration.

Coping with Research Setbacks

In viewing how individual scientists responded to repeated setbacks, whether they blamed themselves, the director, those around them or fate, and whether they cried, shrugged it off, considered leaving science or simply continued to work, Angier felt that she had witnessed the unglamorous side of science, a side which is perhaps closer to reality than the rare success. She says, "If I hadn't seen failure, if by some freak the Weinberg lab had presented only an unbroken string of triumphs, I would have had an inaccurate view of science . . . if I hadn't witnessed so much frustration, I might not have appreciated the sweet triumphs that came later. I certainly wouldn't have appreciated the intricate and contradictory characteristics that make Weinberg a genuinely great scientist."

Given the constant frustrations of research, keeping the atmosphere optimistic and smoothly functioning can be difficult. Weinberg told Angier, "I must spend sixty percent of my time trying to maintain a sense of harmony in the lab. I want people to get along, to cooperate. It's very difficult to do, you know. It's hard enough to do that with your own family, but managing with twenty people is almost impossible. But really that's what my job is all about."

Whether he actually achieves harmony is open to interpretation. Angier says, "The Weinberg groups seems, at least to an outsider, like a family: a disputatious [argumentative] family, certainly, and a difficult family whose problems occasionally stray toward the Southern Gothic. But it is Bob Weinberg's ability to domesticate the work place that makes the lab so intense."

A Non-University Affiliated Rival Lab

Angier left the Whitehead Institute to spend time at Michael Wigler's laboratory at Cold Spring Harbor, which is 35 miles from Manhattan, in a quiet, unspoiled area of Long Island. The 40 acres of the central laboratory grounds fall within a state-run bird sanctuary. The laboratory buildings date back to the 19th century. During the summer months, the laboratory grounds are crowded with 3,600 scientists who come from around the world to attend the famous Cold Spring Harbor meetings on biology. From September to May, the lab contains only about a hundred or so senior and junior scientists, who make up the staff. The lab has no formal affiliation with a university. Occasionally graduate students from the nearby Stonybrook branch of the State University of New York study with Cold Spring Harbor researchers.

Michael Wigler, Weinberg's counterpart at Cold Spring Harbor, is a child prodigy who has grown to adulthood and continues to be a genius. Angier describes him by saying, "He's more sheerly intelligent than many of his peers, and his peers will admit as much. On the Scholastic Aptitude Test (SAT), he scored a perfect 1600. He majored in math at Princeton and took only graduate-level courses from his sophomore year onward."

After college, Wigler decided to go to medical school, but was so bored by it that he switched to molecular biology. He was offered an independent position at Cold Spring Harbor after only six months of postdoctoral work, an incredibly short time. He soon became known as the protege

of the legendary James D. Watson, the director of Cold Spring Harbor. Watson won the Nobel Prize in 1962, with Francis Crick and Maurice Wilkins, for his work on the structure of DNA, which he describes in his book *The Double Helix* (1968). During spectacular oncogene research races of the early 1980s, Wigler stayed even with Weinberg and on occasion outpaced him.

The first major difference Angier noted between Wigler and Weinberg was Wigler's "omniscience." She said, "Wigler's lab belongs to Wigler, it is his fiefdom. He is always there and he is always aware."

Weinberg's normal work schedule is 10:00 A.M. to 6:00 P.M. five days a week. He rarely works on weekends. By contrast, Wigler works 9:00 to 6:00, goes home for dinner and returns at 8:00 and stays until midnight. He always works weekends. He never takes vacations and he seldom goes on trips.

An average of 10 postdoctoral fellows work for Wigler. Like Weinberg's scientists, the postdocs don't want to be thought of as his subordinates. Nevertheless, Angier asserts that the genius of the Wigler lab is Wigler's omnipresence. She says, "Shuffling from room to room, sneakered feet dragging across the floor, thumbs hooked in pockets, Wigler confronts his people with his stock query, 'anything

Normal and Cancer Cells
Cell Division

Normal

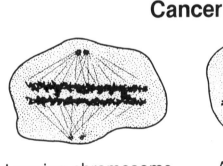

Normal mitosis

Cancer

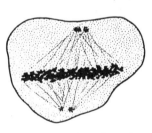

Lagging chromosome

Arrested mitosis

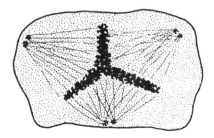

Multipolar mitosis

Normal and Cancer Cells

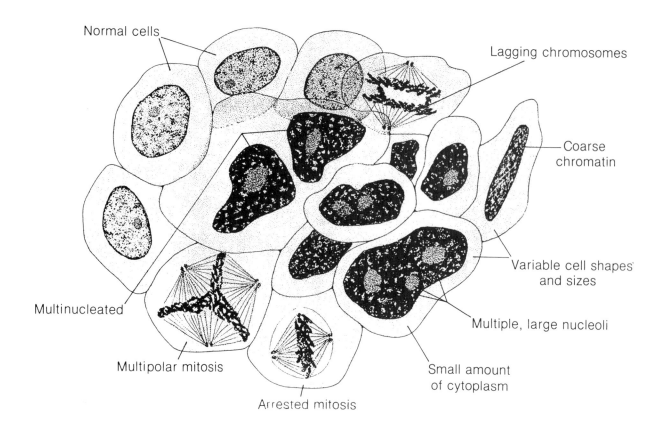

new?' . . . Sometimes he'll ask the question of the same person two, four, six times a day. Usually the postdocs will reply . . . 'No, Mike,' but on occasion they have some problem or result to discuss. By keeping in touch with the daily progress of his lab, Wigler helps salvage stranded projects and points out where mistakes were made."

Wigler sets the tone and pace of his lab. Not only is he always there, everyone else is too. Most of the postdocs live communally in one of the four large Victorian houses owned by the lab. Food is partially subsidized and recreation is provided in the form of a lab-owned tennis court and sailboats. Wigler likes to have people around him when he is bored or has an unpleasant task to perform. He spends far more time with his postdocs than with his peers.

The operative norm at Cold Spring Harbor is hard work. When projects are not going well, the scientists may work hundred-hour weeks. Wigler is addicted to results.

Yeast

During the winter of 1986, when Wigler permitted Angier to stay at his lab for a few weeks, Wigler seemed on the verge of discovering a fail-safe method for discovering the function of *ras*, a cancer gene. Wigler's lab had recently found an analogue (an organ or structure that is similar in function to one in another kind of organism, but is of dissimilar evolutionary origin) of the *ras* gene in yeast, one of nature's simplest and most genetically rational organisms. The yeast's version of *ras* was strikingly similar to the human cancer gene.

When one of Wigler's scientists, Scott Powers, presented Wigler with evidence of a homologue (structural relationship between parts of different organisms) of *ras* in yeast, he instantly grasped the significance for oncogene research. Yeast geneticists have developed elegant techniques for popping genes in and out of yeast chromosomes. The peculiarities of yeast reproduction make it possible for a biologist to replace a yeast gene with a manipulated copy of the gene, a swap impossible in the cells of mammals.

When scientists introduce foreign genes into cultured animal tissue, they can only add new genes on top of old genes. They cannot eliminate the activity of the animal tissue's resident *ras* gene, which means that the resident gene's impact cannot be separated out. Wigler also recognized that the task of distinguishing between the *ras* protein in yeast and all the other proteins would be simplified. A human cell has about 30,000 entangled, communicating proteins, yeast has only 4,000.

Wigler explained why he threw his efforts behind working with yeast by saying, "I was sick and tired of working with mammalian cells. There are no tools to approach them. You have no idea what's going on inside a mammalian membrane or mammalian nucleus . . . you do need a certain amount of faith, because there isn't much else to go on."

From 1984 to 1985, the lab was open 24 hours a day. Wigler picked the brains of every yeast expert at Cold Spring Harbor, and soon could follow the intricate lineages of yeast in his head. He hired biologists from Japan, whom their colleagues describe as the hardest-working scientists in the world.

After months of intensive labor, the Wigler researchers were able to demonstrate that the *ras* protein controlled a familiar and potent enzyme, adenylate cyclase, which produces an equally familiar and potent molecule, adenosine monophosphate (AMP). The two compounds were already known to function in cells throughout the body. They assist the heart to race, the thyroid to secrete thyroid hormone, the liver to metabolize sugar, and the ovary to release progesterone, another hormone.

In October of 1984, Wigler announced the adenylate cyclase results at a cancer conference in New York City. The audience was awed. However, the euphoria at the Wigler lab did not last long.

Carmen Birchmeir came to Cold Spring Harbor from the University of Zurich. Her task was to shift the adenylate cyclase cycle up the evolutionary ladder from yeast to complex animals.

Birchmeir was an expert on the *Xenopus* oocyte, a popular biological system. The oocyte is the unfertilized egg of an 8-inch long toad native to Africa. Like any egg, an oocyte is a single cell; however, because its volume is about a thousand times greater than an average body cell, the *Xenopus* oocyte is suited to studying protein activity within the cytoplasm. With ultrathin needles, micro amounts of purified proteins can be injected into the oocytes and then observed under a microscope.

Birchmeir injected purified *ras* protein into a batch of oocytes and allowed them to incubate overnight. The eggs responded with a rash of white spots that Birchmeir knew was the beginning of maturation prior to fertilization, a condition associated with a decline in adenylate cyclase rather that a surge, which would have been in keeping with the lab's earlier findings. Further experiments provided no better results. There seemed to be no significant relationship between *ras* and adenylate cyclase.

Wigler had to resign himself that what had been true for yeast was true for yeast alone. Nevertheless, he did not reject the idea that yeast was the proper route to further discoveries. He reasoned that the *ras* gene had two functions in yeast. Modulation of adenylate cyclase might be the primary task of *ras* in yeast, but the *ras* gene had to have another function. Many cellular proteins speak several languages. They communicate with different target enzymes at different moments in the life cycle of the cell. Thus evolved the idea of the "Alternate Pathway." During Angier's stay at Cold Spring Harbor, the alternate pathway was the lab's new mission. In her view, the conviction held by Wigler and his nine scientists lent the lab coherence and a harmony of purpose.

Yeast turned out to be less simple than Wigler had expected. In the absence of encouraging data, Wigler became volatile and unpredictable. One day he would be festive and affable, the next glowering and snappish. Nothing upset Wigler more than to think that his scientists were losing heart. Yet for every loss of temper, Angier observed a dozen examples of his generosity. Moreover, he fiercely defended the interests of his scientists.

Angier described Wigler by saying, "Through his intermittent arrogance and tantrums, his impatience and what's-new nosiness, Wigler's conscience shines. He's no altruist and he's as competitive as any other molecular biologist . . . Yet Wigler talks freely about his feelings, and he often thinks about how his work might be put to some practical, medical good."

Wigler's feeling that the *ras* gene was an open-ended narrative kept him interested in continuing with yeast as other outside observers gradually gave up hope. In 1987, Wigler told Angier,

> There are still a lot of unknowns about *ras* in yeast. We still don't know, for example, whether *ras* acts directly on adenylate cyclase, or whether there's an intermediary protein that argues that there could be an alternate pathway. There's an excellent chance that our biochemical understanding hasn't kept pace with our knowledge of genetics, of DNA sequences . . . Your basic yeast cell is every bit as complicated as your basic mammalian cell . . . Having said all that about the complexity of yeast, we know that the tools we have to approach the organism are still light years ahead of what we have in mammalian cell biology, so it's still worth my time and the time of my lab . . . I believe that basic science is the best way to attack human cancer, and that's why I'm doing what I'm doing.

On her last night at Cold Spring Harbor, Wigler asked Angier if she planned to put funny stuff in her book. On the train going back to Manhattan, she mused that she had a hard time finding humor in science. She had seen experiments fail, young scientists spar over turf, authorship and bench space. She had seen senior scientists at their wits' end, confronting or fleeing crises. She had traveled from one famous lab where big, promising projects fizzled and died to another famous, brash, upstart lab where the solution to cancer turned out to be a red herring.

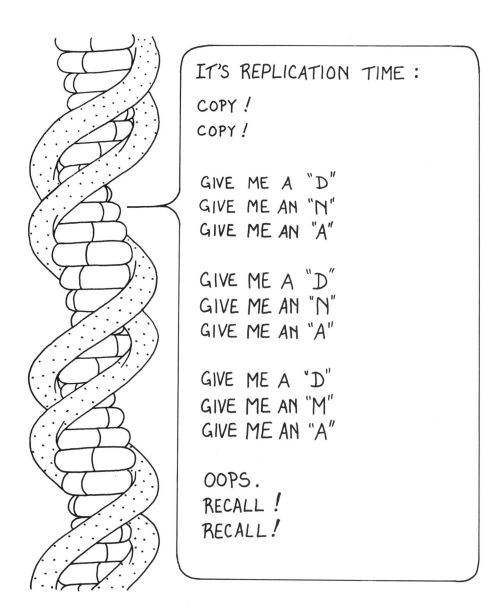

IT'S REPLICATION TIME :

COPY !
COPY !

GIVE ME A "D"
GIVE ME AN "N"
GIVE ME AN "A"

GIVE ME A "D"
GIVE ME AN "N"
GIVE ME AN "A"

GIVE ME A "D"
GIVE ME AN "M"
GIVE ME AN "A"

OOPS.
RECALL !
RECALL !

Even the best-laid plans can go awry.

A Return to Whitehead

Two weeks after leaving Cold Spring Harbor, in early 1986, Angier returned to the Whitehead Institute, six months after the lab had hit its lowest low.

An amiable new postdoc, Steve Friend, an M.D.-Ph.D., had come aboard. Given Friend's geniality, Weinberg found it difficult to say no when Friend wanted to study retinoblastoma, a rapidly growing tumor of the eye that may invade the brain, although Weinberg did not believe that the area lent itself to breakthroughs any time in the near future. Treatment involves removal of the eye and much of the optic nerve.

Retinoblastoma exclusively strikes children under the age of eight. The disease is rare but, from a scientific standpoint, it has long fascinated scientists, who have suspected that it held the clue to the genesis of many, if not all, human malignancies.

The idea that retinoblastoma was caused by two missing genes rather than genes gone awry struck several interested people simultaneously. One of the people interested in retinoblastoma was Ted Dryja, an ophthalmologist at Massachusetts Eye and Ear Hospital in Boston. He had no formal training in molecular biology, but decided that he wanted to make an attack on a disease that he had seen too often.

Dryja talked with Weinberg and one of his scientists in early 1985. They told Dryja that the method he was using had virtually no chance of pinpointing the gene and making an exact replica. After 18 months without success, Dryja found the right probe (technique to identify the location of genes) that could be used to clone the whole retinoblastoma gene.

However, Dryja's lab, which wasn't much bigger than a closet, was not equipped to take the project to its conclusion. Having been an instructor at Children's Hospital when Steve Friend was an intern, Dryja turned to Friend for help.

A couple of weeks later, Friend confirmed that the probe was the right one. Once they had the probe confirmed, the whole gene had to be cloned. Once again, Weinberg's scientists entered into a race. Other scientists were closing in on the retinoblastoma clone.

Friend had never cloned a gene before. Another postdoc, Snezna Rogelj, agreed to help him. By early spring, Friend and Rogelj thought that they had a working clone of the retinoblastoma.

The October 1986 issue of *Nature* reported their success in a paper on retinoblastoma coauthored by Dryja, Friend and Rogelj. Their work on the retinoblastoma clone has been heralded as a genuine breakthrough. It is the first true human cancer gene to be found, and scientists can say unequivocally that the retinoblastoma gene is involved in particular human cancers. Wigler described their finding by saying, "It's like getting through to the other side of the mirror."

The success of the search for the retinoblastoma gene exerted an impact on Weinberg. He told Angier, "I'm having ideas again, one after another . . . The creative juices are flowing. I'd been worried that I was all dried up . . . But I'm coming up with new models . . . They're not profound ideas—my ideas usually aren't—but they're enough to keep me happy."

The Rarity of Success

The process of inquiry, not the rare success, is what keeps scientists working. The process of puzzle-solving uncovers other problems to be solved in a never-ending sequence. A lack of success is not necessarily a failure; it often points the way to a new line of inquiry.

The Weinberg and the Wigler labs are unusual in the degree of success they have compared with other labs, but they otherwise represent the daily, ongoing routine of "doing science."

SLEEP RESEARCH

Circadian Rhythms, Sleep Deprivation and Sleep Disorders

One-third of life is spent sleeping. Despite a half-century of observation, researchers still cannot explain why. British sleep researcher James Horne in his book *Why We Sleep* confesses, "All we can conclude about the function of sleep is that it overcomes sleepiness, and the only reliable finding from sleep deprivation experiments is that sleep loss makes us sleepy."

In a September 19, 1989, *Boston Globe* column called "Mysterious Sleep," physicist and science writer Chet Raymo wrote,"The mountain of science has labored mightily and brought forth a mouse. Nay, not just a mouse, but thousands of mice, rats, puppies, chimpanzees, dolphins, and drowsy undergraduates, all allowed to sleep or kept awake, and watched—watched by eager researchers keen to discover why we sleep, to no avail."

Over the centuries, there has been no shortage of opinions about the function of sleep. Sleep occupies the hours of darkness (a variation on this theme is that sleep occupies unproductive hours). Sleep conserves energy. Sleep rekindles the brain. Sleep provides an opportunity to dream. None of the opinions has been supported by research, and sleep's biological function is still not clear. Rats deprived of sleep die within a week or so. On the other hand, a schoolboy who set a record by staying awake for 11 days, while not particularly alert at the end of his trial, nevertheless recovered quickly after a long sleep.

This dozing college student is just one of over 100 million Americans who suffer from chronic daytime sleepiness.

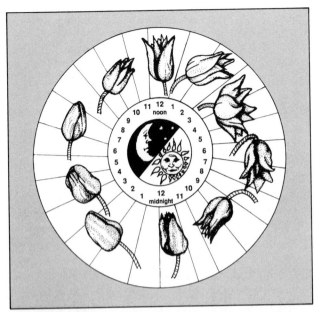

The body follows a biological clock that controls such things as brain waves, heart rate, lung function, body temperature, sleepiness and alertness.

A sample of the puzzlement researchers feel at the lack of sleep's clear function can be seen in a comment Raymo included in his column by sleep researcher Allan Rechtschaffen, who said, "How could natural selection with its irrevocable logic have 'permitted' the animal kingdom to pay the price of sleep for no good reason? Sleep is so apparently maladaptive that it is hard to understand why some other conditions did not evolve to satisfy whatever need it is that sleep satisfies. Unless we have missed something, sleep is the biggest mistake evolution ever made."

There are several reasons why Rechtschaffen suspects that sleep was an evolutionary mistake. Sleep takes away time that could be used to search for food, to locate mates, to procreate and to feed the young. Moreover, sleep makes creatures vulnerable to predators.

Research Has Not Been in Vain

Scientists may not have discovered why there seems to be a biological need for sleep, but they have made many other discoveries. Defined by electrical changes in the brain, scientists have learned that normal sleep occurs at various stages and in cycles.

Routinely, there are four cycles each night. During each cycle, there is an interval called REM (rapid eye movement) when the eyes twitch beneath the closed lids. By waking people up when this happens, researchers know that dreaming occurs during this period. Animals, including rats and dolphins, have REM sleep. Dolphins sleep while remaining in constant motion. Knowing that people dream

during REM, raises questions about whether creatures such as rats and dolphins dream.

Experts know that the deepest stage of sleep, a period they call "slow-wave" sleep, is a time when it is most difficult to be awakened. Therefore, they suspect this period is important for feeling well-rested.

Circadian (Daily) Rhythms

From sleep research, scientists have learned a great deal about "circadian rhythms," the so-called "biological clock," a daily cycle of alertness and sleepiness found in all creatures.

The clock is normally synchronized by the amount of light entering the eyes. Alertness, temperature and various levels of chemicals rise and fall throughout a daily 24-hour cycle, each adhering to its own separate pattern.

A typical 24-hour cycle is as follows: During the period midnight to about 6:30 A.M., body temperature and alertness drop steadily. At the temperature's lowest point, about 5 A.M., the circadian cycle begins. The temperature begins to rise and continues upward all day until its highest point at about 6 P.M., when it starts downward again.

The alertness cycle's lowest point is reached later than that of the temperature cycle. It bottoms out about 6:30 A.M. Thereafter, alertness begins to rise. Looking like a series of wiggles on a chart, alertness rises, plateaus and rises again the whole morning. Oxygen use is at maximum efficiency about 9 A.M., which makes it a good time to exercise.

Alertness continues to rise until about noon, its highest point. At about 1 P.M., alertness begins to slump toward the "midafternoon dip or trough," which occurs about 3 P.M. Oddly enough, this is the point in the cycle at which more people report that they feel happier than at any other time.

After the midafternoon trough, alertness begins to rise again, until about 4:30 P.M., when it plateaus until about 6 P.M. It then begins to rise once more to a high point at about 8 P.M., a peak time of alertness. Following the 8 P.M. peak, alertness begins a downward slide to a typical bedtime of 10 P.M. While some people may vary from the specific times, they tend to follow a similar pattern of peaks and troughs.

Scientists call the normal bedtime the "primary sleep gate" and the midafternoon dip, the "secondary sleep gate." These are the times when it is easiest to fall asleep. They call the peaks of alertness, the "forbidden zones." These are the times when it is most difficult to fall asleep. The sleep gates and the forbidden zones are critical to people who have sleep disturbances and to people who must make do with less than enough sleep.

While circadian rhythms are influenced by such cues as daylight, they operate independently of them and account for the problems of people who have jet lag or who work rotating schedules. When people stay up late on weekends and get up early to go to work on Monday, the malaise that they suffer is a result of their body rhythms being out of synchronization with their work and social schedules.

Experiments on circadian rhythms with people living temporarily in caves or in windowless rooms without cues to the time of day have revealed that the natural daily sleep-wake cycle is 25 hours. Scientists don't know why there is this natural tendency to lengthen the day. However, this propensity explains why it is easier to stay up late than it is to get up early, and why jet lag is less severe traveling west than east. (Going west, bedtime will be later than normal and getting up the next morning will also be later. Going east, bedtime will be earlier than normal and getting up the next morning will also be earlier.)

In the short run, circadian rhythms seem to affect alertness to a greater extent than sleep deprivation does. In an interview for an April 17, 1988, *New York Times Good Health Magazine* article called "Exploring the Forces of Sleep," Richard Coleman, an instructor in psychiatry and behavioral sciences at Stanford University Medical School, described a circadian research experiment that underscored the link between alertness and circadian rhythms.

Subjects were asked to complete a routine task on a computer terminal every hour for 24 hours. They generally did well during the day and poorly after midnight, hitting a low point at 3 or 4 in the morning. However, their performance picked up again at 7 or 8 A.M., indicating that their inner clock had partially compensated for their loss of sleep.

Even after an inadequate night's sleep (four to five hours for those accustomed to eight hours), subjects performed better during the day than they did at night. However, after a number of nights of insufficient sleep, the circadian rhythms were not enough to overcome exhaustion.

Some people perform better early in the morning and others late at night, a factor that seems to reflect variations from the norm in the biological clocks. Such individual differences only matter when a "morning person" must work at night or a "night person" is expected to deliver a peak performance in the morning. Undoubtedly, it makes a difference when a morning person and a night person live together.

Work Scheduling

About 22% of all American employees work at night or on changing shifts. Employees who work the graveyard shift (generally 11 P.M. to 7 A.M. or midnight to 8 A.M.) have great difficulty keeping their work schedules and inner clocks aligned. This misalignment carries great hazards. In the view of sleep researchers, it is not coincidental that the Three Mile Island nuclear plant accident in Pennsylvania, the Chernobyl nuclear plant accident in the Soviet Union and the Bhopal chemical plant explosion in India all

happened deep in the night, a time when operators could be expected to be least alert.

The human biological clock is flexible enough to accept slight changes in the work schedule. However, most industries set up shift work so that it creates havoc in body rhythms. Sleep scientists, in some cases, are able to bring their research to bear to reduce some of the impact.

An experiment with the Philadelphia Police Department demonstrated that some methods for rotating schedules are better than others. The experiment was conducted by the Center for Design of Industrial Scheduling, a nonprofit organization, headed by Dr. Charles Czeisler, who is on the faculty at Harvard Medical School and associated with the Brigham and Women's Hospital in Boston, in cooperation with the Police Union.

The Philadelphia schedule in operation at the time of the experiment required the police officers to work for six straight days, followed by two days off, and a new shift. This schedule meant that the officers had to adjust their sleep habits every eight days.

The scientists designed a new schedule to minimize disruptions. Two hundred and twenty officers of Philadelphia's 35th Police District, in 1987, participated in the experiment. The officers stayed on the same shift for three weeks at a time. Then their shift moved forward, from day to evening, to take advantage of the natural propensity toward a 25-hour cycle. (The customary shift had been from evening to day.) The number of consecutive work days was cut from six to four, allowing officers a chance to catch up on their sleep. In addition, fewer officers were scheduled for the early morning shift, a statistically low-crime period.

In a survey at the end of the experiment, most officers said that they slept better at home, suffered less fatigue on the job, and used half as much alcohol and tranquillizers to induce sleep as they had before the new schedule. Moreover, officer's families were happier with the new schedule, falling asleep on the job declined by 29%, and the incidence of on-the-job automobile accidents was 40% lower than in previous years.

Because Philadelphia Police management felt that the experimental schedule did not meet some of their needs, the shift was not adopted throughout the system. However, a new system-wide schedule was subsequently adopted that better addressed the sleep needs of officers.

Skipping Sleep

A great deal of sleep deprivation in modern life is unrelated to unhealthy scheduling, sleep research experiments or sleep disorders. Much of it is due to a societal-wide norm to make due with less sleep. During an interview for a May 15, 1990, *New York Times* article entitled "Cheating on Sleep: Modern Life Turns America into the Land of the Drowsy," Dr. Howard Roffwarg, director of the Sleep Study Unit at the University of Texas Southwestern Medical School in Dallas, said, "People cheat on their sleep, and they don't even realize they're doing it. They think they're O.K. because they can get by on six and a half hours, when they really need seven and a half, eight or even more to feel vigorous."

Sleep scientists are convinced that there is an epidemic of sleep deprivation. Although there has not been a large-scale epidemiological study (research on the occurrence of a disease in a mass population), scientists base their conclusions on a variety of sources of information. The sources are: recent surveys; data from sleep disorder treatment clinics; labor force trends toward more shift work and more night work; an apparent growth in the number of Americans who suffer from sleep pathologies and chronic fatigue; and the scientists' own studies of certain populations. From their studies of the defined populations, mostly the elderly and young adults, the scientists have been able to make estimates about how many people in the national population are getting less sleep than they need.

One study of a defined population done by the National Institute of Aging analyzed several health surveys covering a total of 21,000 people who were 65 years of age or older. The researchers reported that 50% of the respondents claimed that they slept badly and felt poorly rested when they awoke. Making projections from the base of the surveys to the entire U.S. population, Institute of Aging sleep researcher Dr. Andrew Monjan concluded that at least 13 million Americans are sufficiently aware of their chronic sleep deficiency to cite it as a source of woe.

These police officers look relaxed and alert after a long parade. But the police, like other workers who must deal with emergencies, often find their normal work schedules extended, resulting in potentially dangerous sleep deprivation.

Measuring Sleep Deprivation

The most accurate measurement of sleep deprivation is the Multiple Sleep Latency Test, devised by Dr. William Dement, director of the Stanford Sleep Disorders Center, and by Dr. Mary Carskadon of Brown University. To track the precise moment when a subject falls asleep, subjects are hooked up to electroencephalograms, which record their brainwave patterns.

While being tested, subjects are allowed to lie down in a dark room for a short period every two hours. Those who fall asleep in under five minutes are considered to be severely sleep deprived, comparable to someone suffering from a sleep disorder. Those who take an average of 5 to 10 minutes before falling asleep are considered borderline pathological. Those who take between 10 and 15 minutes are viewed as having sufficient sleep, but not an optimal amount. Those who stay awake 15 minutes or longer are considered to be at their peak of restedness.

Unnoticed sleep deprivation was highlighted by another series of studies done with several hundred college and graduate students between the ages of 18 and 30. The studies were done over several years at Stanford University, Brown University and the Henry Ford Hospital in Detroit.

In a typical representative study, 20% of the students who reported that they had an average of seven or eight hours of sleep a night, when given the Multiple Sleep Latency Test could fall asleep almost instantly throughout the day. The students' apparent sleep deprivation was comparable to that of people who have known sleep disorders, such as narcoplexy (chronic, recurring attacks of drowsiness) and apnea (periods during sleep when breathing ceases).

During an August 1990 telephone interview with Dr. Mark Chambers of the Stanford Sleep Disorders Center, questions were raised about whether students participating in the Multiple Sleep Latency Test might have been exaggerating the amount of sleep they claimed to be getting each night or whether book-oriented work might increase a need for sleep. Dr. Chambers answered that researchers did not believe that those issues were responsible for the apparent sleep deprivation of the students.

Confronted with the apparent widespread sleep deprivation among college students, Chambers reported that scientists had become convinced that adolescents need more sleep than they normally get. Children's sleep patterns change drastically when they reach adolescence. Scientists believe that the abrupt change is not a reflection of a lessened need for sleep, but instead reflects a change of life-style.

Support for the scientists' theory about adolescent sleep deprivation comes from other studies with students. Researchers found that even alert students who did not fall asleep during the test conditions benefited from more sleep. If the students spent a week going to bed 60 to 90 minutes

Insomniacs could find contemplation of the bear's long winter nap irritating. In an effort to discover why humans sleep, researchers have studied the sleep of animals. Researchers have discovered that rats have REM sleep and that dolphins sleep with half their brain at a time, presumably to prevent drowning. But no explanation has been found for why they sleep.

earlier than usual, they markedly improved their performance on psychological and cognitive tests.

The findings from the students' studies suggests to researchers that most people, not just adolescents, who think that they are sleeping enough could probably gain from an extra bit of sleep. Dr. Wilse Webb, a psychologist and a sleep research pioneer at the University of Florida in Gainesville, points to the bedside alarm clock as a symbol of sleep deprivation. To Webb, waking up regularly to an alarm clock indicates that the natural sleep pattern is being shortened.

Another piece of evidence that researchers use to bolster their contention that sleep deprivation is widespread among the general population is the constantly rising number of people who consult sleep-disorder clinics each year, complaining of constant fatigue. In 1980, there were only 25 accredited sleep disorder clinics in the United States. By 1990, there were 140. In 1985, only 710 clinicians belonged to the American Sleep Disorders Association. By 1990, the numbers had climbed to 1,200. Some clinics annually experience as much as a 50% increase in patients. An estimated 40% of the patients who come to those centers are suffering from severe sleep deprivation.

Competitors to Sleep

Diaries and personal journals provide evidence that a century ago, the average person slept nine and a half hours. In the absence of electricity, there wasn't much else to do except work by candlelight or go to bed. Apparently most people went to bed. By the middle of the 20th century, the hours in bed had been trimmed to eight or seven and one-half hours. Trends suggest the time spent in slumber continues to be whittled down.

TV and around-the-clock entertainment continue to play a role in depriving people of sleep. The most relentless thief of sleep is the complexity of everyday life. Pressures from work, family, friends and community leave sleep as the only expendable item in the schedule.

A rising contributor to sleeplessness is the burgeoning number of workers keyed into the international economy. For example, even after the New York Stock Exchange closes, the Tokyo and London markets are tracked by those who have a stake in them. In the face of strong competition at home and abroad, many companies and industries have turned to round-the-clock operations.

Coping with a high cost of living forces many people to "moonlight," thereby reducing the hours available for sleep. Some not only have second jobs, they have third jobs. Boston police officers refused to consider a schedule that would have been kinder to their sleep needs because the present system permits them to accept a substantial amount of outside work.

Regulations about limited working hours are often flouted. Federal statistics show that long-haul truck drivers are involved in a high number of fatal accidents during the early morning hours. Performance of routine tasks, such as driving, and passively monitoring automated machines, is degraded by sleep deprivation.

A Social Trend That Threatens Personal and Collective Well-being

The effects of sleep loss are cumulative. An individual who regularly sleeps 90 minutes less than needed each night during the work week will feel far worse on Friday than on Tuesday. By Friday, seven and a half hours, or almost a whole night's sleep will have been lost.

Despite the malaise generated by regularly losing sleep, Neil Cavey, the director of the Sleep Disorder Center at Columbia-Presbyterian Medical Center in New York, pointed out the social pressure to continue to lose sleep. He said, "It's considered dynamic, a feather in one's cap, to say you only need five and a half hours' sleep. If you say you've got to get eight and a half, people look at you askance, as though you lacked ambition."

As a cause of traffic accidents, sleepiness is second only to drunkenness. In 1989, the U.S. Department of Transportation reported to Congress that 40,000 traffic accidents a year may be sleep-related. More than 20% of all drivers have fallen asleep behind the wheel. Dr. Thomas Roth, the director of the Sleep Disorder Center at Henry Ford Hospital in Detroit, found that it takes smaller quantities of alcohol to affect sleep-impaired people than it does rested people, a factor that could additionally contribute to traffic accidents.

During an interview for a May 28, 1990, *Boston Globe* article entitled "Getting the Most Out of a Little Sleep," David Dinges, a biological psychologist at the University of Pennsylvania Medical School, said, "The consequences of human failure are much more disastrous and costly than they used to be." Dinges believes that the *Exxon Valdez* oil spill

The mid-afternoon biological trough sees a rise in the automobile accident rate.

in Alaska was "a classic fatigue accident" caused by inattention and an improper steering decision made by the third mate who had been working long shifts.

An estimated 330,000 commercial airplanes operated by domestic airlines and tens of thousands of foreign-owned carriers routinely carry passengers destined for jet lag from one locale to another.

Congress became sufficiently concerned about the hazards of chronic sleep deprivation that, as a part of an omnibus health bill passed in 1988, it asked a panel of a dozen sleep scientists to conduct a comprehensive study of the subject, to be completed by mid-1991. The scientists' task was to attempt to assess the economic and medical impact of sleep deprivation and sleep disorders and to suggest ways in which the government might be able to ease the problem.

Making the Most of Opportunities to Sleep

Getting a good night's sleep is not always possible. Disaster-relief workers and medical professionals suffer sleep deprivation and are expected to make crucial decisions. Long space flight may one day require unusual sleep and wakefulness patterns.

The military has special problems concerning sleep. Soldiers may be flown into a trouble spot on short notice, arriving sleep-deprived and jet-lagged, and yet be expected to perform in combat. Drugs to induce sleep and stimulants to hold off sleep have built-in problems for the military because they reduce flexibility. Dr. Gregory Belensky, chief of behavioral biology at Walter Reed Army Institute of Research, described the problems by saying, "If you gave troops a stimulant and then the enemy backed off, you'd have lost a chance to get 8 or 10 hours of sleep."

Napping

The long tradition of siestas around the world coincides with the mid-afternoon slump, suggesting that naps might be a good idea. However, some researchers believe that people who have had a truly good night's sleep don't need a nap.

Napping is one of the most-studied countermeasures to sleep loss. Scientists' interest may have been drawn to the examination of naps by the examples of such famous nappers as Winston Churchill, Thomas Edison and Napoleon. Leonardo da Vinci is said to have prospered on less than two hours of sleep daily by napping for 15 minutes six times a day.

In one nap experiment, David Dinges of the University of Pennsylvania kept 48 young adults awake for 54 hours. Some were allowed two-hour naps at various times during the study. Others were allowed no sleep. Those who napped did better on alertness tests, but those who napped

Researchers disagree about how effective cat naps are at forestalling sleepiness—at least in humans.

Despite many experiments, no one has found a single best regimen for prophylactic napping. Some experts are in favor of getting at least one substantial nap, referred to as "anchor sleep," that is at least half as long as a normal night's sleep. This approach helps the circadian rhythms to stay synchronized.

A Role for Bright Lights

Adding bright lights to the workplace during night shifts helps to stimulate alertness. During a study for the Air Force, George Brainard of Jefferson Medical College kept volunteers up for 30 hours, some working under normal interior lighting, and others under lighting 30 times stronger. Those under stronger lighting performed better on mental tests and had faster reflexes, but they didn't report feeling any less fatigued.

During an April 11, 1990, broadcast called "The Infinite Voyage: The Living Clock," produced by WQED/Pittsburg and the National Academy of Sciences, sleep researcher Charles Czeisler discussed efforts to reset a patient's biological clock. For more than 10 years, the patient, Pat Phillipps, had been unable to stay awake after 8:30 or 9 P.M. To her consternation, she would wake up at 3:30 or 4 A.M., wide awake and too energetic to stay in bed. Czeisler prescribed treatment to reset the patient's biological clock that involved exposure to light 25 to 50 times brighter than ordinary indoor light.

Research had determined that the response to light as a therapy depended upon the time of day the light was administered. Czeisler said, "There are times of day when we're exposed to light where there is no phase-shifting effect at all . . . The response of the system depends on what time it is in the body when it receives the signal."

To determine what time it was in Phillipps's body, Czeisler confined her for 48 hours to an isolation chamber with no clocks and no cues to time. The key indicator of body time is internal temperature. When temperature reaches its lowest point, it is dawn in the body. To ensure an accurate profile, the patient had to remain inactive. Small meals kept her metabolism constant. Her vital signs (respiration, pulse and temperature) were monitored continuously. Because sleep causes profound physiological changes, technicians helped the patient to stay awake.

Once dawn was established in the patient's body, treatment could be administered at that time. The treatment to reset Pat Phillipps's clock consisted of three consecutive days of spending five hours in front of the lights, beginning at the time that coincided with her dawn.

Czeisler believes that efforts to change the biological clock may help those with sleep disorders, facilitate changes in shifts and enable those who have crossed time zones to reset their clocks at the local time.

earliest—six hours into the experiment—benefited most. This suggests that "prophylactic" preventive napping (as most mothers of young children would suspect) is useful when sleep will be lost later. The longer intense sleepiness can be held off, the better.

In another study of prophylactic sleep by Michael Bonnet at the Long Beach, California, Veterans Administration Hospital, volunteers stayed up for two days and two nights after having naps of two, four or eight hours on the first day. The longer the nap, the better the performance on the first day. By the second night, everyone's performance went downhill.

One of the factors that makes naps ambiguous as a universal solution is the phenomenon called "sleep inertia," the stunned, drowsy feeling many people experience when they awake after a daytime nap. Researchers believe that the inertia is caused by waking up from the deepest level of sleep, the "slow wave sleep," which is more common in daytime naps. Military scientists believe that some people, like fighter pilots who are on ready alert, should not be allowed to nap.

A researcher at the Institute for Circadian Physiology in Boston, Claudio Stampi, has found that the best transatlantic sailboat racers break up their sleep into many naps of about an hour each. In order to shorten overall sleeping time, he believes that humans could adopt the multiple-nap style of cats and other animals.

A subsequent study by Czeisler and his colleagues, reported in the May 3, 1990, issue of the *New England Journal of Medicine* documented the team's successful effort to readjust the human sleep-wake cycle to night work. In the study, Czeisler's research overcame the obstacle of bright, outdoor light to which night workers are exposed on their trip home from work.

In 45 resetting trials, a combination laboratory and field study, Czeisler and his researchers used timed exposures to bright lights, ordinary room light and darkness to reset the subjects' biological clocks. The study demonstrated that even those who had worked a night schedule for years had physiologically failed to adapt, although they did so after Czeisler and his team administered treatment.

In the June 16, 1990, issue of *Science*, Czeisler reported that the research had established a "phase-response" curve to light in humans that provides precise information on when and in which direction (earlier or later clock time) the biological clock will be reset. Czeisler expects the findings to be useful in the treatment of seasonal affective disorder (SAD).

SAD

In 1984, a team of scientists at the National Institute of Mental Health (NIMH) in Bethesda, Maryland, identified a syndrome (a collection of signs and symptoms that together indicated a disease or condition) that they named "seasonal affective disorder," or SAD. Annually, those afflicted with SAD gradually find themselves in October or November trying to cope with declining energy, difficulty in processing information, depression and an urge to withdraw from friends and family.

During an interview for the "The Infinite Voyage: The Living Clock" broadcast, Dr. Norman Rosenthal, one of the NIMH team who identified SAD, explained that humans are quite "seasonal," especially in the far north and far south. In winter, they eat more, gain more weight, and sleep more. While a high percentage of the population reports such phenomenon, the change of seasons becomes a significant problem for only a few. For those people, therapy with light seems to help. Even for

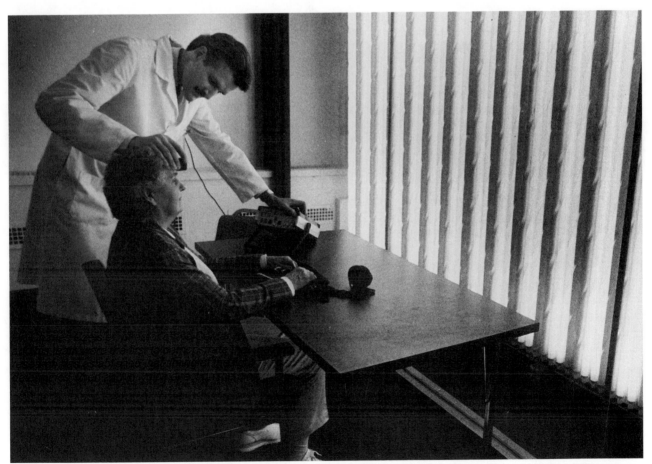

Dr. Charles Czeisler, director of the Center for Circadian and Sleep Disorders Medicine at Brigham and Women's Hospital, and his team were the first to demonstrate that the human biological clock could be reset by the use of light. Further research has established that timing of the light exposure is important. There is a "phase-response" curve to light that determines when and in which direction the biological clock will be reset.

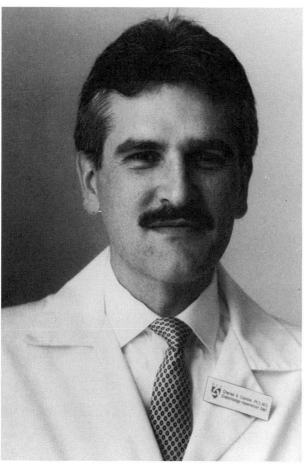

During resetting trials, Dr. Czeisler and his researchers used not only bright light but also ordinary room light and darkness after discovering that ordinary room light has an effect on the biological clock by modulating exposure to bright light.

those who only get mild winter blues, exposure to bright light seems to offer relief. Czeisler's new research is likely to make treatment of SAD even more effective.

Sleep Disorders

Research suggests that the degree to which people feel rested depends on the number of times they awaken during the night. "Micro-arousals" of less than 10 seconds are frequent among those over age 50, who may have hundreds of micro-arousals a night. While they may not be aware of or remember waking up, they are apt to feel unrested when they get up. Twice the proportion of older people also wake up outright more often than younger age groups, and have a harder time falling asleep. The total time in deep sleep appears to diminish with age.

Some sleep problems that afflict people of all ages are potentially dangerous and should receive medical attention. They include insomnia that is specifically linked to depression, medicines or illness; narcolepsy, a frequent and uncontrollable urge to sleep; and apnea (from the Greek for "want of breath"). Those with apnea stop breathing as many as several hundred times during the night, for periods anywhere from 30 seconds to one minute. Episodes of apnea occasionally may initiate strokes or heart attacks.

The most common risk of sleep apnea is daytime drowsiness, which is probably responsible for many car accidents and blighted careers. The apnea syndrome does not usually strike until middle age, when it most often strikes obese men. In later years, apnea affects many women too.

For persistent and severe insomnia, medical or psychological help may be necessary. For occasional insomnia, experts advise against: sleeping pills; alcohol; bringing books, puzzles or work to bed; and late evening exercise, heavy meals and caffeinated beverages. Lying in bed worrying about not sleeping tends to make the worrier more wide awake. Researchers recommend getting out of bed to do some quiet activity, such as read.

Mark Chambers of the Stanford Sleep Disorders Center reported in an August 1990 phone interview that he and his colleagues are engaged in an effort to develop a behavioral profile of patients to determine which patients are most likely to respond to treatment for insomnia.

Mathematical Models of Sleep

Harvard scientists Richard Kronauer, Steven Strogatz and Charles Czeisler are trying to understand the interaction between the circadian rhythm and the sleep-wake cycle. Kronauer has developed a mathematical model consisting of two differential equations, one representing each of the two cycles.

Dutch scientists Serge Daan and Domien Beersma and Swiss researcher Alexander Borbely have developed a different mathematical model. Their model proposes that a "sleep propensity" builds up during waking hours and dissipates during sleep. The buildup and dissipation have been linked with chemicals called peptides that have been extracted from the brain. No one knows whether the peptides are the cause of natural sleep or simply a component of whatever takes place on the way to becoming sleepy.

In an interview for the February/March 1987 issue of *Technology Review*, Strogatz pointed out that models can suggest ideas that are not obvious. He said, "Most people think you need eight hours of sleep. That's not true. How long you sleep depends mainly on when you got to sleep in the body's temperature cycle."

Most of what is known about sleep continues to come from laboratory data rather than mathematical predictions. From laboratory experiments, Strogatz, Kronauer and Czeisler developed the concept of the "forbidden zone," a period when falling asleep is very difficult. One forbidden zone is about eight hours before the temperature trough and another is about five hours after the trough. For example, in the sleep cycle of a person who goes to sleep at 11 P.M., the forbidden zones occur approximately at 9 P.M. and 10 A.M. Forbidden zones help to explain some cases of insomnia.

Kronauer has investigated dividing sleep into two increments, pointing out that two-thirds of the world has naps or siestas. A night worker might do well on four hours before work and four hours after work. Kronauer explained by saying, "It seems like people can move freely between the usual eight hours and the split cycle."

The Basic Difficulty Remains

A significant problem sleep researchers continue to face, including mathematical modelers, is the fact that the underlying biology of sleep is not yet understood. Why there is a need for sleep, what triggers sleep and what causes awakening remain unknown. Nevertheless, they have learned enough to recognize a national epidemic of sleep deprivation, and to offer treatment to shift workers and those suffering from jet lag and sleep disorders.

4
The Changing Environment

THE POPULATION EXPLOSION

At the Top of the List of Most Environmental Experts

By the year 2025, the earth's current population of 5.2 billion is expected to rise to 14 billion, surpassing the 10 billion predicted earlier. Scientists concerned with global warming note that the benefits of cutting carbon dioxide emissions in half would be wiped out if the world's population were to double.

Paul Ehrlich, an ecologist and population forecaster, says, "Nobody in their right mind thinks we can solve these other environmental problems if we don't deal with the population issue." Ehrlich, a Bing Professor of Population Studies and a professor of biological sciences at Stanford University, has written two widely read books on the issue of the world's burgeoning population. The first, *The Population Bomb*, was published in 1968. The second, *The Population Explosion*, written with Anne Ehrlich, a senior research associate in biological sciences at Stanford University, was published in 1990.

In the first chapter of *The Population Bomb*, Ehrlich recalled how he came to sense emotionally the population problem, which he felt that he had understood intellectually for years. On an extremely hot night in Delhi, India, while returning to his hotel in an ancient taxi, accompanied by his wife and daughter, he was confronted with the reality of daily living with overpopulation.

Ehrlich described the incident by saying,

The seats were hopping with fleas. The only functional gear was third. As we crawled through the city, we entered a crowded slum area. The temperature was well over 100, and the air was a haze of dust and smoke. The streets seemed alive with people, people washing, people sleeping. People visiting, arguing, and screaming. People clinging to buses. People herding animals. People, people, people, people. As we moved slowly through the mob, hand horn squawking, the dust, noise, heat, and cooking fires gave the scene a hellish aspect . . .

The Doubling Rate

The human population, it has been estimated, numbered about 5 million people in the year 8000 B.C. Almost 10,000 years passed before the population reached 500 million about 1650 A.D. At that rate, the population was doubling about every thousand years or so. The next doubling took only 200 years, when the world's population reached a billion about 1850 A.D. The next doubling took only 80 years. The population reached 2 billion about 1930. By 1990, the population was past 5.3 billion, increasing annually at a rate of 95 million people a year in contrast to 20 years earlier when it was increasing at an annual rate of 75 million a year. Even though falling birthrates in a majority of countries have slackened the average global growth *rate*, the annual increment of additional people in 1990 is at an all-time high because the lowered growth rate is being applied to a much larger population base.

A large population has a multifold effect on the relationship between food production and land. Forests, marshes and grasslands needed to sustain wildlife and some hunting and food gathering are converted to agricultural or industrial use. Because of the price of land in industrial nations, good farmland is purchased by developers for housing and taken out of food production.

The Discovery of Agriculture and Its Long-Range Effect

In *The Population Bomb*, the Ehrlichs describe the historical process by which the growth of agriculture contributed to the growth of the human population. The development of agriculture was probably gradual, beginning with an increased fund of knowledge among food gatherers about the ecology of their favorite food plants. Deliberate planting of seeds and casual weeding that met with success led to more systematic behavior. Eventually the control of herbivorous animals provided access to a steady supply of meat. However they began, farming and herding represented a radical change in the ability of humans to manipulate their environments. Food supplies were more dependable and abundant and many more people could be supported by agricultural production on a given area of land.

The increasingly efficient use of renewable and nonrenewable resources to support people, together with the expansion of farming to ever larger areas, supported an increase in the human population from 5 million before the invention of agriculture about 8000 B.C. to 200–300 million

in the first century A.D. (Nonrenewable resources are resources, such as ancient forests, minerals in the ground, and species that become extinct, that cannot be replaced once they are gone.)

That population growth, while extraordinarily slow by today's standards, represented an unprecedented change. The change brought with it substantial modifications in the biotic (plant and animal) communities over much of the planet's land surface, particularly in Southern Europe and parts of Asia. More and more, agriculture displaced natural ecosystems (organisms of a natural community together with their environment). Forests were cut down for fuel, construction and to clear additional land for farming.

The Industrial Revolution and Its Long-Range Effect

By 1800, with the world population grown to a billion, the industrial revolution was under way in Western Europe and North America. Over the next century, the world was transformed. Better housing and food, along with advances in sanitation and medicine, led in the West to a decline in death rates, especially among infants and small children.

Present-day agrarian societies without modern sanitation and medicine generally have annual birthrates around 40 to 45 and annual death rates at 38 or more per 1,000 in the population. These are rates that were typical in most of the world in the 18th century. During the 19th century, in some Western nations the death rates crept downward to 30 per 1,000 and below.

The widening gap between the persistent high birthrates and the falling death rates in Western nations resulted in an acceleration of population growth in those countries at unprecedented levels of 1.5% (15 per 1,000) per year or more in the late 19th and early 20th centuries. Within one or two generations (a generation is roughly 30 years, between the birth of one generation and the birth of the next), birthrates too began to fall slowly, as the apparent result of couples' individual decisions to limit their offspring.

The impetus to limit family size appeared to stem from two factors: large numbers of children were no longer dying in infancy or early childhood, and a large number of children had become an economic burden in industrial societies. In an agricultural society, children can be put to work and contribute to the family income. Work opportunities are limited for children in industrial societies. Other factors contributing to the decline in birthrates were late marriages, moderately high rates of nonmarriage, the feminist movement and increasing employment of women outside the home. By the 1930s, birthrates in the United States, Canada and most European countries had fallen well below 20 per 1,000. They were accompanied by death rates of 12 to 15 per 1,000, producing growth rates under 1% per year.

Despite the fall of population growths in the West, the average worldwide rate of growth continued to rise after 1930, mostly due to the control of insect-borne diseases and the spread of modern medicine.

After World War II, the birthrates, particularly in the United States, Canada and Australia, climbed to produce the so-called baby boom from 1946 to 1964. The baby-boom birthrates, coupled with spectacular declines in death rates in Asia, Africa and Latin America, at a time there was no change in high birthrates, resulted in a global population explosion.

Population impact is not always directly proportional to numbers of people. In the United States the "population" of automobiles has increased disproportionally faster than the number of people. From 1960 to 1990, the U.S. population grew about 39% from 179 million to 249 million. From 1960 to 1988 the number of registered motor vehicles swelled 148% from 73.9 million to 183.5 million. Between 1960 and 1987 new highway lane miles increased by 9% while the number of vehicle miles traveled in a year increased to 168% by 1987. Now, 50% of the world's vehicle miles are driven in the U.S. By contrast mass transit use, at a fraction of the fuel consumption, has dropped nearly two-thirds since the mid-1940s.

Environmental Decline

The continuing increase in the number of people on the planet and their use of fossil fuels such as petroleum, coal and natural gas are critical factors in the accelerating decline of the global environment. The discovery of fossil fuels marked a shift from human dependence on renewable resources (such as trees for heat, dung for fertilizer and pack animals for transport) to enormous dependence on nonrenewable resources.

By the 1980s, exhaustion of many nonrenewable resources, mainly petroleum, became evident. Moreover, intensification and expansion of agriculture were fast approaching their limits. Both processes were doing serious damage to soils and draining groundwater (underground water in rocks and soils, as in a spring). Communities of plants, animals and microbes were rapidly disappearing. Many had already vanished. Life-supporting services performed by natural ecosystems had been impaired or lost.

The Ehrlichs describe the consequences of the spread of people into natural ecosystems: "Human beings now occupy and use, at one level or another, some two-thirds of the planet's land surface, and are striving to find ways to exploit the remaining inhospitable third . . . The assault that we are carrying out upon the environment and resources of the planet is not just a matter of the brute numbers of people. Rather, it is what those people *do*; it is their *impact* on the things we care about—on each other, on nonrenewable resources, and above all on the environmental systems that sustain us."

The Ehrlichs offer an equation to demonstrate the effect that any human group has on the environment. The impact is a product of three factors. The first two factors are the number of people (population) and a measure of the average per-person consumption of resources (an index of affluence). The third factor is the product of the first two (population times average consumption) multiplied by an index of the environmental disruptiveness of the technologies needed to provide the goods consumed (technology). In other words, Impact = Population x Affluence x Technology, or I = PAT.

The I = PAT equation helps to explain why population growth remains a serious problem for rich nations. The A and T multipliers are so large for each person that a decrease in population size is not enough to offset the collective high level of consumption. The equation also helps to explain why nations with huge populations like China have an enormous impact on the planet. The P multiplier is so large that the smaller A and T are not enough to offset it. The overall impact of a society on the planet can be lowered by decreasing any of the three factors as long as the others are not increased.

Replacement Reproduction and Demographic Momentum

Births take place among young people and deaths take place primarily among old people. When the average couple in a population has slightly more than two children, the population is said to have reached "replacement reproduction." One child takes the place of each parent when they die. (Slightly more than two births compensate for the percentage of children who die before reaching reproductive age.) In countries that have high infant and child mortality rates, replacement rates require slightly more births per family. In the United States, the replacement reproduction rate is 2.1. The actual birthrate in 1989 was 1.9. In India, where infant deaths are higher, replacement would be about 2.4.; however, the actual birthrate in 1989 was 4.3.

The trend toward the world population doubling itself in ever shorter periods is based on a phenomenon called "demographic momentum"—the tendency of a previously growing population to keep expanding long after reproductive rates have been reduced. In a fast-growing population, only a dramatic rise in the death rate could produce zero-population growth (ZPG).

The driving force for demographic momentum is the age of rapidly growing populations. In 1989, the average age of the populations of the less-developed nations was under 15. This meant that more than a billion young people had not yet entered their prime reproductive years, ages 15 through 30.

It will take this group a half a century before they reach their 60s and start contributing to the death rate. Barring plunges in the birthrate that take family sizes well below replacement reproduction or substantial rises in the death rates, it takes five or six decades *after* a rapidly growing population reaches replacement reproduction to achieve ZPG.

Migration as a Source of Population Growth

Births are not the only source of additions to an area's population. Unequal access to resources prompts people to move from place to place. When assessing the size of the global population, migrations do not make any difference in the overall total. However, migrations can be an important problem in how global resources are used. Increasing numbers of ecological refugees are fleeing from areas where ecosystems are collapsing.

For example, in Brazil, many refugees from desertified (desertlike) northeastern Brazil have fled to Brazilian cities. Many others have joined migrants from southern Brazil and moved into the Amazon basin, where they are cutting down the rain forest for farming. Rapid deforestation of the Amazon rain forest is a major factor contributing to global warming, an element that could substantially reduce the planet's ability to sustain much of its human population.

Migration from poor to rich nations carries a different kind of threat. To the extent that the immigrants adopt the life-styles of their new, affluent countries, they will begin consuming more of the earth's resources per person.

Food: The Limiting Resource

When ecologists think about population problems, they think about food. The amount of food available restrains the size of any animal population, including humans, unless space, disease, predators or other factors set even lower limits.

In 1988, an estimated 950 million people were getting deficient diets—roughly one out of three people living in developing nations outside of China. Almost 400 million were so undernourished that their health or growth were jeopardized. The great majority were infants and small children whose parents lived on the edge of survival.

The Ehrlichs point out that many people subscribe to the notion that the only "population problem" in terms of food is one of maldistribution of food rather than total number of people to be fed. To the charge of maldistribution, the Ehrlichs respond, "If the excess food of the rich were somehow made available to the poor, the poor would be better fed; but there wouldn't be much left to accommodate a population increase."

Moreover, distribution is not always easy. Food destined for famine victims often lingers on docks waiting for transportation to become available or is detained by governments who want to use it as a political tool.

During the summer of 1990, the Soviet Union faced a unique distribution crisis. The farmers had a bumper wheat crop at the same time major cities had significant bread shortages. People who had once been conscripted by the government from the cities to work in fields to harvest crops, given the changed political climate, felt free to refuse to work as farm laborers. The result was an abundance of wheat and a shortage of bread.

Among some scientists and most of the general public, there has been complacency about food production because, for the last four decades, food production worldwide has continued to increase somewhat faster than the population. However, the Ehrlichs believe that the tide has already turned. China's grain production peaked in 1984 at a level three times that of 1950. Since then, production has fallen.

Nonagricultural sectors of China's economy are diverting water from agriculture and each year, some 4,000 square miles of China's farmland are taken out of production, three-quarters of it for construction. This represents an alarming trend for a nation with 7% of the earth's farmland and 21% of the human population.

China's difficulties are replicated in other countries. India made dramatic increases in wheat production from 1965 to 1983. However, since 1983, wheat production has been dropping for many reasons related to the deteriorating condition of the environment. About 40% of India's land is degraded from overuse. Soil erosion results in an annual loss of 6 billion tons of topsoil. In some areas, water levels in aquifers (subsurface zones of permeable rock that provide substantial amounts of water to wells) are dropping rapidly. Aquifers are unable to recharge due to rapid runoff brought about by deforestation. (In the absence of trees, the water is not held long enough in place to sink into the ground.) In a report to the Indian government, an environmentalist said, "At the rate we are destroying our forests, we will not have to wait for long to see India become the biggest desert in the world."

Most hungry countries are tropical, and growing more food in the tropics is not easy. Observers often fall into the assumption that because tropical rain forests are luxuriant and extremely productive biologically, crops that replace them when they are removed will be similarly productive. However, except in cases of rich volcanic soil, as in Java, or regularly flooded areas, as in parts of the Amazon Valley, the soils beneath rain forests are generally poor and thin. The rain forest's nutrients reside in the vegetation, so when the forest is cleared of vegetation, the nutrients are removed.

Agriculture in the tropics outside of rain-forest areas is also problematic. The absence of a strongly defined winter, or dry season, makes it difficult to suppress pest populations. Modern high-yield agricultural systems usually plant a single crop of genetically similar individual plants on large areas of land, thereby creating a potential bonanza for pests. Because heavy tropical rainfall erodes soil and washes away fertilizers and pesticides, farmers are prone to frequent reapplications of both types of chemicals, thereby contaminating water supplies.

Biotechnology (the application of engineering and technological principles to the life sciences) is often held out as the solution to increasing global food production. However, much biotechnological development holds little promise for the agriculture of poor nations. A great deal of the research is aimed at improving the interactions between crops and agricultural chemicals. Peasant farmers in poor nations are unlikely to have access to specially developed seeds or herbicides. Moreover, poor nations are likely to face problems because of the successes of biotechnology. For example, efforts to produce "natural vanilla" flavor in the laboratory threaten the livelihood of some 70,000 farmers in Madagascar, the world's biggest producer of vanilla beans.

In addition, governments in developing countries with many hungry people frequently concentrate their economic and technical support on cash crops intended for export, rather than on food for local markets. The

The earth's farmers are trying to feed about 86 million more people each year with about 24 billion fewer tons of topsoil. In addition to population encroachment, poor agricultural and forestry practices have contributed to erosion.

People can derive sustenance and economic gain from lands that are allowed to remain in a wild state. Tapping rubber and harvesting Brazil nuts (shown above) do not require clearing away forests, forests that must be kept intact if medicinal plants are not to be lost. Yet many native populations have not been recompensed for these medicinal plants.

income from cash crops helps the relatively well-off in cities of those countries, but does little for subsistence farmers or the urban poor.

Overpopulation's Effect on Global Health

A chapter in *Population Explosion* called "Global Ecosystem Health," describes the two ways in which population size influences health and life expectancy. One way is indirectly through an impact on the health of the global ecosystem—the earth's life-support systems (air, water, climate, etc.). The other is directly through what is known as "public health."

The Ehrlichs view the two ways as linked. "Food is intimately involved in both kinds of health," they write. "Human attempts to produce more food more often than not reduce ecosystem health, which in turn undermines the ability of terrestrial and aquatic ecosystems to supply humanity with sustenance. Undernourished people are more susceptible to diseases and more likely to die from them."

They then illustrate the repercussions from overpopulation on a variety of environmental problems—greenhouse warming, acid rain, the depletion of the ozone layer and desertification. To demonstrate the consequences that overpopulation can have on a global level, the Ehrlichs offer an area of America, south Florida, as a living laboratory.

If Florida were an independent nation, it would be one of the fastest-growing in the world, with an annual growth rate of 2.8% per year, equivalent to that of Bangladesh. Florida's growth rate is due to migration not to a high birthrate.

The signs of explosive growth are everywhere. Lake Okeechobee is heavily polluted, and groundwater tables are dropping. Developments are rapidly encroaching on the once teeming wildlife of the Everglades and in the process are draining marshes and destroying ecosystems. The highest point in flat south Florida is "Mount Garbage," the Miami sanitary landfill. Informal dumps line the area's back roads.

Before European settlers came, water drained along a gentle slope from northern Florida into Lake Okeechobee. From there it flowed as a sheet, many miles wide and a few inches deep, to Florida Bay, a body of water between the Florida Keys and the mainland. The flowing sheet of water, the famous "river of grass," forms the central part of the Everglades. The rich waters of the enormous Everglades and the Florida Bay once supported a wide variety of plant and animal life; however, the influx of people, agriculture and industry has put heavy demands on the water supply, resulting in a disaster for the area's wildlife. Bird populations have been reduced by about 90%. The coral reefs of the Florida Keys are in decline.

In addition, Florida is the state most at risk from a sea-level rise due to global warming. The predicted 2- to 3-foot rise in sea level that could occur as a result of global warming would flood a substantial portion of the state over the next half-century.

Economists' Assumptions

In a chapter of *Population Explosion* entitled "Population, Growthism, and National Security," the Ehrlichs point out that for a long time, population growth and economic growth were uniformly considered good. More people meant more security, allowed divisions of labor and made possible economies of scale. Based on this kind of thinking, economist Colin Clark, in 1969, announced that India within a decade would be the most powerful nation in the world, because of its growing population.

Ecologists have long been frustrated by the extreme growth orientation of mainstream economics, a theory they hold responsible for the failure of politicians, business-people and the general public to recognize the increasing seriousness of the population crisis.

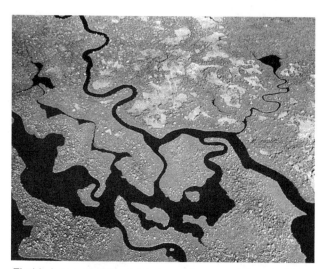

Florida has one of the fastest-growing populations in the United States, greatly taxing state resources. The Everglades are particularly vulnerable to water loss and are showing strain.

A few economists have bucked the trend. One group at the World Resources Institute has engaged in developing a new method for measuring a nation's economic performance that includes an accounting for depletion of natural resources, such as wildlife, forests, fishing grounds, groundwater, soils and minerals.

However, many mainstream economists continue to share the view of British economist Wilfred Beckerman, who believes that economic growth has gone on since the time of the ancient Greeks (around 400 B.C.) and there is no reason to suppose that it cannot continue for another 2,500 years.

In the view of the Ehrlichs, the failure of mainstream economists to recognize a need for population control is rooted in their belief in two axioms: that there is an infinite supply of resources, and that a satisfactory substitute can be found for every resource.

Biologists unfamiliar with economic theory have been shocked when they have come upon an industry that appeared to be destroying its resource base. The whaling industry, for example, has harvested whales at a rate that ensures their extinction. The behavior of maximizing current return on capital at the expense of long-term sustainable yields is rooted in the premise that when one resource is destroyed, another can take its place and be profitably exploited to extinction. The fallacy of this assumption is that even if there were an infinite supply of resources, some resources, such as fresh water, have no substitutes. Moreover, the quality of substitutes is not always comparable. Insecticides are a poor substitute for natural predators.

Waiting for the Demographic Transition

During the 20 years that elapsed between publication of *Population Bomb* and *The Population Explosion* little appears to have been accomplished in slowing population growth. The small reduction in global growth that was achieved during those years was mainly due to fertility reductions in China and in the industrialized West. A few developing nations had managed some fertility declines, but most were growing as rapidly as ever.

The decades of the '70s and '80s had been wasted waiting for what has long been believed to be an automatic demographic transition—a decline in birthrates as a consequence of industrial development. Since fertility reductions occurred in Europe and North America more or less simultaneously with industrialization, it has been assumed that the latter promoted the former.

Those who put their faith in the idea of an automatic demographic theory did so by ignoring fertility declines in developing countries with little or no industrial development, such as Sri Lanka, Costa Rica and China, and a lack of fertility declines in other nations that had made substantial industrial progress, such as Brazil and Mexico.

In fact, industry has little to do with a fall in fertility. Research has established that factors related to women and families are more important than overall national industrial development in promoting declines in population. The critical prerequisites to a reduction in fertility are: adequate nutrition, proper sanitation, basic health care and education, and equal rights for women.

Even a few years of schooling prompts women to improve the lives of their families through more balanced meals, better home health care and sanitation. These factors, in turn, lessen infant and child mortality, thereby making men and women more receptive to the idea of smaller families. Educated women are more receptive to learning about contraception and better able to use whatever method they choose. Moreover, when women have sources of status other than children, family size declines. Factors related to an improved status of women helped to explain, in substantial part, why China's "birth planning," a national effort to restrict family size, was more successful than India's similar effort.

It is no accident that developed nations with lower fertility rates also have lower rates of illiteracy and malnutrition. A high per-capita income is not required in order to have widespread literacy and a satisfactory diet.

Global Cooperation

In trying to explain the decline of some past civilizations, historians have usually looked at social, economic or political factors. Seldom have they looked at population pressures and the impact they might have had on environmental deterioration and resource depletion.

The general decline the Ehrlichs cite is not that of a single country or empire, but that of the entire planet. To reverse the ongoing deterioration, they believe, will take international collaboration.

Population control—let alone the alleviation of global environmental problems—will not be easily achieved in a world plagued by racism, religious prejudice, sexism, and gross economic inequality. The notion that numbers give strength is strongly ingrained—often leading to fear of being outproduced by other groups . . . To resolve any element of the human predicament, xenophobia [fear of strangers or foreigners] must be overcome. The list of tasks is daunting: the rate of climatic change must be slowed, its effects minimized, and general global environmental deterioration—especially the extinction of populations and species of other organisms—reversed. That is the only way that nations can find anything resembling security for the future.

EARTH DAY'S 20TH BIRTHDAY

The Focus Has Broadened

Conceived by Wisconsin Senator Gaylord Nelson and organized by Denis Hayes, a Harvard Law School student, Earth Day 1970 was a relatively simple event. It was planned as a nationwide afternoon teach-in about the environment, at some 1,500 colleges and 10,000 other schools. Nine staff members, most of them students in their 20s, coordinated the grass-roots movement from a small office in Washington, on a budget of $125,000. Throughout the United States, an estimated 20 million people participated.

The 1970 celebration continued some of the protest techniques of the 1960s. For example, in West Virginia, demonstrators dumped 5 tons of roadside trash on the steps of a courthouse to highlight the problem of litter. Students in San Jose, California, buried a car to protest auto emission pollution.

Earth Day 1990 was a vastly more elaborate affair, involving the expenditure of millions of dollars and months of preparation. The original half-day of events had grown to a weekend of participation in 3,600 communities in the United States and in 140 other countries.

The format of the planned demonstrations, which were expected to include 100 million people, varied widely. Scheduled were parades; proclamations; protests; teach-ins; trash-ins; ecofairs; a bicycle procession in Bengal, India; and the efforts of a team of climbers from the United States, the Soviet Union and China, who intended to climb Mt. Everest to clean up debris left by previous expeditions.

A main goal of Earth Day 1990 was to broaden the environmental movement beyond its so-called upper-class, bird-watcher base. In February, a group from Earth Day 1990 embarked on a nation-wide tour to urge minority members to become involved. Gerry Stover, the executive director of the Environmental Consortium for Minority Outreach, in a December 18, 1989, *Time* article entitled "Let Earth Have Its Day," observed: "In this country 4 out of 5 toxic waste dumps are in or near minority communities."

Denis Hayes, now a San Francisco lawyer, chaired Earth Day 1990, headquartered in Palo Alto, California. The organization served as an umbrella group, lending assistance to local and international groups. Earth Day 1990 had a staff of 120 and a board of 115 directors made up of celebrities, prominent politicians, religious leaders, labor officials and business executives.

Fears That a Broadened Base of Support Weakened the Message

The Earth Day 1990 headquarters staff plotted strategy as if the event were a political campaign. Moreover, they adopted ideas from Madison Avenue. Posters and ads carried the slogan: "WHO SAYS YOU CAN'T CHANGE THE WORLD?" As a part of a drive to raise $3 million, Earth Day 1990 licensed its logo.

Although spectacular accidents get a great deal of publicity, the world's oceans and lakes are more at risk from everyday pollution than from events such as the Exxon oil spill. Despite some success at cleaning up various waterways, sewage, trash and bilge water remain great dangers.

Fuel consumption for the average 1991 model car is 28.1 mpg, no greater than that of the average 1986 model. Yet old advertisements for what are now antique cars make fuel efficiency claims of 30 mpg. Although earlier cars did not have gas-consuming air conditioners, they were heavier. Transportation uses 63% of U.S. petroleum. Automobile exhaust makes up 40–60% of urban smog.

Planned obsolescence contributes to the world's trash problem, as do junk mail, multilayered containers (a bottle inside of a box wrapped in cellophane), and leaves and lawn clippings that could be turned into compost. Recycling has increased but so has the overall amount of trash.

The marketing of Earth Day and the sincerity of the apparent change of opinion by American businesses about the event drew some sharp criticism. A March 26, 1990, article entitled "The Selling of Earth Day," expressed some of the negative feelings by saying, "The greening of the boardroom raises questions of whether slick marketing techniques don't contradict the original spirit of Earth Day." The article went on to say that in Earth Day 1970 "Corporate involvement was basically limited to CEOs drawing up plans to evacuate their offices if the protestors stormed the citadels . . . This time the CEOs are more likely to invite the participants in for herbal tea."

Change of Focus

Besides the differences in size, format and packaging of the event itself, there were other more fundamental differences between the first and the 20-year anniversary celebrations. Earth Day 1970 dealt with local and regional problems, such as the Cuyahoga River, which was prone to catch fire from pollutants, as it made its way through Cleveland, Ohio.

Earth Day 1990 dealt with broader, global issues. The targets of environmentalists have changed over the span of the two decades from concerns mostly centered on narrow issues, such as a stream in a valley or creatures threatened by a dam, a development, or even the building of a telescope, to broad concerns that threaten the entire planet, such as industrial gases that are trapping heat and leading to global warming.

Earth Day 1970 was a national event limited mostly to the United States. Earth Day 1990 was a worldwide protest in 140 nations aimed at among other things: pollution in Eastern Europe, destruction of the Latin American rain forest and the deterioration of the ozone layer.

Despite much greater public interest and involvement in 1990—76% of Americans now refer to themselves as environmentalists—many long-term environmentalists believe that the environment is in far worse condition than it was on Earth Day 1970.

An April 22, 1990, *New York Times* article entitled "Guarding Environment: A World of Challenges," by Matthew Wald, described the shift in the focus of environmentalists by saying, "Scientists have discarded the image of Mother Nature with a black eye for one of Mother Nature stumbling toward a cliff." Wald quoted Michael Oppenheimer, a senior scientist at the Environmental Defense Fund, who said, "The ozone hole is a smoking gun." Oppenheimer called the thinning of the ozone layer, "real proof that humans threaten life on earth."

Despite the worsened condition of the earth, there have been some remarkable changes in attitudes. In the wake of the first Earth Day, agencies and protective measures came into being, among them the institution of the Environmental Protection Agency, the Clean Air Act, and the Clean Water

Act. Many corporations have dropped frequently proclaimed arguments, that presented to the public the alternatives of pollution control versus a loss of jobs. Moreover, a marked change in the public's view of the environment has corporations scrambling to demonstrate how "green" they are, in order to gain a competitive edge.

Progress on Preventing and/or Repairing Damage: Mixed Results

The nearly unanimous agreement in Montreal in January 1989 to reduce worldwide production of chlorofluorocarbons is cited by many experts as evidence that global efforts can be addressed to problems of the planet. Yet many such gains are offset by losses. For example:

- Utilities in the United States are emitting 15% less sulfur dioxide, the coal by-product that causes acid rain; however, they are burning more than twice as much coal as they did in 1970.
- The tailpipes of new cars emit 96% less carbon monoxide and hydrocarbons and 76% less nitrogen oxides than older cars. However, there has been such an increase in cars on the road and such an increase in congestion that in 1988 half of all Americans lived in counties that violated the clean air standards.
- Fish have made a comeback in Cuyahoga River and Lake Erie into which it empties, and in other Great Lakes. Yet the bodies of Great Lakes fish carry such high levels of toxic chemicals that they are unfit to eat and restocking the lakes to increase the numbers of fish seems of questionable value.

In contrast to problems recognized in the 1970s, such as dwindling populations of animals, which appeared to have a solution based on existing knowledge, the problems of the 1990s may require solutions without there being time to fully understand the symptoms. The *New York Times* quoted Kenneth Keller, a chemical engineer, formerly the president of the University of Minnesota, who wrote, "Our ability to affect our ecological niche is accompanied by an inability to assess the effects of doing so. In contrast to similar problems in the past, we are faced with the situation that the negative effects may be irreversible if we do not act to correct them, but that forces us to act before we can be sure that we understand them."

Solutions Proposed in the 1970s May Worsen Other Problems

Acid rain is reduced through the use of scrubbers that remove sulfur dioxide from power plant emissions.

However, the use of scrubbers requires a greater use of coal for each unit of electricity, thereby raising carbon dioxide emissions. The increased emissions accelerate the buildup of gases over the planet, such as greenhouse gases, which trap the sun's warmth like panes of glass in a greenhouse. Moreover, the elimination of chlorofluorocarbons to protect the ozone layer has made many industrial machines less efficient, thus raising their fuel use and their output of carbon dioxide.

While the passage of the Endangered Species Act in 1973 has helped to bring back some plants and animals from the verge of extinction, by 1990, species were being lost faster than they could be counted. Since the passage of the act, the federal government has annually added 35 to 50 plants, animals and insects to its endangered list, but, by 1990, the government had removed only 10, six of whom had been determined to be extinct. The length of the government's endangered list in no way mirrors the number of species threatened. It simply reflects the slowness of the legal process required to list a species as endangered.

Conversion to an Environmental Ethic

The *New York Times*, seemingly less skeptical of an actual change in the mentality of corporate America than *Time*, proposed that the reasons why industry has changed its attitude toward the environment during the two decades since 1970 is tied to the change in the public's attitude. For example, Conoco, the world's 20th-largest oil company, announced it was changing its recipe for gasoline to reduce air pollution. From coast to coast, the company received a flood of phone calls to ask where the gas could be bought.

The reason for the public's increased concern for the environment is less clear. Some observers trace it to a merger of two popular opinions: the need for preservation of the wild and a fear of cancer as a consequence of new chemicals.

Translation of the Public Ethic into Practice

Although many more Americans claim to be apprehensive about the welfare of the environment, actual practices raise doubts about the level of their concern. The average gas mileage for car models in the United States declined 4% from 1988 to 1990, but the number of miles driven continues to rise by about 2% year after year. The amount of garbage discarded per person in the United States rose from 2.5 pounds in 1960 to 3.6 pounds in 1986.

The realization is growing that if the planet is not safe for wildlife it is not safe for humanity. To this end many organizations have formed to work to preserve and expand habitat, to eliminate hazardous wastes and to prevent hunting species to extinction.

Similarly, for years, water heaters have been available that use only 1,500 kilowatt-hours of fuel a year and they are expected to improve to just over 1,000 kilowatt-hours in the 1990s. But few consumers appear willing to take out the old model and replace it with a new one. Even when the old heater breaks down, the consumer tends to balk at the increased cost of the more efficient model. The 3,000 kilowatt-hours difference in fuel expenditure between the 1985 model and the anticipated 1990's model is equivalent to the annual consumption of about 1.25 tons of coal.

Living Smarter

Most environmentalists agree that the constant growth of the world's population poses a severe threat to the environment. A dissenter against that view is Julian Simon, a professor at the University of Maryland business school, who believes that a bigger population means more human creativity and more progress. His thesis is that standards of living, the availability of raw materials and life expectancies are all rising because the world is progressively inventing its way out of its problems.

Even less sanguine experts than Simon agree that some progress in solving environmental problems has been made. With some help from governments, some scientists are trying to lay the foundations for an economy that does not consume scarce resources and thereby continuously add to pollution.

The most promising invention of the last two decades is the photovoltaic cell, which turns sunlight into electricity. The price of such cells, while still too high to compete effectively with oil, is falling rapidly. With continued progress, many experts hope that solar cells, coupled with cheap energy storage systems, will supplant the use of oil, coal and natural gas.

There are other hopeful signs. During the last two decades, according to American Council for an Energy Efficient Economy spokesperson, Marc Ledbetter, the American economy has grown by roughly 50%, while energy use has risen by only 10%. The increase in efficiency has come from improvements in products used by consumers.

Toward a Philosophy of the Environment

The 20th anniversary of Earth Day fell as five major concerns threatened the planet: acid rain; the loss of the rain forests; global warming; the threat to the ozone layer; and the population explosion. All are sufficiently menacing that they require extensive changes in behavior.

To make change effective, the impetus behind the idea of never-ending growth must be addressed. World Bank economist Herman Daly, in an interview for an April 22, 1990, *Boston Globe* article entitled "20th Earth Day: Global Effort to Heal Our Home," disputed the conventional economic wisdom that calls for continuing economic growth.

Daly argued in his book *For the Common Good*, written with philosopher John Cobb, that the scale of human activities has grown too large for the natural ecological systems that support it. Costs of growth, such as congestion, pollution, deforestation and acid rain, now outweigh the benefits. He said, "I think the reason we've been so eager for growth is we want to cure poverty, but we don't want to do it by redistribution or sharing . . . we have to move away from this easy solution of growing our way out of everything. The cure for poverty should be sought in population limitation and the redistribution of wealth and income. This would be within countries and between countries. The industrial countries first and foremost have to limit their consumption."

Other prominent thinkers agree. In her book the *Ecological Revolution*, Carolyn Merchant sees signs of a fundamental change in human society, as people wrestle with the contradictions at the heart of the environmental crisis. The growth of a new "ecocentric" ethic rests on the idea of a network of mutual obligations between humans and nature.

Yale environmental historian William Cronon believes the environmental challenge facing the world is essentially a moral one. Cronon's view appears to be part of a trend toward thinking of the environment in moral terms. In an interview with the *Boston Globe*, Father Thomas Berry, a Passionist priest and the author of *The Dream of Earth*, said "We have a general sense of the evil of suicide and homicide and genocide, but we commit biocide and 'geocide' and we have no moral principles to deal with it. Our sense of morality stops with humans."

An April 22, 1990, *Boston Globe* column entitled "Earth Day's 'Gideons'" told the story of one person's effort to spread the word that environmental issues are ethical ones. Steve Wright was Vermont's fish and wildlife commissioner before becoming the president of Sterling College, a small environmentally focused school in northern Vermont. In a talk before the Vermont Audubon Council, Wright made the comment, "*A Sand County Almanac*, ought to be in every hotel room in Vermont. It could be the Gideon Bible for those who love land and wildlife."

Wright was referring to a book first published in 1949 and rediscovered in the late 1960s, *A Sand County Almanac*, by Aldo Leopold, the founder of ecological science and of the American wilderness protection movement, which inspired many people to become a part of the environmental movement. More than a year after Wright's talk, an officer of the Council called to tell him that the group planned to make an effort to meet his challenge as a part of their observance of the 20th anniversary of Earth Day. In mid-April 1990, the Vermont Audubon Society announced that, with the help of Sterling College, Oxford University Press, two bookstores and an anonymous donor, they would begin distribution of *A Sand County Almanac* to 1,000 inn and motel rooms along Route 7 between Bennington and Burlington.

If Aldo Leopold, who died in 1949, were still alive, he might have been uncomfortable with the parades, the proclamations and the coffee cups carrying Earth Day 1990 logos, but he would surely have been uneasy with the apparent adoption of "green" slogans by corporations that at the same time were major polluters. In *A Sand County Almanac* he wrote, "In our attempt to make conservation easy, we have made it trivial."

On the other hand, Leopold might have agreed with mule trainers, who claim that in order to get a mule to move, you have to first get his attention.

5

Archaeology and Anthropology

THE DEAD SEA SCROLLS

A Dispute Among Scholars Over an Ancient Treasure

The Dead Sea Scrolls, hundreds of ancient Jewish and Aramaic documents, are the literary remains of a Jewish community started about 150 B.C. and destroyed in A.D. 68. They were discovered by Bedouin tribesmen between 1947 and 1956 in caves on the northwestern shore of the Dead Sea, 20 miles east of Jerusalem, in an area variously referred to as Khirbat Qumran, Wadi (valley, river, or dry riverbed) Qumran, or simply Qumran. The documents, written on leather or papyrus, have become the source of a bitter, ongoing protest by scholars who have criticized the long delay in making some of the most important documents available.

The possible links between Jesus and the Dead Sea Scrolls have made them one of the most talked-about archaeological finds of the century. Despite the widespread interest, more than 30 years later approximately one-fourth of the material remains unpublished. The original informal target date for issuing transcriptions of all the scrolls was 1970. In 1989, the 18 scholars who constitute the official scrolls team told the Israeli government that complete publication could not be expected until 1997.

Dr. John Strugnell, a professor of Christian origins at Harvard, the head of the scrolls team whose job it is to piece together and analyze the fragments, explained that fund-raising problems and the Arab-Israeli wars had interfered with progress. He admitted that the 1997 deadline was only an "intelligent guess" and that the work could extend for years beyond the deadline date.

The new timetable further aroused scholars already angry at being denied access to the material. The team members, 12 of whom labor in Jerusalem, responded to the criticism by pointing out that the difficult task takes great precision. In 1989, Israel's antiquities committee set up an oversight committee to monitor the team's progress.

The Ongoing Arguments

An August 14, 1989, *Time* article entitled "Secrets of the Dead Sea Scrolls: A Scholarly Squabble Over an Archaelogical Treasure" described some of the participants in the quarrel and their points of view. A principal among the critics is *Biblical Archaeology Review* (BAR), a well-respected laypersons' magazine, which has long expressed unhappiness with what the magazine's staff considers unconscionable foot-dragging.

The editor of the magazine, Herschel Shanks, labeled the new timetable a "hoax and a fraud." In Shanks's opinion the scrolls are unlikely ever to be published by the current team. A November 21, 1989, *New York Times* article entitled "Scholars Clash Over Origins of Dead Sea Scroll," described a heated confrontation between Herschel Shanks and John Strugnell, during which Shanks demanded that Strugnell resign. To which Strugnell responded "Give me a little time."

The Khirbat Qumran, Israel, site and some of the caves on the escarpment above it where the Dead Sea Scrolls were discovered.

Extensive coverage of the controversy appeared in the March/April 1990 issue of BAR and was followed by shorter pieces and a flood of letters from readers in the May/June, July/August, and September/October issues. The readers were unanimous in their condemnation of the team's failure to make the documents available to scholars.

Assessing Blame

Of the 11 caves in Qumran in which texts were found, the contents of all but two have been completely published. The text from caves 1 through 3 and 5 through 10 have been fully published and most of the 25 texts found in Cave 11 have been either published or are soon to be published. But these texts represent less than half of the finds.

Cave 4 is the source of the scholarly battle. All of the texts from this cave were found in fragments. An estimated 15,000 fragments were rescued from the debris and had to be pieced together like a puzzle into an estimated 520 or 521 scrolls. Only 98 of the texts have been published.

The major portion of the unpublished texts was assigned to Jozef Milik, a Polish refugee priest, who had been pursuing his doctorate at the Pontifical Biblical Institute in Rome. Milik is alleged to have been given the assignment because he was presumed to be "the fastest man with a fragment."

Many critics contend that Milik, now with the National Center for Scientific Research in Paris, is the scholar most responsible for the slow progress of the team. Subsequent to his assignment, Milik became quite ill, left the priesthood, and married. Except for a few small articles, his last

publication, a hefty volume entitled *The Books of Enoch: Aramaic Fragments of Qumran Cave 4*, came out in 1976.

Over the years, Milik, for the most part, has been unresponsive to phone calls, letters or requests for interviews. He has remained unimpressed by the criticism and *Time* quoted him as saying "The world will see the manuscripts when I have done the necessary work." He described the criticism as "unhealthy curiosity."

In 1989, Milik reassigned some of the most important texts to other scholars. The May/June issue of BAR reported that one of the scholars to whom Milik had reassigned some of the work, James VanderKam of North Carolina State University, was willing to show photographs of the texts in his possession to other scholars. He said that Milik had told him to do with the documents as he wished.

A staff member at BAR was able to reach Milik on the phone and it was reported in the May/June 1990 issue that he had agreed to authorize other scholars to see the remaining scrolls under his control. Then, apparently, Milik changed his mind. BAR reported in the July/August 1990 issue that Milik had branded VanderKam's decision to share the scrolls as irresponsible.

Milik May Not Be the Only Obstacle

An article entitled "A Visit with M. Jozef T. Milik, Dead Sea Scroll Editor," by Joseph Fitzmyer in the July/August issue of BAR suggested that the fault may not all lie with Milik. Fitzmyer described international political involvement that may be an equally significant stumbling block.

When Qumran Cave 4 was discovered by Bedouin tribesmen in 1952, it was a part of the kingdom of Jordan, in the area of the so-called West Bank. The Palestine Archaeological Museum, as it was then known, did not have sufficient funds to buy Cave 4 fragments from the negotiator for the Bedouin. Rather than risk having the fragments sold piecemeal, the museum appealed to foreign institutions for financial help.

In exchange for their help with the purchase price, the museum had an agreement with the foreign institutions that the fragments would stay at the museum until they were published by the international team assigned to do the work. Once published, an agreed-upon distribution of the pieces would take place among the institutions. For reasons known only to themselves, the Jordanian government in 1961 nationalized the fragments and scrolls with no acknowledgment of any obligation to reimburse the foreign institutions.

During the Six-Day War (1967), Israel took possession of the West Bank. The Palestine Archaeological Museum

At right is a fragment from the scrolls. The fragments are so darkened with age that the ink and the leather are approximately the same color. However, fragments can be photographed by means of infrared light, rendering them legible as black ink on a gray background. Photos are also safer to handle than the fragile scraps salvaged from the caves.

became the Rockefeller Museum under the jurisdiction of Israel. According to Fitzmyer, it is at the feet of the Israeli committee in charge of the scrolls that Milik lays the blame for holding up publication.

In 1990, a philanthropic group, the American Foundation, wrote to the Israeli government with an offer to support the cost of publication up to $100,000. The Israeli government took the offer under advisement.

There Is Enough Blame for Everyone

In the opinion of Lawrence Schiffman of New York University, the material could be published in a short time if the circle of scholars were enlarged. Enlargement of the circle has been prevented thus far by a system of control imposed shortly after the discoveries. The initial finds were rapidly published by Israeli scholars. Jordan responded by authorizing the creation of a select group of antiquities experts, all of them Christians, who were given exclusive rights to study and publish the rest of the manuscripts.

The circle of scholars parceled out the various texts among themselves. Some of the scrolls went on display at West Jerusalem's Shrine of the Book, but most were lodged in the museum in East Jerusalem. When Israel acquired jurisdiction over the museum, they left the existing team in place. In time, some of the members consigned some of the scrolls to their own graduate students, thereby by-passing better-known scholars.

The Case for Slow Publication

Eugene Ulrich, professor of Hebrew scriptures at Notre Dame University, is in the process of bringing to completion the work of more than three decades begun by the late Professor Patrick Skehan of Catholic University. Skehan and Professor Frank Cross of Harvard University were the two Americans originally selected in 1953 to join the international team charged with editing the scrolls. Skehan, who died in 1980, had before his death designated Ulrich to carry on his work. As he neared retirement in the mid-1980s, Cross too appointed Ulrich as the successor for his share of the scrolls.

Ulrich linked the extended timetable to the difficulty of the work. He described the material as being in thousands of tiny, fragile, hard-to-decipher pieces that he characterized as darkened, brittle, cracked and moth-eaten. He felt that some of the criticisms were based on an erroneous notion that the documents were being suppressed because they might be embarrassing to Christians or Jews.

Ulrich made the case that only the most skilled scholars could handle the work with the scrolls. In an interview for the July/August issue of BAR, Professor Ulrich said, "The vast majority of people who will use these editions—including average university professors . . . are barely able to judge competently difficult readings."

He pointed out that hasty publications had already introduced errors and gave as an example a 1950s publication by Hebrew University Professor E.L. Sukenik, who, with the help of his son and Hebrew University professor Nahman Avigad, had edited one of the Isaiah scrolls. In Ulrich's opinion, the volume is filled with errors and questionable readings. Ulrich believes that hasty editing could introduce errors that would for the next century become the basis for ill-founded scholarship.

BAR responded to Ulrich's position by arguing that publication of the texts is the beginning of the editing process and not the end of it. They called attention to the current preparation of a whole new edition of texts that had already been published by the current team of editors. For example, Johns Hopkins professor P. Kyle McCarter is preparing a new edition of the *Copper Scroll* (the only scroll made of metal rather than leather or papyrus), previously published by J.T. Milik.

Yields and Scholarly Clashes from Already Published Texts

The scrolls that have been published have proven to be important to both scholars and to ordinary religious participants. Insight into ancient Jewish life was provided by a hitherto unknown text called the *Manual of Discipline*, which provided a list of the rules for group living within an ancient Jewish sect. With the exception of Esther, portions of all the books of the Old Testament were found in the caves, including a complete scroll of Isaiah, which is 1,000 years older than any known surviving manuscript. The scrolls attest to the considerable accuracy with which Jewish scribes over the centuries have preserved the text of the Bible.

A fundamental question that has become the source of heated scholarly arguments is whether the scrolls were the work of one small sect or the accumulated Judaic wisdom of that era. Unfortunately, to settle the far-reaching dispute over the hypothesis of the scrolls' origin and nature, scholars need access to the remaining unpublished scrolls.

Shortly after the discovery of the first scrolls in 1947, scholars proposed that they had been written by the Essenes, a small ascetic Jewish sect, who were believed to have strongly influenced the early Christians. The Essene monks were thought to have had a monastery at nearby Qumran. Subsequent scroll discoveries were also ascribed to Essene monks. A link between the scrolls and the Essenes was forged in the public's as well as in academics' minds by the 1955 publication of Edmund Wilson's book *The Scrolls from the Dead Sea*. A few historians have contended that

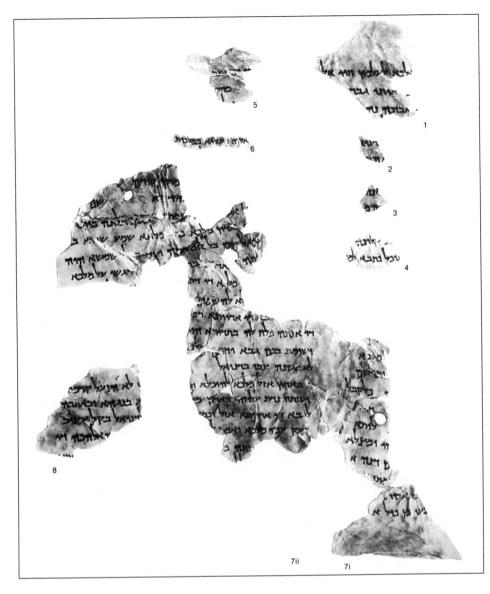

Assembling the scroll fragments is like assembling a very incomplete jigsaw puzzle. For example, working from known scripture scholars might deduce that the fragments of a particular scroll are from the Book of Daniel (as are ones to the left). Scholars must locate the proper position of a fragment on the proper page, the proper line and proper position within the line, and eventually chart all these pieces. Eight fragmentary manuscripts of the Book of Daniel were found at Qumran, dating from the late second century B.C. to the middle of the first century A.D.

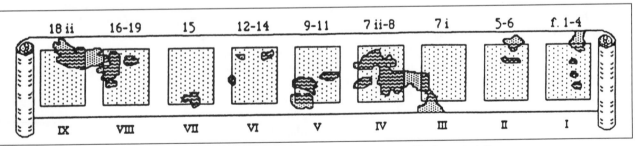

The figure above shows a distribution of fragments from the Book of Daniel found in Cave 4 at Qumran.

John the Baptist and possibly Jesus himself were Essenes. Essene life was described by Pliny, the Roman writer and by Josephus, the Jewish historian, in the first century after Christ. In Pliny's and Josephus's contemporary accounts, the Essenes never numbered more than 4,000 and were said to have prospered in Palestine from 150 B.C. to A.D. 70.

Opponents of the Essene Hypothesis

Some scholars have concluded that the estimated 800 different scrolls are not the works of the Essenes, but instead represent the thinking of a wide spectrum of Palestinian Jews. If their assessment is correct, historians and theologians will gain a new perspective on post-biblical

Judaism and its influence on early Christianity. Because the scrolls contain ideas that resemble later Christian doctrine, the documents could suggest that Christianity grew out of a mainstream Judaism that was in a state of transition and turmoil, rather than out of a narrow dissident sect.

A vigorous dissenter against the notion of an Essene link is Dr. Norman Golb, a professor of Jewish history and civilization at the University of Chicago. In an interview with the *New York Times*, Golb said, "There is no rational basis for the Essene hypothesis, except for 40 years of commitment to an old idea by a clique of scholars."

Golb supports his contention by pointing out that as more of the scrolls have been analyzed it has become clear that none of the documents relates to Qumran, even though it was thought to be the headquarters for the sect. Moreover, *The Manual of Discipline* includes such rules as avoidance of the accumulation of personal wealth and maintenance of a communal life, but it makes no mention of celibacy, a fundamental tenet of Essene life.

In support of his arguments against an Essene link, Golb points out that additional examination of the stone ruins at Qumran has not confirmed that the site was a monastery, Essene or any other kind. Moreover, excavations of graves revealed the presence of women, which would not have been likely if the site had been a monastery.

Based on the remains of several large cisterns, food storage areas, stables, stone fortifications and a stone watchtower that commands an excellent view of the Dead Sea, some archaeologists suspect that the site was a military outpost. During the presentation of a report at a November 1989 Dead Sea Scrolls symposium, held at the Institute of Semitic Studies at Princeton, Dr. Golb said, "There's nothing to show it was anything but a fortress." He contends that Qumran was one of several armed bases around Jerusalem that formed a perimeter of defense against Roman invaders during the war from A.D. 67 to 73.

Golb asserted that the scrolls were transferred from Jerusalem to the caves for safekeeping during the siege. The scrolls, he believes, represent the accumulated treasure of Jewish writings and were not the works of Qumran monks.

In the Spring 1989 issue of *The American Scholar*, Golb restated his hypothesis. In the autumn issue of the journal, Dr. John Trever of the School of Theology at Claremont California, an expert on the scrolls, responded to Golb's position by citing flaws in the argument that Qumran was a military fortress. He pointed out that no military hardware of any kind has appeared in the excavations, except for that used by the Romans to destroy the site.

The presence of earlier documents in the caves, as Golb contends, would raise the possibility that the scrolls could have been a collection of documents varied in time and origin, rather than the original or transcribed work of a single group. When Strugnell, one of a small group of experts who have built their careers around the scrolls and support of the Essene hypothesis, acknowledged that several scrolls being prepared for publication in the next few years may date back before the time of the presumed Qumran monastery, a further blow was struck against the Essene hypothesis. A scroll called the Damascus Document includes a legal section from about 200 B.C. that was later incorporated into the Qumran legal code.

Because Dr. Golb and a growing number of younger researchers believe that the scrolls provide some missing links in theology and history between the Old and New Testaments they want the scroll's team of scholars to accelerate publication and in the meantime to furnish qualified scholars with photographs of unpublished documents. Otherwise, Dr. Golb said, "a generation of scholars will never get the chance to study these documents."

In Golb's opinion, "liberating" the scrolls would make possible a new appraisal of the ferment 2,000 years ago when Christianity took root and most Jews turned away from a priest-dominated Judaism to evolve into the rabbinical Judaism that still survives.

The Debate Shows No Signs of Winding Down

The ferment among scholars does not appear to be related to controversial ideas in the documents themselves. P.Kyle McCarter, Jr., who is translating the *Copper Scroll*, said, "It's a shame that the material has taken so long to become available. Nobody thinks there's a conspiracy to withhold information. There is no motive for it. The unpublished material is not controversial in any way." Rather the critics' thinking seems to be that while the scrolls' editors want all the scholarly credit, there is enough credit for everyone to share.

In mid-December 1990, Strugnell was dismissed as the chief editor of the scrolls after having called Judaism "a horrible religion" in an interview with an Israeli journalist published in a Tel Aviv newspaper.

THE REVISION OF OLD OPINIONS

The Philistines Were Not Boors and the Early Israelites Were Probably Canaanites

The Philistines were a group of Aegean seafarers who lived in southwestern Palestine from about 1200 B.C. onward. The Bible depicts the Philistines as thieves and war mongers and ancient Egyptian paintings represent them as thieves and marauders. Since then, this image has undergone an odd transformation. Beginning in the 17th century, the term *philistine* became synonymous with smugly conventional, lacking in culture, and anti-intellectual. Recent archaeological excavations in Israel have suggested that the Philistines' boorish reputation is unwarranted.

The discoveries were made in the ancient city of Ekron, 20 miles west of Jerusalem, one of five major Philistine city-states, which included Gaza, Ashkelon, Ashdod and Gath. Finds at the Ekron site suggest that the Philistines were one of the most highly civilized people of their time. They were successful merchants and industrialists, accomplished in the production of pottery and metal tools, and expert architects and town planners.

During an interview for an August 29, 1988, *Time* article entitled "Giving Goliath His Due," Seymour Gitin, the American director of the William F. Albright Institute of Archaeological Research in Jerusalem, said, "While they existed, the Philistines served as a link between the East and the West. They introduced a new culture to this part of the world. Eventually they became a great trading power and a powerful industrial nation with their individual style."

The excavation site was first surveyed in 1923; however, it was not identified as the city of Ekron until the 1960s. Excavated as a joint American-Israeli venture, the 50-acre area was described by Gitin as a "time capsule." Over the course of seven seasons of digging, the scientists have uncovered a wealth of materials that has led to the new perspective on the Philistines.

The Varied Fortunes of the Philistines

During a time of great political upheaval, the Philistines, settled in the Levant region, on what is now the southeastern coast of Israel, between the Israelite tribes to the east and the Egyptian empire to the south. It was a period in which the Hittite empire was in the midst of crumbling and Greece had begun 500 years of decline. Trude Dothan of Hebrew University, a co-director of the Ekron dig, has said of the Philistines: "Their culture was a unique product of tradition and innovation in a time of international catastrophe."

Because they possessed a monopoly on iron smelting and may have even had the capacity to make steel, the Philistines gained a reputation as fierce warriors. The Old Testament provides accounts of the Philistines' frequent clashes with the neighboring Israelite tribes. The Philistines sent Delilah to discover the secret of Samson's strength, and later slew King Saul and his sons in battle, and stole the Holy Ark of the Covenant. The Israelites pursued the Philistines to the gates of Ekron, following an incident in which David killed the giant Philistine Goliath with his slingshot. To cope with the military threat of the Philistines, Israel and Judah united against them. Defeated first by David and then by the Egyptians, the Philistines went into a decline in the 10th century B.C.

Less is known of the Philistines' history from 1,000 to 600 B.C., which is why Ekron is a particularly important archaeological site. At the end of this period, Ekron was only 10 acres in size, a reflection of the decline in power of the Philistines as a consequence of the rise of the Israelite monarchies. Conquest by the Assyrian kings of Mesopotamia, at the end of the eighth century B.C., brought peace and prosperity.

Philistine Industrial Complex

As a vassal state of the Assyrians, the Philistine civilization flourished during the seventh century B.C. The Assyrian-imposed peace permitted the import of olives from neighboring Judah, a former enemy, and Ekron became a major oil processing center.

During the seventh century B.C., olive oil was used for an enormous variety of everyday activities, such as in lamps, religious rituals, condiments and medicine. Ekron's production and distribution of olive oil was a lucrative trade. Moreover, since olive oil was in great demand and could be shipped easily, it offered a source for heavy taxation.

The excavation of only 2% of the Ekron site has uncovered the presence of 100 olive oil installations. The most installations found at other comparable sites has been 15, the typical number being only 3. At a concentration of about 100 per room, the remains of 1,000 ceramic vessels used to store olive oil were found in Ekron's industrial area. Lids were also found, which indicated that the ceramic jars were used to ship the oil. Engineers working at the Ekron site have estimated that the city's annual oil output surpassed 1,000 tons, an equivalent of 20% of modern-day Israel's annual production. Much of the oil was shipped to

Building and Planning

The sophistication and size of Ekron's structures indicate that the Philistines were master builders. A 2,300 square-foot complex, possibly a royal palace, has been uncovered. The picture that has emerged from the Ekron site is one of a people who had advanced ideas about town planning. The city was surrounded by fortification walls and made up of distinct districts. Just inside the walls, on the periphery of the city, lay an industrial belt, separate from public buildings and residential areas. The residential areas included upper- and lower-class neighborhoods.

Accommodation of the water needs of the city was well thought out. Ekron was built in a stepped-down fashion, with a gradual descent from the outer perimeter to the city center, taking advantage of natural water runoff. Because the city was shaped like a basin, the wells in the center city had to be dug only a modest 5 to 10 feet. During the interview for *Time* Seymour Gitin described the layout of the city as "a highly sophisticated way of building."

Religion

In every district in Ekron, small four-horned altars used to burn incense have been discovered in the same rooms as the olive-processing equipment. Such altars have been found nowhere else in the country. The presence of the altars suggests a religious or cultic involvement with the industry.

A priestly class affiliated with the rulers may have participated in the administration of the oil-processing industry. In his interview with *Time*, Gitin said, "In most places in the Middle East, there was a close relationship between cult, religion, and kingship. Priest and king often worked together. The priest controlled the water supplies in some cites. In Ekron the large royal financial investment in production was overseen by the priests."

Since the oil processing probably took place no more than two months per year, archaeologists suspect that another industry may have taken its place during the other 10 months of the year. The presence of loom weights at the site suggests that the plants may have also served as a textile dying center. This theory is supported by records of Assyrian kings, which list linen robes and tent cloth exacted as tribute from the Philistines.

Food as an Index of Philistine Culture's Complexity

Bones unearthed at Ekron indicate that the early Philistine diet consisted of pork and beef, which was replaced during their latter period by sheep, goat and fish. Scholars speculate that the shift in diet signaled increased interrelationships within the society.

David and Goliath. Until the excavations at Ekron, Israel, there was little physical evidence from which to construe what the Philistines were like. Much of what was "known" was derived from accounts written by their enemies.

Egypt, where it was exchanged for grain and other foodstuffs.

By ancient standards, Ekron appeared to have been unusually large and in the seventh century B.C. may have contained the largest industrial complex in the Middle East. A wide street in the industrial zone with buildings on either side was served by a complex sewer system comparable to those still in use in the Old City of Jerusalem and other Middle Eastern cities.

Private livestock pens are common to cultures that subsist on the labor of individual cottages. In Ekron the presence of great quantities of sheep and goat bones indicates that great herds were grazed in the surrounding hills and presumably sold within the city, suggesting a significant level of social interdependence.

Artistic Skills

Among the earliest finds at the Ekron site were large quantities of ceramics. The Philistine pottery, some of which dates back to their earliest period, was decorated with birds, fish and geometric designs and was painted black, red and white. Archaeologists at first thought that the pottery had been imported from the Aegean region. However, scientific analysis revealed that the clay used in the pottery was of local origin. Metal and ceremonial objects of the Philistines demonstrate a high level of skill.

Unanswered Questions About the Philistines Remain

In 603 B.C., Ekron was conquered by the Babylonians and the Philistines' advanced culture disappeared. About 500 years after the Philistines disappeared, the Romans named the coastal plain Palestine, "land of the Philistines," and the name was eventually extended to the rest of the country.

The destruction of Ekron and abandonment of the site left the city's remains intact and made the archaeologists' tasks much easier. There is no evidence that a remnant of the Philistine people persisted after the destruction. Scientists don't know whether the race died out or was assimilated into neighboring tribes. Experts believe there is no connection between the Philistines and modern Palestinians.

The Genesis of the Israelites

Recent research has not only changed long-held views about the Philistines, it has also revised scholarly thinking about the early Israelites. Whether basing their thoughts on scrutiny of the Bible or on the excavations of ruins, scholars have long disagreed about the origins of the Israelites.

In keeping with the biblical story of Joshua, some scholars viewed the Israelites as conquerors who swept through the fortified countryside of Canaan. Others believed that they were nomad shepherds from the east. Still others believed that they were breakaway Canaanites, who had forsaken the cities near the sea to live in the hills. (The land area once called Canaan is now divided among modern Israel, Sinai and Jordan.) Nonetheless, scholars have agreed that the Israelites emerged in the hill country of Canaan more than 3,200 years ago, a people living in remote villages, who developed their own religion and ethnic identity.

A major step toward understanding who the early Israelites were and how they emerged as a distinct society was made with a recent reinterpretation of carvings on the wall of the temple of Karnak in Egypt.

The Process of Detection

Egyptologist Frank Yurco of the Field Museum of Natural History in Chicago was examining inscriptions and carvings when he found what he believes to be the earliest pictorial representation of Israelites. The Karnak depiction was made more than 600 years before the reliefs found in Nineveh, the ancient capital of Assyria on the Tigris River, which show Israelites being led into exile.

Yurco's discovery was a consequence of his work with the University of Chicago's epigraphic survey of Egyptian temples. While engaged in his doctoral dissertation research, Yurco noticed that four battle scenes carved on the Karnak wall had been mistakenly attributed to Ramses II, the pharaoh who had ruled Egypt for much of the 13th century B.C.

The centerpiece of the wall he was examining is the hieroglyphic text of the peace treaty that concluded the battle of Kadesh in Syria in 1275 between Ramses and the Hittite army. The four battle scenes that frame the treaty were assumed to depict combat scenes during that war.

Yurco learned that a practice of succeeding pharaohs of the times was to have their predecessor's names hammered out of such works of art and replaced by their own. By scraping away the plastered-over superimposed names, Yurco learned that the original inscription was not of Ramses II, but that of Merenptah, who had been pharaoh from 1212 to 1202 B.C. Moreover, he noticed that the facial features of a pharaoh carved on a nearby block did not resemble Ramses but did resemble the figure found on Merenptah's tomb. In an interview with the *New York Times*, Yurco said, "It was then that I made the conceptual leap that the battle scenes were from Merenptah's campaign against Canaan."

To lend support to his hunch, Yurco reexamined the Merenptah Stele, a black granite tablet inscribed with the account of the pharaoh's military exploits. The text, which was discovered a century ago and is now housed in the Egyptian Museum in Cairo, contains the earliest known mention of Israel.

In a description of Merenptah's four victories in Canaan, the text says: "Ashkelon has been overcome. Gezer has been captured. Yano'am was made non-existent. Israel is laid waste, his seed is not."

The text suggested a connection to the four battle scenes at Karnak. Yurco learned that in Karnak's first carved scene the town of Ashkelon had been specifically identified. The

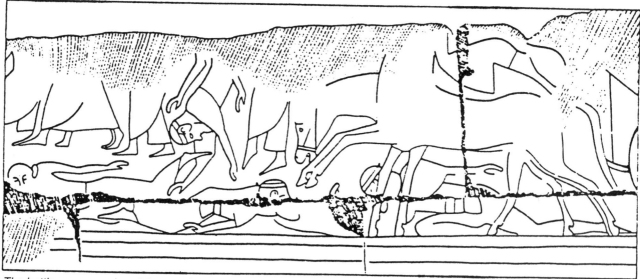

The battle scene carving at the temple of Karnak in Egypt that may show the earliest known rendering of the Israelites.

next two scenes are of fortified places lying in a line between Ashkelon on the coastal plain into the hill country. The fourth scene, which depicts the pharaoh's horse and chariot team in the center running roughshod over fallen soldiers, includes no suggestion of walls or towers or evidence of a fortified city.

Yurco was reminded that the hieroglyphic writing of the Merenptah Stele consists not only of signs meant to be vocalized but also so-called determinatives. The sole function of a determinative is to indicate the category or type of word to which it is attached. In the stele, the determinative that is used with the names of the first three states mentioned is the one normally used to designate city-state areas. However, the determinative used with the name Israel is the one normally used only for peoples without a fixed city-state area or a rural or nomadic people. Thus the carved reliefs provide confirmation of accumulating archaeological evidence that the original Israelite settlements were in the highlands and in open, dispersed villages with no substantial fortified towns.

In an article published in the September issue of *Biblical Archaeology Review*, Yurco recounted his theory. In one battle scene, he writes, the Israelites are wearing ankle-length cloaks, the style worn by the Canaanites, rather than the turbans and short kilts of the Shasu, a nomadic people, whom many scholars have recently associated with the origins of the Israelites.

The Karnak reliefs seemed to suggest that the Canaanites had withdrawn to the hill country, which is in keeping with impressions derived from archaeological findings and biblical texts. Yurco's find has led to a growing consensus among Egyptologists, biblical scholars and archaeologists that most of the early Israelites were Canaanites who settled along the ridge running through Jerusalem from Hebron,

which lies 20 miles south-southwest of Jerusalem and is thought to be one of the oldest holy cities in the world. Yurco concluded that early Israelites probably coalesced out of the Canaanite society in the 13th and 12th centuries B.C.

Assuming some historical basis for the biblical story of the Exodus, which describes the departure from Egypt of the Israelites under the leadership of Moses, the account may refer to the presence among the Canaanites of some nomadic shepherds and others from east of the Jordan River who had fled from Egypt.

Although most biblical experts deemphasize the Exodus story because they are not sure of its historical reality, Yurco and some other scholars do not rule out the possibility that people from the Exodus were a component of the new rural society.

During an interview for a September 4, 1990, *New York Times* article entitled "Battle Scene on Egyptian Temple May Be Earliest View of Israelites," Dr. Lawrence Stager, a professor of archaeology at Harvard University, praised Yurco's research as a "brilliant comparison of a literary work with an artistic work."

Dr. Stager went on to say that the Israelites were probably a "hodgepodge of different segments of society," who were brought together by their rural experience. Stager was of the opinion that modern scholars do not believe that the early Israelites came as conquerors. Some scholars assert that the Israelites broke off from Canaan in a peasant revolt against an upper class or were escaping from crowded lowlands. Many Israeli scholars contend that the early Israelites were pastoralists (shepherds or involved in rural life) who migrated into the hill country of Canaan.

Hershel Shanks, editor of *Biblical Archaeology Review*, during an interview with the *New York Times*, said, "If we read the Bible, we get a simpler version of a group of people who simply wandered from Egypt to Canaan. The reality is much more complex and equally fascinating."

The creation of the Karnak carvings precedes by nearly a century the use in the biblical Song of Deborah, recorded in the Book of Judges, of the name Israel to designate the tribal confederacy. The tribes did not unite under a monarch until the 11th century B.C.

Many Mysteries Remain

Not only did the Philistines disappear as a race, no trace of their language has been found. The archaeologists engaged in uncovering Ekron relish the fact that they have been able to redeem the Philistine's tarnished reputation. Dothan remarked during her interview with *Time* that "The Philistines need no longer bear the burden of biblical scorn."

Like the Philistines, the Canaanites from whom the early Israelites seem to have emerged disappeared after the time of Christ, after being known for some time as the Phoenicians.

In Stager's opinion, the whole constituency of the early Israelites remains unknown but, based on their representation on the Karnak wall, it is at least now accepted that they dressed like Canaanites who lived in remote rural settlements.

One of the two vessels used by the SEA Education Association for their seagoing research training program.

PART TWO

Earth and
Space Science

EVENTS AND TRENDS IN EARTH AND SPACE SCIENCE

The wonders and woes of the Hubble Space Telescope dominated much of the 1990 astronomical news. Concerns about the well-being of the environment were heightened as increased access to Eastern Europe made it possible to assess damage that has been heretofore hidden. Serendipity played a role in the discovery of a possible earthquake detector and in the mechanism that may be used in mating by a large number of the ocean's predators and scavengers.

The Earth and Its Oceans

The early 20th century New England naturalist and author Henry Beston recognized that animals possessed some senses that humans do not have. In his 1928 book, *The Outermost House*, he wrote "They move finished and complete, gifted with extensions of the senses we have lost or never attained, living by voices we shall never hear." During the more than six decades that have elapsed since Beston's words were published, scientists exploring the sensory biology of animals have found support for his ideas.

Some bats and dolphins explore their world with beams of sound, a form of sonar known as ecolocation. Elephants and whales broadcast and receive information over enormous distances using infrasound below the threshold of human hearing. Birds can see polarized light and bees are able to see both ultraviolet and polarized light. In 1966, Ad Kalmijin, a Netherlands biologist, demonstrated that sharks and rays use electric fields to sense prey.

Discoveries made in the spring of 1990, reported in an article entitled "For Stingrays, A Current Affair," in the October 8, 1990, *Boston Globe*, demonstrated the crucial role electroreception, the ability to sense electric fields, may play in the complex reproductive strategies of stingrays, sharks and skates, the premier marine predators and scavengers of the world's oceans. The findings may serve as a breakthrough in understanding the mating system used by more than 1,000 fishes that are a part of the taxonomic group elasmobranchs, which includes stingrays, sharks and skates.

The research about electroreception, done in Sonora, Mexico, revealed that the electric field signals picked up by rays are extremely weak and are generated, continuously and passively, by all members of the species. All organisms, including humans, have a passive bioelectric field when immersed in water, a current generated between biological membranes and the surrounding water.

During the stingray's mating season, which begins in late February, females do one of three things: In groups of 40 to 50, some pile one atop the other on the ocean floor, four or five animals deep. In groups of up to 40, some lie partially buried their rounded side fins overlapping. Others bury themselves alone. The males patrol the water singly looking for mates. Since they ignore the piles of females, they obviously don't use sight in their search.

In the clear shallow waters of a quiet bay in Sonora, a stingray breeding ground, Scott Michaels, a University of Nebraska biologist, who was visiting the area for the first time, recognized that he had stumbled on a research gold mine. During the course of his observations Michaels watched a male swim near a single, invisible buried female. When the male was about a yard beyond the buried female, he abruptly wheeled to return, excavate her and begin a violent courtship, biting at her side fins while she stung him with her tail.

With a videotape of stingray courtship encounters, Michaels sought help from Timothy Tricas of Washington University in St. Louis, an expert on shark studies. Watching the films, Tricas noted that the males homed in on the buried females so quickly that their cues could not have been odors, which typically take considerable sampling. During an interview with the *Boston Globe* Tricas explained that since the males were not using vision or odors, "It clicked in my head that there was probably only one other sense that would give such rapid directional information—the sensitivity of sharks, skates, and rays to weak electric fields."

Tricas and Michaels designed a "dummy ray" equipped with electrodes to generate a field to attract the stingray males. At Ad Kalmijin's lab at Scripps Institute of Oceanography at La Jolla, Tricas measured and digitally recorded a captive ray's electric field. In addition, he designed a portable, high-speed computer that could record and play back a ray's electric field signals.

Electrodes connected to the computer were implanted in a plastic model of a ray and the model was buried in the sand and turned on. Within minutes a male swam by, turned abruptly and tried to excavate the model. The behavior was repeated 60 out of 100 times when a male came near the model. Moreover, a real female, who had successfully fought off a male suitor, swam within about a yard of the buried model, turned abruptly and buried herself beside the model.

Weather and Climate

The field of forensic meteorology is thought to have begun with Oscar Tenenbaum. In addition to being chief meteorologist at Boston's Logan International Airport, Tenenbaum was a practicing lawyer. His familiarity with the courts prompted him to offer his services in cases where weather was a pertinent legal factor.

An April 1989 *Technology Review* article entitled "Forensic Meteorology," described one of Tenenbaum's cases. The famous blizzard in the Northeast United States in 1978 destroyed homes miles from the seashore, apparently by flooding. Homeowners hired Tenenbaum, who investigated weather records and found that hurricane-force winds had preceded the flooding. He theorized that the strong winds had demolished the homes, which had later been covered by water. Because their insurance policies had included wind damage, two homeowners won settlements based on his findings.

Although 20 years ago, the term forensic meteorology did not even exist, by 1989 there were 20 consulting firms in the United States with scientists licensed by the American Meteorological Society to do forensic meteorology. The companies use U.S. Weather Service data, supplemented with their own tailored technology, but the skill of meteorologists remains key to their success.

To amass a more detailed, accurate history than that provided by the National Weather Service, most forensic meteorological companies have developed extensive observation networks. They use a wide range of data-collection methods ranging from public telephones equipped with automated recording devices to very-high-frequency radio communication systems that bounce signals off meteor trails, a relatively inexpensive, reliable way to transmit data from locations as remote as Alaska.

R-Scan Corporation, a Minneapolis-based company, has a consumer forensic service for lightning damage similar to the service the National Lightning Detection Network supplies for researchers. (R-Scan provided some of the equipment to start up the Lightning Detection Network.) In the continental United States, R-Scan can pinpoint a lightning strike to within a quarter of a mile.

Because insurance companies were often unable to verify or challenge lightning damage claims, some customers took advantage of them. For example, a Minnesota company submitted a $10,000 claim for a computer system and cited lightning damage as the cause. R-Scan records revealed that there had been no lightning on the day the computer was alleged to have been damaged.

In New England, where weather can vary dramatically within a relatively small area, a wealth of information is necessary to achieve accuracy. From a network of 15 weather observers in the Boston area, plus several in New Hampshire and Maine, the New England Weather Service stores information phoned in daily for its local forecasts. The company also collects observations from small airports and utility companies. The stored information serves as a basis for New England's forensic work.

Weather Surveys of New York was able to come to the aid of the operator of several Kentucky coal mines who went broke. The mines' stockholders sued because they believed they had been misled when investing. The operator, who claimed that heavy snows had been a factor in his financial woes, hired Weather Surveys, who produced 15 years of snowfall records that showed snowfalls had been heavier than normal. The operator won the suit.

The Earth in the Past

A Navy submarine communications study may yield a long-sought earthquake alert system. On October 17, 1989, at 5:04 P.M., when the third most lethal earthquake in U.S. history struck the San Francisco Bay area, an instrument that was a part of an Office of Naval Research study was in operation just 5 miles from the quake's epicenter (the point on the earth's surface directly above the earthquake's first movement).

The purpose of the Navy's research was to improve its ability to communicate with submarines. The project director, Antony Fraser-Smith, a Stanford research associate in electrical engineering, has been studying low-frequency radio waves for 25 years. This particular effort involved a long-term study of radio noise at frequencies from 10 hertz (Hz) down to 1/1000 Hz, far below the range of radio frequencies used for communications. (A Hz is one wave cycle per second.)

Such ultralow frequencies pass freely through deep water and solid rock, making them a promising means for communicating with distant submarines. The Navy wanted to know how the frequencies might be affected by electrical storms and electrical power plants. One of two such devices (the other is in Grafton, New Hampshire), the instrument's receiver was located in Corralitos, in the Santa Cruz mountains. The instrument was set up to average out the noise that it had received during the previous half hour and record the figure on a computer disk.

Among other things, the device picks up changes in the earth's magnetic field. Prior to the October quake, the highest activity levels detected had come the previous March, during an intense magnetic storm (violent disturbances in the magnetic force of the earth) triggered by solar flares. About two weeks before the October quake, signals began coming through that were 30 times greater than normal. Three hours before the earthquake struck, with a magnitude of 6.9 on the Richter scale, the signals' intensity jumped to more than 100 times the normal level and kept climbing—until the earthquake knocked out the power.

In an interview for a March 26, 1990, *Boston Globe* article entitled "Predicting Earthquakes," the chairman of the geophysics department at Stanford University, Amos Nur, speculated that salty water flowing underground, pushed by deep movements of rock building up to a quake, could produce an electrical current and generate low-frequency waves. The project director, Fraser-Smith, leaned toward the idea that pressure on the rock itself generated an electrical current based on a phenomenon known as piezoelectricity, electricity induced in a crystalline structure by the application of pressure.

For years scientists at the University of Athens had reported signs of low-frequency earthquake precursors. Because their equipment was not top quality and because scientists tend to be skeptics, the Greek scientists' data were not accepted. However, Fraser-Smith's instrument was too precise to be ignored. Nevertheless, one recording on one instrument was not enough to form conclusions. The U.S. Geological Survey paid for two duplicates of the sensitive apparatus to be set up near Parkfield, California, a heavily instrumented rural area where a magnitude 6 earthquake is expected in the near future.

The Stars and the Universe

Thirty years of spaceflight have accumulated an enormous amount of data, all of which was collected at great risk and expense. Yet much of it is so badly labeled or stored that extracting information from it requires imaginative and highly skilled detective work.

Even when tapes are in good condition, they are apt to be missing the documents needed to decode them. Some tapes are so old that present-day computer experts are no longer able to understand how they were programmed. Some of the tapes can only be processed on machines that have not been built by their companies for a quarter of a century.

Sorting out what is on the tapes can be daunting. Eric Eliason of the U.S. Geological Survey learned in 1988 that 3,000 images from the Viking mission to Mars had never been processed. Although there were copies of old computer programs necessary to turn the raw data into pictures, the source codes needed to run the programs could not be found and the computers they had been designed for no longer existed.

Eliason tracked down the people who had designed the camera and other instruments. After a year of scientific detective work, Eliason succeeded in writing a computer program to extract the images. For his effort, he found the highest resolution image ever taken of Mons Olympus, the most significant feature on Mars and the largest volcano in the solar system.

During an interview for a March 20, 1990, *New York Times* article entitled "Lost on Earth: Wealth of Data Found in Space," Arthur Zygielbaum, manager of the Science Information System's Office at the National Aeronautics and Space Administration's (NASA's) Jet Propulsion Laboratory, said, "These data are a national treasure. Our goal should be to save everything. Without tomorrow's context, we don't know what is valuable today."

As well as information about the moon and the planets, the Jet Propulsion Laboratory's 200,000 space mission tapes contain information on long-term trends like global climate change and tropical deforestation. In the 1970s, NASA scientists ignored ozone data gathered during flights because they were so low that they thought they were in error. After British scientists in the 1980 suggested that there was a dangerous thinning of the ozone layer, NASA data were able to confirm it.

Tapes that were properly stored and documented contain so much information that scientists have barely begun to catalog and transpose the data to modern computer tapes, using more advanced storage systems. As the scientists work their way through already accumulated data, plans call for a much greater accumulation of information ahead.

NASA's "Mission to Planet Earth" program, which will collect information about the Earth, is expected to collect more data in a day than has been generated by the entire previous history of the space program and scientists at the Jet Propulsion Laboratory are developing new technologies to make better use of archived data. Moreover, data are being made available to scientists on compact disks, as well as through a special computer network associated with six universities.

6

The Earth and Its Oceans

LIMNOLOGISTS EXAMINE THE WORLD'S DEEPEST LAKE IN THE SOVIET UNION AND ENCOUNTER EUROPE'S PROLIFIC ZEBRA MUSSEL AT HOME

Lake Baikal in southern Siberia is the oldest, deepest, cleanest large lake in the world. Most estimates claim that the 400-mile-long lake holds one-quarter of all the fresh water in the world—more than 14,000 cubic miles. The lake's basin is the deepest continental depression on earth.

After years of being barred from access, in late summer of 1988, 1989 and 1990, American limnologists (scientists who study the conditions for life in lakes, ponds and streams and the living things that inhabit them) were permitted to join Soviet scientists in research at Lake Baikal. In late summer of 1990, Soviet and American geologists delved beneath the surface of the lake and made discoveries of creatures never before seen.

The first expedition in 1988 was recounted in a March 1989 *Earthwatch* article entitled "Baikal: Americans and Soviets Team Up to Probe the World's Deepest Lake," by Mark Cherrington, a senior editor of the magazine. The group included two American limnologists from Wisconsin, three graduate students, six Earthwatch volunteers, 14 Soviet scientists, including limnologists, mathematicians, chemists and biologists, and the ship's crew.

The effort was the first time in more than 30 years that American and Soviet limnologists had been able to work together on Lake Baikal, and one of the first times that Soviet and American scientists had collaborated. The project was sponsored by Earthwatch, the Soros Foundation, the Soviet Academy of Sciences and the Irkutsk Limnology Institute.

The goal was to increase understanding of how freshwater ecosystems (the interaction of all living and nonliving things in a particular environment) work throughout the world by sampling and analyzing the lake's chemistry and microbiology (the study of microorganisms, including protozoans, algae, fungi, bacteria and viruses). The research effort was not intended to discover anything radically new, rather the collaboration was aimed at bringing together American equipment and techniques with Soviet scientists' superior knowledge of Baikal.

The American team was led by Drs. Ken Nealson and Art Brooks of the University of Wisconsin's Center for Great Lake Studies. Nealson's purpose was to determine the distribution of manganese and iron in Baikal, two minerals that are active in the lake's carbon cycle, and to assess their impact on the food chain. Brooks's task was to look at the lake's chlorophyll production and the distribution of phytoplankton (floating microscopic plant life used as food by fish). He wanted to learn where phytoplankton was most dense and the effects on it of depth, temperature and currents. The Soviet team was also interested in the lake's microbiology and chemistry.

Nealson and Brooks brought with them a hydrolab and a fluorometer. A hydrolab contains sensory equipment to measure depth, dissolved oxygen, pH, salinity (amount of salt) and temperature, together with electronic equipment that converts the collected information into a digital signal

The Veretschagin, *one of two vessels used by Russian and American scientists for the Lake Baikal project.*

and sends it via a cable to a portable computer. As the unit is lowered into the water, the computer gives a constant readout.

A fluorometer uses a small pulsating light and a light meter to measure chlorophyll in the water. The laser strikes the chlorophyll (photoreceptors of light energy for photosynthesis) in phytoplankton and the chlorophyll fluoresces briefly. Between bursts of the laser, a light meter registers the fluorescence as a level of light. The signal is carried back by cable to a transcription device in the lab to make a permanent record.

Most of the Earthwatch volunteers' work involved collecting water samples from various depths to mix with a variety of reagents to check for nutrients. The Soviets and the Americans, however, differed in their thinking about how the water samples should be collected.

The Americans used plastic cylinders with ball-shaped, spring-cocked valves on either end. The valves were operated by stretched rubber hose. The cylinders were attached to a cable at measured intervals and released over the side from a calibrated winch. The cylinders descended in the water with the valves cocked open so that the water could flow through them. At the desired depth, a brass weight was slid down the cable to close the valves and trap a water sample.

The Soviets used old-fashioned metal cylinders with flat lids. The Americans were concerned that the metal from the Soviet's cylinders would contaminate their samples. The Soviets were amused that the Americans' plastic cylinders often failed to shut, while theirs, outfitted with brass armatures and steel springs, never failed.

Baikal's Unique Geography

The size of the Baikal is difficult to comprehend. In surface area, half a dozen other lakes are larger, but in sheer volume nothing else matches it. To convey a sense of its immense size, author Mark Cherrington made a comparison between Lake Baikal and other large bodies of water.

The Amazon drains an area the size of the United States and discharges enough water to meet on a daily basis the water needs of the population of the United States. If the basin of Lake Baikal were empty and the Amazon flowed into it, together with the Nile, the Congo, the Mississippi, the Ganges, the Thames and every other river and stream—in other words, all the running water in the world—it would take a year to fill the empty basin.

The lake's great volume is due to its depth. The basin is more than mile deep in several spots and almost that deep on the average. The depth is a consequence of tectonic action, changes in the structure of the earth's crust. (Plate tectonics is a theoretical model of the earth in which 10–25 semi-rigid plates drift on molten rock to collide and form continents.)

Lake Baikal fills a rift valley (a crack in the earth's surface) where two tectonic plates are drifting apart, causing the lake's banks to constantly widen and land between the plates to drop lower. The split is part of a huge fault (a break in rock layers that causes a section to become dislocated along a line of fracture) that stretches from the Hindu Kush (a central Asian mountain range on the border of Kashmir and Afghanistan) to the Sea of Okhotsk (an inlet of the Pacific Ocean on the coast of the Soviet Union).

A wave of geologic activity about 20 million years ago created the rift that made Baikal the oldest lake in the world. The same forces that created the rift also pushed up the mountains that surround Baikal. (A particular set of circumstances creates rift lakes so that they all are apt to have similar morphologies, forms and structures. The second-deepest and second-oldest lake in the world is Lake Tanganyika in Africa's Western Rift Valley.)

An Unusual Glimpse of Evolution

Baikal is home to more than 2,000 species of plants and animals that live nowhere else, a total far higher than any other lake. The abundance of native species is a consequence of the lake's great age. Most lakes have a short life span because the river waters that feed them bring loads of silt and sediment to the essentially still water of the lake. Artificial lakes tend to fill up quickly. Natural lakes last longer, but at best their spans measure in thousands of years, while Baikal has been in existence for 20 million years.

The rift in which the lake rests separates at a rate of about 3 millimeters (.118 inches) a year. The rate of growth of the lake's basin is almost the same as the rate at which sediment fills it.

Twenty million years has permitted Baikal's animal life enough time to evolve into forms quite different than their ancestors. An additional factor makes evolution in Baikal singular. The lake is a closed system. All the waters in the lake come from the runoff of the surrounding mountains. Even the lake's longest and largest contributor, the Salenga, flowing from Mongolia, has no connection to any outside rivers or watershed.

By contrast, the Great Lakes in the United States are connected over an enormous area via rivers and streams to other lakes and lake systems. As a consequence, the organisms in any lake in the Great Lakes system are open to genetic influence from a wide variety of other life. Baikal's closed system makes the lake ideal for the study of ecology in general and the origin of species in particular.

The enormous length of time that Baikal's native species have been in isolation has permitted them to adapt magnificently to the lake's singular conditions, but has made them vulnerable to outside influences, such as pollution. A study by a Soviet limnologists revealed that Baikal's endemic (native) species were 10 times more susceptible to water-borne pollution than were ordinary Siberian species. The northern part of the lake is so pure that the expedition's members were able to drink water straight from the lake, but the southern part of the lake has been heavily polluted by a paper and pulp mill built 20 years ago.

Mikail Grachev, head of the Irkutsk Limnology Institute, believes that 23 square miles of the lake have been severely damaged because of the mill. Fortunately, Soviet environmentalists persuaded the government to convert the mill to a relatively harmless furniture factory. Unfortunately, Nealson's data suggested that the southern basin might be the biochemical nursery for the entire lake.

Wildlife is abundant in the forests that surround Baikal. They contain some of the world's largest bears, weighing nearly three-quarters of a ton. Bird species are plentiful, including the capercaillie, a turkey-size grouse that eats pine needles and buries itself in the snow. There are several kinds of weasels, including the sable, whose fur is the most valuable on earth.

The Soviet translator told Cherrington that it was unfortunate that the Americans could not see Baikal during winter when the forest is draped with snow and the ice is crystal clear, despite being 3 or 4 feet thick. The frozen lake once temporarily supported the Trans-Siberian Railroad tracks. For the phytoplankton population, the ice serves as a shield against the cold air and magnifies the sun's light. The population booms under the ice. The lake's enormous fish population, on the under hand, moves into deeper water and feeds little during the winter.

Getting to Know One Another

At the beginning of the voyage, the Americans and the Soviets, for the most part, avoided interaction. The Earthwatch volunteers were confusing to the Soviets because they were neither scientists nor tourists. Until the Soviets understood that the volunteers paid to come on the trip, they dismissed the volunteers as not worth their attention, even when Cherrington suggested that the volunteers were an example of a pure socialist concept, people at all levels of society working together to get a job done.

Two Russian scientists examining water samples taken from the lake.

Researcher Ken Nealson with an instrument that, when dropped through the water, can measure such things as temperature, salinity, pH levels etc.

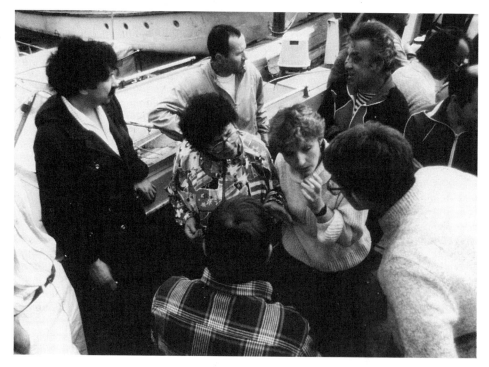

The two principal American investigators, Ken Nealson in the plaid shirt and Art Brooks in white, are listening to the Russian interpreter.

Despite the fact that the Americans spoke little Russian and the Russians spoke little English, once the work started, most of the awkwardness between the two groups disappeared. Each group was working on the same questions and often using similar techniques. Cherrington described the interaction by saying, "Like strangers admiring a baby, we realized we had the same interests, the same motivation, the same fascination with this lake. In almost no time, both Soviets and Americans felt free to make fun of one another, and even tease one another about failing equipment."

Parties around a campfire on the lake's cobblestone shore, at which Ken Nealson played songs on a guitar belonging to one of the ships' captains, helped to break the ice between the Soviets and the Americans. Songs by the Beatles were particularly appreciated. At the end of the trip, the captain presented Nealson with the guitar as a momento of the camaraderie.

Findings and Plans

The Americans' main research finding from the first year was that the Salenga River is the main source of dissolved metals, such as manganese, in the lake. The second year confirmed the findings on the Salenga River and gathered preliminary data on sedimentation rates and the part microbes (microorganisms, especially bacteria) play in the cycling of metals as nutrients.

In 1990, David Edgington, an associate of Ken Nealson, took Earthwatch volunteers to Baikal to do a study of sedimentation (the rate at which matter settles to the bottom of water) rates using natural and man-made radionuclides, such as cesium left over in the atmosphere from nuclear bomb testing. (A nuclide is an atom capable of existing for a measurable lifetime. A radionuclide is a nuclide that exhibits radioactivity.) They also planned to do preliminary studies on levels of PCBs (polychlorinated biphenyls, a highly toxic chemical). Future plans call for Nealson to do a shore-based study concentrating on the shallows and waters close to shore. Nealson hopes to study hot springs on the lake's outskirts.

Baikal Yields Two Discoveries for the Price of One

Hot water springing from the earth thrust a joint research project of Soviet and American scientists into the news in 1990. A brief article in the August 20, 1990, issue of *U.S. News and World and World Report* entitled "An Ocean Aborning a Steppe from Moscow" reported the outcome of a Soviet-American expedition on the bottom of Lake Baikal. The expedition was led by geophysicist Kathleen Crane of Hunter College.

During the summer of 1990, the Soviet-American expedition went looking for the source of heat in Lake Baikal. Under the auspices of Columbia University's Lamont-Doherty Geological Observatory, in Palisades, New York, the scientists explored in a submersible at a level 1,350 feet below the surface, towing cameras with temperature gauges.

After days of looking at nothing but mud, they came upon cracks in the earth that were hot-water vents in the lake bed. Around the vents, they found communities of strange creatures similar to those only seen living around hydrothermal vents in the ocean. The hydrothermal vents are openings in the ocean floor where molten rock oozing up from the interior of the earth heats water ladened with minerals, which serve as nutrients for bizarre organisms that live around them. Baikal's organisms included bacteria, translucent shrimp and mushroom-shaped sponges.

The Soviet-American scientists' discovery lends support to a theory that Baikal is in the process of becoming an ocean. The vents suggest that an enormous tear in the continent made when the Indian subcontinent collided with Asia 40 million years ago is slowly widening. If the continent continues to split, another ocean will be born. The last ocean was created 150 million years ago when the Atlantic was born.

The Immigrant Mollusk

The strange creatures at Baikal were not the only recent discoveries from the Eurasian continent.

Sometime in late 1985 or 1986, a ship leaving a freshwater European port for North America took on ballast water. Ships "ballast up" for many reasons. A lightly loaded vessel rides too high and becomes vulnerable to being capsized, or the propeller of an underloaded ship may rise partially out of the water, reducing some of its propulsion capacity. When the unknown ship in the European freshwater port opened its sea cocks and started its pumps, it took on more than water. It boarded the hardy and destructive Asian bivalve (a mollusk with a two-part shell hinged to open and shut) *Dreissena polymorpha*, the zebra mussel.

With its stowaway the ship crossed the Atlantic, traversed the St. Lawrence Seaway and sailed on through Lake Erie. When the ship reached its destination, somewhere above Detroit, and emptied its ballast to take on cargo, it flushed a founding population of zebra mussels into Lake St. Claire. The zebra mussel had immigrated to colonize a new continent.

Since ballast flushing is not a new practice, biologists wondered why the zebra mussel had not arrived earlier. The answer is pollution. For many years, the mussels could not survive in Europe's polluted major freshwater ports. Once environmental cleanups made European harbors more habitable, the mussels began colonizing, with the potential to be taken on board as ballast.

Like the European harbors, for a long time North America's freshwater ports were too dirty for the mussels to make a new home, but North American ports, like their European counterparts, were subjected to environmental controls and became habitable for the Asian bivalve immigrants.

Over a period of 150 years, the zebra mussel spread from the region of the Caspian Sea, which, except for its southern shore in Iran, is mainly in the U.S.S.R., into much of Europe, plugging water pipes and clasping itself to boat hulls wherever it went. But the mussels' migration through Europe was slow. They seem to have found North America particularly hospitable for getting around.

In a July 1990 *Atlantic Monthly* article entitled "Invasion of the Zebra Mussels," author Matthew Hart described the astonishing travel feats of the new migrant. Since the zebra mussels' arrival, they have already worked their way down the length of Lake Erie and into Lake Ontario. In time,

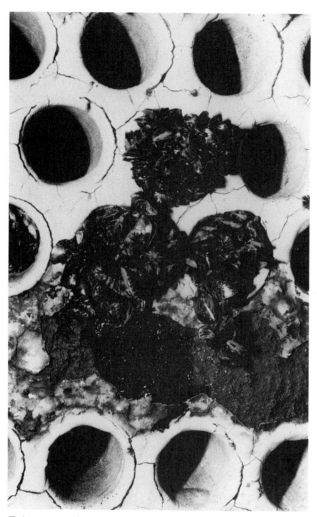

Zebra mussels are attracted to pipes. The mussels don't care whether the pipes belong to a water treatment plant, an industrial plant, a water supply system or a power plant. Zebra mussels have been found in the intakes of the Cook Nuclear plant in Bridgman, Michigan, and the Perry Nuclear Station of Cleveland, Ohio. They have forced a partial shutdown of Detroit Edison's largest power plant. A combination of zebra mussels and ice completely blocked the flow of water through a 30-inch pipe in Monroe, Michigan.

Population Counting

The discovery of the unwelcome newcomer was made by a research technician and two summer interns at the University of Windsor's Great Lake's Institute on June 1, 1988. As part of a program to monitor water quality, the three were conducting a routine sampling of the invertebrate population on the bottom of Lake St. Clair. Using a Ponar grab (a scoop that takes samples from the bottom of a lake or river), they brought up a rock to which a strange mollusk clung.

The three discoverers called Gerry Mackie, a professor of zoology at the University of Guelph, near Toronto, and a freshwater-mussel expert, and described their find. Because he feared he knew what they had discovered, Mackie asked them to bring the mussel in. Unhappily, his suspicions were correct.

When the news of the zebra mussel's arrival spread to other biologists, they began a count. At the beginning of August 1988, the Great Lakes Institute sampled zebra-mussel densities at 10 sites in Lake St. Claire. At some sites, they found as many as 200 mussels per square meter (1.196 square yards). Because zebra-mussel populations tend to increase each year by an order of magnitude (such as doubling or tripling), the biologists reasoned that the next time they counted, the population could be 20,000. Through a process of working backward from the population they found originally, the biologists were able to pinpoint the probable time of arrival as late 1985 or 1986.

By 1989, the zebra mussel had spread through most of Lake Erie. In May, zebra mussel colonies found in one premier walleye (any of several freshwater North American perches with large staring eyes) spawning ground had a density of 1,200 to the square meter (1.196 square yards). By October, the density had increased to 9,000 a square meter (1.196 square yards). At another spot, the May count of 3,500 to the square meter (1.196 square yards) had reached 23,000 by October.

Downstream from Lake St. Charles is Lake Erie, the largest freshwater fishery in the world. The lake is warm and fed by nutrients from surrounding agricultural lands, and it is strewn with rocky shoals (shallow places), which make it an inviting place for zebra mussels. A limnologist at Ontario's Lake Erie Fisheries Station, Joseph Leach, who already had some plankton stations in the western basin of Lake Erie, started to look for zebra mussels as well. Leach found zebra mussels everywhere he checked.

Zebra Mussel Characteristics

A female zebra mussel can produce 40,000 eggs each year and the male a comparable amount of sperm. Even if only a small percentage of the eggs reach maturity, the reproductive rate is enormous.

biologists expect the zebra mussels to sweep from the Great Lakes to the Ohio and Mississippi River drainage system and into the waters of approximately two-thirds of the United States.

The zebra mussels breed rapidly and unceasingly. They clog the intakes of power stations, entangle fishing nets and foul marine engines and boat hulls. They colonize navigation buoys in numbers sufficient to force the buoys under the water.

Over many decades of dealing with zebra mussels, Europeans have developed measures to cope with them. For example, they use pipes with wider diameters to make cleaning easier and to reduce the potential of colonies to close them.

On occasion, some species reproduce so fast that they develop genetic alterations. An expert on biological invasions, James Carlton, the director of the Williams College Mystic Seaport Maritime Studies Program, said, "Sometimes they go into hyperjump. It took the zebra mussel a single year to get from one end of Lake Erie to the other."

Mussels use tongue-like "feet" to push themselves along the bottom. In addition, they are unique among freshwater mussels in that they have byssuses (or byssi), which are long, lustrous, silky bunches of filaments secreted by bivalves to attach themselves to hard surfaces, including rocks, metals and other mussels. Because zebra mussels can attach to other zebra mussels, populations of 10,000 to a square meter (1.196 square yards) are common in Europe.

North American mussels migrate by catching rides on fish. Zebra mussels don't need to hitchhike. As larva, they are veligers, which means that they have a cluster of cilia (small, hairlike projections) that enables them to hang suspended in the water to be carried swiftly by the current.

Lake St. Clair, where the zebra mussels initially arrived, has a significant current. Within nine days, a volume of water equivalent to the lake's entire volume flows into the Detroit River. At a rate of 5,400 cubic meters (1.308 cubic yards) per second, the Detroit River subsequently pours Lake St. Claire's water into the superb habitat of Lake Erie's western basin.

Only a few conditions deter the zebra mussels' spread into a new habitat. They require a minimum level of calcium in their environment and cannot cope with extremes of acidity or alkalinity, therefore they are not expected to colonize such locations as the acidified lakes of the Adirondacks. They can cope with a wide range of temperature and probably will be deterred only by Canada's cold northern lakes and the warm waters of the American South.

Ecological Threat Posed by Zebra Mussels

Limnologist Joseph Leach explained why the zebra mussels are a threat. In Lake Erie's western basin, some of the pitted limestone reefs are ideal spawning grounds. The pits in the reefs serve as places for the eggs of walleye, lake whitefish and white bass to settle, and the reefs are swept by currents that supply the spawn with oxygen. Leach expects the zebra mussels to compete with the spawn for oxygen. Moreover, as the mussels' own feces and organic debris decompose, they can be expected to draw additional oxygen from the water.

The zebra mussel threatens native species in other ways. It has a ravenous appetite for phytoplankton, the microscopic green plants at the bottom of the food chain. Zooplanktons that eat phytoplanktons serve as food for many fish. If the zooplanktons disappear, the process could work its way up the food chain, even as far as the ducks and people who catch and eat the fish.

Scientists are not agreed on the extent of the threat that the zebra mussel poses. David Garton, a professor of zoology at Ohio State University, who has done field research in Lake Erie's western basin, believes that oxygen starvation may not be a problem because the water is cold when the walleye spawn and cold water contains more

These tiny creatures are extremely hardy. Although they do not survive well in acidified water (lakes and rivers contaminated by acid rain), under lab conditions zebra mussels have survived being starved for months at a time.

oxygen. He said, "Not only that, the mussels are always jostling around. They let go of their byssal attachments in order to rise to the top of the heap. They're always playing king of the mountain, because whoever is on top has a better crack at the food. This jostling would tend to promote circulation." Circulation replenishes the supply of oxygen in the water.

In the spring of 1990, divers found oxygen levels still adequate on the reefs; however, Leach wondered if they would stay that way when the mussels became thicker. "When you introduce a new biomass," he argues, "and there is no change in the productivity of the system, then something has to give."

In addition zebra mussels tend to clarify water by cleaning it of algae pollution. Walleyes are dark-adapted fish that prefer to hide. Clarity will drive them into deeper water.

In 1989, Leach used a secchi disc to test Lake Erie's clarity. A secchi disc is a flat circle painted in alternating quadrants of black and white. The secchi disc is lowered into the water until it can no longer be seen from above. The 1989 secchi disc records when checked against the 1988 records revealed that the water was twice as clear as it had been the year before. Moreover, the prevalence of phytoplankton in Lake Erie had dropped dramatically, indicating that a lot of food in the water was being consumed.

Threat Posed by the Zebra Mussel to Human Structures

While it may be too early to tell whether the zebra mussel is going to disrupt the ecological balance, there is no question that it is destructive to human-made structures. Detroit Edison's generating station in Monroe, Michigan, a 3,000-megawatt coal-fired facility on Lake Erie, is an example of how fast the zebra mussel can get out of hand.

The Monroe plant has a forebay, a reservoir feeding the penstocks (a valve or sluice gate for regulating water flow) of a hydroelectric plant. The forebay draws in water for coolant, is lined with steel-sheet pilings and includes concrete as well as steel grates. The conditions are ideal to attach byssuses. A factor that makes the site even more attractive is that a unidirectional water flow brings new food and dissolved oxygen and carries away waste.

When crews checked the Monroe plant's forebay in February 1989, they found densities of up to 1,000 zebra mussels per square meter (1.196 square yards). When they returned in the fall, they found densities of 700,000 mussels per square meter (1.196 square yards). The spaces between bars placed 3 inches apart were completely jammed.

Ontario Hydro, one of the largest utilities in North America, operating 80 generating stations, found zebra mussels in the forebay of its Nanticoke, Ontario, plant at a density of 100,000 per square meter (1.196 square yards).

Remedies

A bill before Congress in the summer of 1990, the Non-Indigenous Aquatic Nuisance Act of 1990, would force incoming ships to discharge freshwater ballast at sea and replace it with saltwater ballast. The bill would also provide funds to control the spread of imported species that have already recently arrived.

Various alternatives are under way to try to eliminate the zebra mussel. Janiece Romstadt, who runs the water-treatment plant at Oregon, Ohio, a Lake Erie city of 30,000, received federal permission to use a commercial

The zebra mussels will adhere to almost anything and can live out of water for some time. The more humid the conditions, the longer they can last. This ability means an unseen mussel, attached to a boat transferred from one body of water to another, can remain viable to colonize a hitherto uncontaminated lake or river a few miles or hundreds of miles away from the source point. Zebra mussels live an average of four to five years and multiply prodigiously.

Dr. John Stanley, of the U.S. Fish and Wildlife Service, calculates that 1.2 billion dollars will be needed over the next 10 years to retrofit and maintain water supply systems in the Great Lakes area against the zebra mussel invasion.

mollucicide. Ontario Hydro is treating some of its coolant with hypochlorite, an active ingredient in household bleach, a short-term solution that is repugnant to an environmentally anxious public.

Ozonation is one solution that is environmentally benign. Ozone, an unstable blue gas, has various uses: as an oxidant (removes or changes substances by combing them with oxygen), bleach, water purifier and a treatment for industrial waste. However, ozonation is expensive. Ontario Hydro estimated that its per-plant cost using ozonation would be $9 million. John Stanley, of the U.S. Fish and Wildlife Service, estimated that the national annual bill for reengineering, and various forms of zebra mussel abatement, could be about $500 million.

The discovery of zebra mussels as a food by a variety of existing species offers some slim hope of control. The drum,

Zebra mussels attach themselves to many inhabitants of the lakes, often causing them to smother or starve to death and causing damage to the overall food chain.

a fish that is a bottom feeder, likes the zebra mussel. Unfortunately, the drum has not proven to be a popular commercial fish, a factor that might have encouraged increasing the population of drum. A Lake Erie population of lesser scaup, a type of diving duck, also seems to enjoy zebra mussels. Although the scaup population has increased since they discovered the zebra mussels, scaups alone can't make much of a difference.

There may yet be a natural remedy to the zebra mussel problem. A typical pattern for a species new to an area is spectacular growth followed by a crash (a steep drop in numbers). The crash can be prompted by any of several factors: disease, native species discovering the immigrant as a food source, or starvation after the immigrants have eaten all the food available. The crash is usually followed by another period of growth, followed by another crash. The cycle continues until the newcomer achieves a sustainable level. The experts don't know yet whether the zebra-mussel population will crash. In Sweden, the zebra population's numbers have remained high for a decade.

At the moment nothing is expected to stop the zebra mussel's spread. Biologists refer to the extension of an animal's range as "homogenization of the planet," an inevitable phenomenon, as specie after specie casts its lot in foreign environments.

Research Opportunities for Limnologists Look Bright

With areas such as Lake Baikal that were once closed becoming open, and with homogenization of the planet bringing new species to their doorstep, limnologists in the foreseeable future can expect to be kept busy at home and abroad.

THE SEA EDUCATION ASSOCIATION (SEA)

A Semester of Learning on the Deep Ocean

The oceans cover more than two-thirds of the planet Earth. In their book *The Sargasso Sea*, John and Mildred Teal write, "The planet Earth is misnamed, if you consider it from the proportion of land to water. By a fair naming process it would be called the planet Water." But despite water's prevalence on the planet, much remains unknown about Earth's oceans.

One effort to spread information about the sea is being made by the Sea Education Association (SEA), a nonprofit, educational organization, founded in 1971 and headquartered in Woods Hole, Massachusetts, the oceanographic center of the East Coast of the United States. SEA devotes itself to widening the pool of people who are knowledgeable about the oceans. SEA's executive director, Rafe Parker, described the program by saying, "We are the only institution giving college students the opportunity to do deep-sea research. It's the type of experience that even marine science majors don't see until they reach graduate school."

While teaching students, the faculty of SEA's two vessels, the SSV *Westward*, a 125-foot schooner, and the SSV *Corwith Cramer*, a 134-foot brigantine, conduct research in the ocean. The ships regularly sail the North Atlantic Ocean, the Caribbean Sea, and the Gulf of Mexico, traveling as far north as Newfoundland, as far south as South America, and as far east as Portugal. Students learn not only how to properly conduct original or ongoing research, and how to handle a sailing vessel at sea, they also develop a lifelong respect for the oceans and the role they play in the history, literature and ecology of the planet.

Each of SEA's separate programs, the Sea Semester and the Maritime Semester, integrates science, the humanities and practical seamanship in small classes. Each program is divided into two segments, a shore component and a sea component.

Typical Participants

Enrollment is open to men and women 18 and over and most classes are evenly divided between men and women. Completion of one semester of a college-level laboratory science course or its equivalent is required of Sea Semester students but not of Maritime Semester students. The Sea Semester students are not made up solely of science students, but students from a range of disciplines are selected.

The academic component of the program is challenging. The curriculum of both regular SEA programs assumes a college sophomore level of competence and the motivation and emotional maturity to meet demanding courses and long hours of work. All regular SEA cruises sail about 2,500 nautical miles (about 2,878 land miles).

Sea Semester: Shore Component

Sea Semester participants spend their six-week shore component studying at SEA's campus in Woods Hole. They take classes in Maritime Studies, Oceanography and Nautical Science. The curriculum includes lectures, seminar discussions, field trips, innovative labs and hands-on workshops.

An ocean survey of neuston tow net samplings for the presence of plastics conducted by SEA found that 68% of all samplings contained plastic and 28% contained plastic pellets (the raw material from which larger plastic items are molded). There were regional differences in amounts, types and ages of the plastic pieces.

SEA was the brainchild of Corwin Cramer, a former Coast Guard officer, teacher and avid sailboat racer. Frustrated by the rebelliousness of his students in the late 1960s, Cramer decided that the experience of living at sea would teach students that an organized structure protected them from danger.

Maritime Studies includes an introduction to the role that the sea has played in the history of the United States. Such topics as the early fishing industry and the New England whaling industry are covered. Literature about the sea, drawn from a wide variety of authors, including Conrad, Hemingway, Kipling and London, explores the tradition of sea voyages. Maritime art and music supplement the history and literature. Some coverage is given to marine policy and contemporary marine affairs.

Oceanography courses examine the geology, physics, chemistry and biology of the sea and how they fit into the dynamics of the complex marine environment. Such questions as how oceans were formed, what the relationship is between marine life and the circulation of the ocean's water, and the impact of humans on the oceanic environment are raised. Guest lecturers from among Woods Hole's research community of scientists introduce students to current areas of oceanographic focus. During this course, with advice from Woods Hole oceanographers, each Sea Semester student designs his or her own research project to be carried out while at sea.

Nautical Science classes provide students with the theory needed to understand practices they will follow in the operation of the *Westward* or the *Cramer* at sea. In lectures and workshops, the ships' captains and mates lead the students to an understanding of how sailing vessels move in harmony with the wind and water. Included are analyses of the forces acting on the hull in the water and on the sails in the air, along with ideas about stability and the dynamics of water movement. Models of the ships help students to understand the effect of combined forces.

Since students cannot expect that their weeks at sea will bring only fine weather and smooth sailing, during the course in Nautical Science the ships' diesel auxiliary system is also reviewed, as is the electric power system, which is in constant use regardless of the weather. Skills fundamental to the safety of the vessels, such as weather prediction, coastal piloting and offshore navigation, are also covered.

Maritime Semester: Shore Component

The first Maritime Semester class began in the summer of 1989. There are many similarities in the Sea Semester and the Maritime Semester, but there are substantial differences in course work, emphasis and division of time. The Sea Semester is more science oriented and the Maritime Semester is more humanities oriented. The Maritime Semester students spend only four weeks in Woods Hole, preparing for a six-week cruise in Canadian waters, followed by two weeks of courses in Halifax, Nova Scotia. Both groups of students learn to handle the ship on which they sail and learn to do science while on board.

The Maritime Semester's courses include Maritime History and Cultures, the Literature of the Sea Voyage, International Relations: Maritime Dimension, Oceanography and Nautical Science.

Maritime History and Cultures surveys the history and cultures of the Northwest Atlantic. The lectures deal with the exploration and colonization of the Atlantic seaboard, the importance of the early North Atlantic trade routes, the history of nautical technology and the various industries that permitted people to make their livings from the sea. The lectures are supplemented with frequent field trips and discussion groups.

The Literature of the Sea Voyage involves reading literary works that evoke the seagoing experience. English, American and Canadian writers, such as Conrad, Hemingway, Melville, McFee, Mostert, Mowat and Buckley, introduce the student to the varied perspectives of "sea" writers. From the vantage point of their own period in history and unique perspectives, the various writers depict life on the quarterdeck—the afterpart of the upper deck of a ship, usually reserved for officers—in the forecastle—the front part of a merchant ship where sailors' quarters are located—or from the deck or the engine room.

International Relations: the Maritime Dimension examines and compares the maritime concerns of Canada and the United States, given the two nations' geographical proximity on the North American continent. The fishing industry, the merchant marine, offshore drilling for oil and the making of policies that affect those industries are discussed. A comparison is made between the U.S. fishing port of New Bedford and Canada's ports at Lunenburg and St. Johns, and between the U.S. port of Boston and the Canadian port of Halifax. Controversies are discussed involving: the Canadian and U.S. navies; the competition between Canada and the United States over the fish and oil on Georges Bank (a submerged sandbank that is a productive fishing ground in the Atlantic, east of

Massachusetts); and the possibilities of naval competition in the undersea Arctic region.

Instead of completing their own science project as the Sea Semester students do, the Maritime Semester students must complete a term paper drawn from maritime history, literature or international relations.

Students in both programs have two classes a day at sea. When Maritime Semester students leave their ship to study in Halifax, they attend two weeks of lectures at the Maritime Museum of the Atlantic. Guest lecturers are drawn from nearby Dalhousie University and the International Institute of Transportation and Ocean Policy Studies. The SEA students live at Dalhousie University and use the library to finish their term papers, which must be presented in seminar fashion.

Sea Component for Both Programs

At sea, the theory learned in the Shore Component classes is put into practice. Much of the teaching takes place in small groups, with three students and one staff member working together. In addition to the two formal classes each day, students work side-by-side with staff at least eight hours a day. Students become familiar with the ship and its rigging and soon feel comfortable in the lab. Daily life is structured into the rhythm of round-the-clock watches, deep-sea scientific stations, shiphandling and navigation.

For a few students, the Sea Component is their first venture in a career in oceanography. For most students, the Sea Component serves as a means to learn about the ocean, sharpen their analytic skills and increase their adaptability to novel settings.

During their courses in Oceanography, the Sea Semester students learn techniques of data collection, including deep-sea bathymetry (the measurement of ocean depths to determine the sea-floor topography), how to set biological tows and trawls to collect specimens, sediment sampling techniques, and analysis of sea water.

During the second three weeks at sea, students take increasing levels of responsibility for the conduct of research and for sailing the ship. The staff monitor operations to ensure that the safety of the scientific mission and the lives of those on-board are not compromised, but the first line of decision making rests with the student.

Sea Semester cruises usually make only two port stops, at least one of which is foreign. Both ships frequently visit Jamaica, Bonaire (an island off the coast of Venezuela), Bermuda, the Bahamas, and Newfoundland.

Research Capacity

The *Westward* and the *Cramer* are equipped with deep-sea oceanographic equipment. Remote-sensing devices, such as echo soundings, permit mapping of the ocean floor. A hydrographic winch makes it possible to collect water samples, sediment cores and biological specimens from many depths.

The laboratory of each ship is equipped with a variety of instruments necessary for analysis. Biological specimens are examined with microscopes. A spectrophotometer (which measures transmission or absorption of light as a function of wavelength) is used to analyze seawater, and a salinometer measures salinity by means of electrical conductivity. In addition to their science projects, each ship also collects meteorological observations for the National Weather Service.

Because the *Westward* and the *Cramer* track the same annual routes year after year, SEA scientists have been able to gather long-term data in the same regions annually, thereby making unique contributions to oceanographic research. During their annual treks, SEA scientists, with the help of students, monitor offshore seaweed communities, the status of ocean birds and marine mammals, and the environmental impact of floating tar and plastics.

In one typical ongoing project, scientists and students are studying a type of seaweed found in the Sargasso Sea, a large tract of comparatively still water in the North Atlantic. The students collect the seaweed, which is home to a variety of organisms, and observe how it is affected by changes in temperature.

Each SEA voyage has a primary research objective, such as the biology of Gulf Stream rings (eddies that break off and travel in the opposite direction of the flow of water), the physical dynamics of Newfoundland fjords (long, narrow inlets from the sea between steep cliffs and slopes), and the influence of Caribbean islands on water circulation and the distribution of marine life.

Progress of a Long-term Research Project

A journal article entitled "Plastic in the North Atlantic," by R. Jude Wilber in the Fall 1987 issue of *Oceanus* described one on-going research effort carried out by SEA students and faculty. The research began in 1984 along the *Westward's* routes in the open ocean and along the shorelines of islands visited during the cruises. Originally intended as a broad qualitative study, the research evolved into a quantitative survey aimed at assessing the amount of plastic drifting in the western North Atlantic. The scientists also hoped to determine the pathways of plastic pollution in the region.

The survey consisted of beach samplings and open ocean neuston tows. (Neuston refers to the uppermost surface of a body of water and to the organisms that live in that environment.) While traversing 35,000 nautical miles (40,250 land miles), more than 420 tows were made, and more than 150 beach surveys were conducted on Bermuda, the Bahamas, the Lesser Antilles, the Florida Keys and Cape Cod.

Special Programs

After many requests, in the winter of 1988, the first SEA cruise was offered for the parents of students who had sailed with SEA, and in 1988, SEA ran its first course for 22 Massachusetts science teachers, from upper elementary through high school grade levels. Sponsored by the National Science Foundation, the program was later broadened to include science teachers from around the country. The science teachers spend three weeks in Woods Hole studying concepts of marine science followed by two weeks aboard the *Cramer*. A bulletin described the philosophy of the program by saying,

> Only through working and living at sea can the excitement of studying the dynamic ocean be realized. The experience of actually being part of a research group doing field work and dealing with the vagaries of weather and ocean will greatly enhance the confidence of the participants in their knowledge of the subject. In addition, working on one of the few remaining "tall ships" that practice marine research will certainly prove a personal challenge to every participant; this new and very different experience can serve only to refresh them and revitalize their teaching. Finally, our past experience has shown us that groups living and working together in confined quarters for a period of time develop a close-knit awareness of the group as a whole and as individuals and that they tend to remain in close contact with each other. This is of particular importance to our program as we try to set up a supportive network for each individual as he/she attempts to introduce what has been learned into the classroom.

In June 1990, SEA offered for the first time a week-long, 450 nautical mile (518 land mile) cruise aboard the *Westward* for entering and current graduate students of the Woods Hole Oceanographic Institute/Massachusetts Institute of Technology (WHOI/MIT) Joint Program. The object of the cruise was to provide the students with an overview of oceanographic research.

Daily Life On Board Ship

A SEA booklet describes daily living on the ocean by saying,

> Life on board ships requires a new set of social skills. You stand watches—night and day—on a rotational basis. [Watches are six hours long during the day and four hours at night.] The bunks are adequate but not spacious, and amenities such as freshwater showers and water for washing clothes are limited. Adaptive skills, compromise and consideration are necessary elements of living in a community at sea. You may experience fatigue and some physical discomfort, yet your shipmates and the work need your best efforts.
>
> Modern conveniences and diversions (TV, tapedecks, and radios) are unheard of aboard the vessels. Students seeking escape through the possession or use of drugs are put ashore without ceremony.

The chief attraction for students is the emphasis on cooperation. During a interview for a May 22, 1989, *Insight* article entitled "Sailing Through a Rigorous Course," Lori Givonetti, a Hamilton College student, said, "Most of us come from colleges where the name of the game is competition. Here you learn to depend on everyone. You see it clearly from the beginning: that if you're not prepared, you're letting the others down. If you haven't learned what you're supposed to learn, you can be endangering lives. It is the stresses added together that give you the kind of responsibility you've never faced before and that we have come here to learn to face."

There is little time or room for privacy aboard SEA's vessels, but here, student Erin Kelly enjoys a quiet moment alone in her only private corner, her bunk.

7

Weather and Climate

CLOUDS

Clues to Climate

A flood of data from satellite observations and atmospheric probes has brought the unwelcome news that mathematical models of clouds upon which climatologists (those who study weather) have depended are far out of touch with reality. Clouds in the tropics differ from those in temperate zones and they affect the planet's temperature differently. Despite their complexity, some scientists believe that clouds may behave according to a relatively simple set of underlying principles.

To study the role clouds play in global climate, a team of more than 150 researchers is engaged in carrying out a decade-long international experiment, the International Satellite Cloud Climatology Project (I.S.C.C.P.), in several countries under the sponsorship of the World Meteorological Organization. In the United States, a study called Project Fire, conducted under the auspices of the National Science Foundation, the Office of Naval Research and the Department of Energy, is a part of the I.S.C.C.P. experiment. Fire is an acronym for First I.S.C.C.P. Regional Experiment.

The first phase of Project Fire, launched in 1986, collected information on stratocumulus (wispy, thin) clouds found over the Pacific Ocean off the coast of California and high cirrus clouds commonly found over the Midwest. The finding required many changes in theories about clouds. A second phase, scheduled to begin some time in early 1990, was rescheduled to 1991. At this point, theorists are unable to predict whether clouds will prevent or contribute to global warming.

Stephen Schneider, a climate specialist at the National Center, indicated the value of such research during an interview for a June 30, 1987, *New York Times* article entitled "Hints of More Cloudiness Spur Global Study." He said, "The clouds are the shades—they're the blinds. It's a very difficult thing to monitor, because it's so highly variable. Yet I can't think of a more important variable if you want to know what the climate is doing, other than the thermometer itself."

American researchers, in 1987, began a program to analyze low-level sea clouds off the coast of California, using a combination of satellites, aircraft and ground-based observers. Europeans also launched an effort called the International Cirrus Experiments to study high-altitude clouds.

An Increase in Cloudiness

Scientists know that human activities are having an impact on the global climate, but they do not know how big the response may be. By 1987, some fragmentary data and some isolated pieces of research suggested that one effect might be a growing cloudiness over widespread areas.

A survey from 45 American cities revealed that every city except one, Fort Worth, Texas, was cloudier in the second half of the century than it was in the first half. Los Angeles, for example, had an average of 10 cloudless days per month from 1900 to 1936 and an average of only 7.6 per

FIRE's object is to develop improved cloud and radiation parameterizations (a constant, with variable values, used as a point to refer to when determining other variables) for use in climate models. FIRE combines climatic modeling with satellite, airborne and surface observations to study two types of cloud systems: cirrus and marine stratocumulus.

month from 1950 to 1982. A cloudless day was defined as one in which an average of 10% or less of the daytime sky was obscured by clouds, haze, smoke or fog.

The survey of cities was done by William Seaver of Virginia Polytechnic Institute and State University and James Lee of the Mitre Corporation, a nonprofit systems engineering company in McLean, Virginia. The Seaver-Lee study was the first to demonstrate a trend in cloudiness for the nation as a whole. For their study, the researchers compared data available from the U.S. National Weather Service on the number of cloudless days in 45 cities for two time periods, 1900 to 1936 and 1950 to 1982.

A couple of studies of smaller areas showed a similar trend. Research done by Stanley Changnon and his colleagues at the Illinois State Water Survey at the University of Illinois, Urbana-Champaign, documented an increase in cloudiness for the middle third of the United States. A statewide study done by Val Eichenlaub of Western Michigan University in Kalamazoo showed an increase in cloudiness in the state of Michigan. Grand Rapids, for example, was 75% to 80% sunny in the late 1930s and early 1940s but was only 65% sunny in the 1970s.

While the studies agreed that there was a trend toward increased cloudiness, they provided no explanation for the change. Changnon suggested that jet contrails (condensed water vapor that forms in the wake of an aircraft) act as condensation seeds that instigate cloud formation. Eichenlaub proposed that an air mass called the polar

weather front has been drifting southward, bringing with it more storms and clouds. Lee believed that pollution could be providing particles around which waters may condense.

Global Warming and Possible Impact of Life on Clouds

Lack of knowledge about clouds has become of greater significance recently as scientists' concerns about global warming have mounted. Global warming, the so-called greenhouse effect, is caused by the trapping of energy in the atmosphere by carbon dioxide and a variety of gases made by humans. Scientists fear that the trapped energy will raise the temperature of the planet and result in a cascade of other changes, including melted icecaps, increased droughts, more desert regions, destructive winds and a rise in sea level, which could inundate many port cities and shoreline communities.

While scientists are in general agreement that global warming would have a chain of climate effects, they are not in agreement about causes, or outcomes, or whether global warming has already begun. Only recently has there been an effort to include the effect of living organisms on the planet.

Three researchers who have been interested in the impact of life on the overall balance of the planet are Robert Charlson and Stephen Warren of the University of Washington, Meinrat Andreae of Florida State, and James Lovelock of the Coombe Mill Experimental Station in Launceston, England. Dr. Lovelock is the author of the "Gaia Hypothesis," a theory that life on earth has interacted to establish and maintain the conditions needed for continuing existence. The theory implies that actions give rise to counteractions that dampen the original action, thus action and reaction tend to create a balance over time. The idea continues to be controversial; however, it has alerted scientists to the need to examine the ways in which the smallest organisms that participate in ongoing feedback loops can contribute to change on a global scale.

One life form, plankton (algae floating in vast numbers near the ocean surface), may be part of a feedback loop that is related to clouds and global warming. Plankton emit a sulfurous gas, dimethysulfide. When dimethysulfide reaches the atmosphere, it reacts with oxygen to form aerosols (ultramicroscopic particles). The aerosols may serve as seeds for clouds as excess moisture condenses around them to form cloud droplets. The droplets act as reflectors to return the sun's radiation back into space.

Tracing the logic of the Gaia premise that the earth has the capacity to be self-regulating, a proposed plankton feedback loop would involve five steps. 1) The earth's warming would encourage the growth of plankton. 2) The increased plankton would emit more sulfurous gas. 3) The sulfurous gas would float into the atmosphere where it would react with oxygen to form aerosol particles. 4) The aerosol particles would act as seeds for the formation of cloud droplets. 5) The cloud droplets would reflect an increased amount of sun back into space, thereby moderating the increase in the earth's heat.

Whether the earth does have a self-regulating mechanism to slow global warming is impossible to establish, in part, due to the lack of available data on cloud reflectivity. Data from satellites have helped; however, they provide only a unidimensional, top-down view. Clouds are three-dimensional and multi-layered, making measurement difficult.

Satellite photographs of cloud cover are on a scale of 3 to 6 miles, which means that it is impossible to tell whether clouds are solid or broken up into smaller elements. The study of low-level sea clouds off the California coast was intended to examine clouds on the order of 100 feet.

There are a number of variables under consideration. Among them is the relationship of droplet size to reflectivity and the balance between clouds as a reflector of radiation and clouds that serve as a blanket to hold infrared radiation in the atmosphere that would otherwise escape.

Climate Models

More than any other factor, the mysteries of clouds have kept scientists from having confidence in forecasts about global warming and the changes that would accompany it. An April 24, 1990, *New York Times* article entitled "Clouds Are Yielding Clues to Changes in Climate" reported that accumulating data from satellite observations and atmospheric probes indicates that computerized

One project of FIRE is ASTEX, Atlantic Stratocumulus Transition Experiment. How best to delineate stratocumulus and trade-cumulus (boundary layer) clouds in large-scale and mesoscale models is unknown. These clouds are frequently less than 500 meters (548 yards) thick and closely associated with boundary layer turbulence, facts that complicate their representation in models. ASTEX plans to study the physical processes responsible for the transition from stratocumulus clouds to shallow cumulus clouds.

mathematical models on which climatologists rely to forecast climatic changes do not reflect reality.

These models will require reconstruction, not simple adjustment. The *New York Times* quoted Veerabhadran Ramanathan, a climatologist at the University of Chicago and a leader in new research on clouds, as saying, "In some cases tuning may be impossible; you may have to go back to the drawing board and rethink the whole process."

Scientists have long known that clouds both cool and warm the earth; however, the new findings suggest that the effects are more powerful than had been previously thought. Moreover, the heating and cooling are so delicately balanced that even a small change could have far-reaching consequences.

The scientists have also found that clouds themselves are more complex and varied than they had previously realized. Clouds in the tropics are different than clouds in temperate zones and they have a different impact on the earth's heat balance. Clouds over water have different heating effects than clouds over continents. Moreover, the nature and effects of clouds vary with the season and time of day.

At the same time that scientists have become more aware of the variety and complexity of clouds, some have begun to suspect that clouds may have an underlying set of relatively simple principles and are working to distill these principles into concepts that could be included in climate prediction models.

Conclusions Based on Small-Scale Inquiries

Although study of the clouds has been going on for decades, the investigation has been limited to relatively small-scale studies in only a few areas of the globe. Scientists have long known that clouds form when water condenses around dust particles or minute nuclei, and that clouds are mostly air. Stephen Schwartz, a cloud expert at the Brookhaven National Laboratory on Long Island, describes clouds as one part water to a million parts atmospheric gas.

Despite their ephemerality, scientists have also known that clouds are the means by which the oceans and the atmosphere interact and the means by which heat and water are distributed around the planet. Sunlight hits the water, causing it to evaporate. The evaporated molecules rise into the atmosphere where the coolness causes them to form clouds, condense into water droplets, and fall as rain. The process of condensing and falling as rain releases large amounts of heat, fueling the winds in the atmosphere.

William Rossow of the Goddard Institute of Space Studies in New York City describes the lack of knowledge about clouds as a sampling problem. In the absence of satellite observations, scientists in the past, for the most part, limited themselves to studies of clouds in temperate zones and over continents where data collection was most feasible.

Cool-Warm Balance

As part of NASA's Earth Radiation Budget Experiment between 1984 and 1990, Dr. Ramanathan and his colleagues analyzed satellite measurements of the earth's heating. They were surprised to find that on a global scale, clouds amplified the greenhouse warming by a staggering amount. They learned that the warming effect of the clouds was 250 times greater than the effect of carbon dioxide, a major global pollutant. However, they also learned that clouds reflect a still greater amount of heat from the sun; therefore clouds exert a net cooling effect.

The cooling-warming effects of clouds are not uniform around the world. The huge storm systems of the tropics with their towering cumulonimbus clouds (thunderheads) have a disproportionate impact. Compared with other clouds on a global average, they prevent three times as much heat from escaping from the planet. On the other hand, they reflect such a great amount of sunlight that their heating effect is canceled out. Because the tropics account for 20% of the earth's surface, it is critical that they sustain their delicate balance.

On a global scale, a warmer ocean could be expected to cause more cloud formation. In all likelihood, the additional clouds would pile up, building to higher altitudes where it is colder. In the colder air of higher altitudes, clouds emit less heat into space than they absorb below, a factor that could upset the delicate heat balance of the tropics. Moreover, a warmer ocean's production of more clouds could alter global wind circulation patterns, resulting in a shift in the location of desert and moist regions to different latitudes.

Stratocumulus Clouds

Satellite data has revealed that stratocumulus clouds, low-lying layers of clouds with fluffy contours, almost always cover large areas of the North Atlantic, North Pacific and the temperate areas of the Southern (Antarctic) Ocean. These clouds have been found to exert a net cooling effect locally, and appear to be responsible for the overall cooling effect of clouds on a global scale.

The location of the stratocumulus clouds over an ocean is determined by the ocean's temperature. Global warming could cause clouds to shift northward or southward and expose new areas of ocean to the sun. Depending on which way they shifted, the clouds might have either a warming or a cooling effect.

Dr. Ramanathan reported that the new data on the low-level ocean clouds had surprised scientists. They learned that the reflectivity of the clouds is three times greater than that attributed to them by current mathematical models.

The Project Fire study of stratocumulus clouds off the California coast found that they are strongly affected by dust and pollution from the United States. Small particles and aerosols are the nuclei around which cloud droplets form. The more particles, the more droplets and the smaller they are likely to be. The smaller, more numerous droplets have a greater scattering effect on sunlight, making the clouds brighter and more reflective. If particles are large enough, they can form large droplets that fall as rain and dissipate the cloud. The researchers don't yet have a full explanation of the process.

Stratocumulus clouds have a dramatic impact on solar radiation (emitted by the sun) and less effect on thermal radiation (heat absorbed by the earth and trapped in its atmosphere and emitted back toward space). Without clouds, water reflects only about 10% of the incoming solar radiation. Clouds reflect 60% to 70% of the solar radiation.

Cirrus Clouds

Opinions about the heat-trapping qualities of cirrus clouds also had to undergo some changes as a consequence of Project Fire data. At any given time, cirrus clouds cover about 16% of the globe. Often called mare's tails, feathery cirrus clouds form high in the sky at an average height of 33,000 feet and are filled with ice pellets. The major reason that scientists know little about cirrus clouds is that their high altitude has put them beyond the reach of most research aircraft.

In contrast to some other cloud types that block the sun, cirrus clouds let through much of the sun's visible and ultraviolet light. The ice in cirrus clouds also absorbs more infrared (long-wave) radiation headed away from the earth than they are able to emit to space or back to earth. (All objects, including human bodies and clouds, emit infrared radiation; however, cool objects emit less than warm ones.) If cirrus clouds were bright, they would reflect more. But most of the time they are not bright and they tend to have an overall warming effect, rather than a cooling effect.

Scientists had been of the opinion that high cirrus clouds lacked earth-cooling properties; however, Project Fire findings have modified their views. In October 1986, investigators launched a large experiment in central Wisconsin to gather data on cirrus clouds using a wide variety of observing instruments. The experiment nearly doubled the number of in situ (in place, inside the cloud) measurements available to scientists.

During an August 23, 1990, telephone interview, Stephen Cox reported that from the first-phase data, scientists learned that small-scale motions in the atmosphere in the range of 10s to 100s of meters (32.8 feet to 328 feet) have more impact on cirrus clouds than thought heretofore. Such small-scale motions will make the task of fitting cloud information into large-scale climate models even more complicated.

Project Fire data also revealed that cirrus clouds contain an unexpectedly large population of very small ice crystals that reflect more sunlight back into space than previously envisioned. This raised more questions about the heating-cooling effect of cirrus clouds.

Bruce Wielicki of NASA's Langley Research Center in Hampton, Virginia, speculated that while the small bits of ice may account for only a small portion of a cloud's mass, they might overshadow weightier particles in determining the cloud's contribution to the greenhouse effect.

A subsequent cirrus cloud experiment scheduled for the Kansas-Oklahoma region in 1991 is expected to include instruments particularly designed to measure small ice particles. Scientists also expect to include rawinsonde, a method of upper air observation of wind speed and direction, temperature, pressure and relative humidity using a balloon-borne radiosonde tracked by radar or radio direction finder.

The first Project Fire experiment took place over Wisconsin. The second experiment has been set for Kansas-Oklahoma to examine the effect of moving south, where the clouds are higher. The average height of cirrus clouds increases as latitude decreases. Since temperature decreases with altitude, the cirrus clouds in lower latitudes are colder. Scientists hope to learn whether the relationship between sunlight and thermal radiation is the same regardless of latitude.

Marine Stratocumulus Clouds

At a level of only 500 to 1,000 yards above the sea's surface, marine stratocumulus clouds form, cooling the atmosphere. Although marine stratocumulus clouds are thin, no more than a few hundred yards from top to bottom, they are full of water droplets that reflect substantial amounts of the earth's infrared radiation back toward space. Because they are low, warm clouds, marine stratocumulus clouds also have the capacity to radiate into space much of the infrared radiation they absorb coming off the earth's surface.

Atmospheric scientist Bruce Albrecht of Pennsylvania State University in University Park, described marine stratocumulus clouds by saying that they "are probably the most important low-level clouds in a climatological sense because of their large aerial extent and their persistent nature." Drifting above the ocean surface, they often are arranged in sheet-like "decks" that disperse over large regions. Studies have revealed that stratocumulus and other low-level clouds cover 34% of the world's oceans at any given moment.

The Project Fire investigation off the California coast uncovered a complex pattern above and below marine stratocumulus clouds. Prior to the experiments, scientists had thought that air could move easily from the ocean surface through the bottom of the cloud to its top. However, in an interview with *Science News*, David Randall, Colorado State University scientist and co-chairman of the Project Fire science team, noted that 1987 measurements had discovered that a thermal barrier frequently developed at the cloud base and inhibited air circulation. This temperature inversion (when cold air gets trapped under warm air) is the same kind of barrier that holds smog over Los Angeles and Denver. Scientists had previously seen such an effect with marine stratocumulus clouds but did not realize that it was widespread.

A stable temperature inversion cuts a cloud off from a continuing supply of moisture from the ocean. Without a moisture source, the cloud disappears during daylight hours because the sun evaporates the water droplets.

A 1992 Project Fire investigation scheduled to study stratocumulus clouds over the Western Atlantic, headquartered in the Azores, a group of nine islands 800 miles off the coast of Portugal in the North Atlantic Ocean, will focus on how clouds break up and how breaking up affects their ability to absorb and reflect light. The research will involve ships, aircraft, a satellite and land stations, and will be a joint atmospheric science and oceanography experiment. The first Project Fire investigation of stratocumulus clouds was conducted in a location where clouds were usually present. In the Azores, one region may have clouds most of the time; another region may have clouds that tend to break up; and a third may be clear. The purpose of the experiment will be to learn why the clouds form and why they dissipate.

Cloud Variations

Data emerging from the various cloud studies demonstrate what Dr. Rossow of the Goddard Institute calls "a variety of styles of cloudiness" around the globe. The variety is illustrated by a number of new finds. Scientists have discovered that cloudiness over water is 15% greater than over land; cloud tops tend to be higher over land than over water; there tend to be more clouds over land in the morning than in the afternoon, and more clouds over water in the afternoon than in the morning. When the temperature is warmer, there tend to be thicker clouds over land, but when the temperature is cooler, there tend to be thicker clouds over water; and in temperate latitudes, winter clouds tend to be somewhat thicker and higher than in other seasons, while the situation is reversed near the equator.

Scientists are beginning to explore how the varieties of clouds fit together to produce a global climate effect. The Department of Energy's Atmospheric Radiation Measurement Project will establish four to six permanent observation sites to intensively measure cloud properties.

Cloud Microphysics

The 1987 Project Fire stratocumulus experiment, like the cirrus experiment, brought attention to the complicated world of tiny particles, cloud microphysics. Investigators made the first direct measurements of the effect of ship exhausts on cloud droplets. Scientists theorized that the additional nuclei provided by the ship's exhaust, if it entered a cloud, would result in the available water being spread between the old and new cloud-condensation nuclei. Such an effect would increase the number of droplets but make each droplet smaller. Because cloud particles reflect light, the additional drops could be expected to brighten a cloud.

Measurements of actual ship trails indicated that the trails contained more liquid water than did surrounding

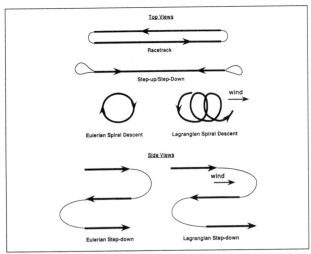

In collection of data, coordination of air, space and surface observation points is necessary. For most missions, aircraft fly the same basic racetrack pattern, over the same geographical coordinates, at altitudes of 65,000 and 10,000 feet. Above is a diagram of standard aircraft flight patterns for FIRE Cirrus Intensive Field Operations-Phase II.

clouds. Scientists speculated that by fostering small drops and thereby allowing clouds to retain water, ship pollution inhibited the life span of a cloud. The breakup of a cloud can be hastened by falling water droplets, which empty a cloud of its moisture and can also form a temperature inversion at the cloud's base.

Taking Clouds into Account in Climate Models

In an August 12, 1989, *Science News* article entitled "Cloudy Concerns: Will Clouds Prevent or Promote a Drastic Global Warming?", author Richard Monastersky said, "Climate experts often call clouds the wild card in the game of global change. (Oceans may be the second wild card in the deck, because they could dramatically affect the pace of a greenhouse warming.)"

Anthony Slingo, who works on one of the large general-circulation models at the National Atmospheric Research in Boulder, Colorado, told Monastersky that the lack of a firm theoretical foundation for the behavior of clouds made it impossible for scientists to say what confidence they put in results they obtained on the climate models.

Within the emerging complexity, some scientists believe there may lie a set of simple principles that can be plugged into reformulated climate models. Dr. Rossow suspects that small-scale phenomena may average each other out. He believes that substantial improvement will come in 5 to 10 years. He tempered his prediction by saying, "There may never be a day when we can say 'I think I understand it.' But our confidence ought to grow."

Contrasts in size complicate the models. An individual water droplet can measure as small as 10 microns. (A micron

is equal to one-millionth of a meter or .0000393 inches.) A cloud system can stretch for more than 600 miles. The general-circulation models, the most advanced climate models, divide the atmosphere and the oceans into thousands of boxes of 100 or or 200 miles square. Using a process called "parameterization," scientists draw up equations that represent a general "cloudiness" based on physical principles and empirical observations. Within such a system, the patterns of individual clouds are lost.

Scientists working with general-circulation models had hoped to avoid the complexities of microphysics; however, the recent data, which suggests that minute drops can powerfully influence the activities of a cloud, mean that modelers can no longer avoid microphysics in the interest of keeping their models simple.

A study of 14 general-circulation models was reported in the August 4, 1989, issue of *Science*. The study found that when researchers forecast a world with double the present level of carbon dioxide, the 14 models agreed, so long as clouds were not included. With the inclusion of clouds, the models failed to agree and made forecasts that ranged over a wide spectrum.

Expectations for Improved Data Loom Promising

With the extensive data already collected and major experiments scheduled for 1991 and 1992, expectations for improved understanding of clouds are high. The introduction of accurate information about clouds and improved theoretical explanations of their behavior would significantly enhance the reliability of climate models. With more reliable forecasts, better plans could be made on behalf of the future climate of the earth.

In tropical storm systems, cumulonimbus clouds, on average, trap three times as much heat as other clouds. But they also reflect so much sunlight back towards space that the warming effect is canceled.

VIOLENT WEATHER

Bombs, Cyclones, Hurricanes and Tornadoes

"Weather is always abnormal," says Jerome Namaias, a research meteorologist at the Scripps Institution of Oceanography in La Jolla, California, and the father of long-range weather forecasting. Natural variations give rise to abnormalities. For example, several times each year, rapidly intensifying storms form with little warning off the Carolinas. They churn their way northeast on a track that brings torrents of precipitation in the form of rain, snow, sleet etc. or bitingly frigid weather to the New England coast. One of the storms, the Blizzard of '78, killed 29 people, demolished 339 homes and deposited as much as 4 feet of snow along the coast from Rhode Island to southern Maine.

Meteorologists call these savage storms "bombs." Officially, they refer to them as explosive marine cyclogenesis. Explosive implies that the storms happen rapidly in the span of six hours, compared to a storm over land that would take 24 hours to reach a similar level of growth. Marine means that they develop over the sea. Cyclogenesis refers to the genesis (creation or generation) of cyclones, a general category of storms with rotating winds around a calm center, which includes bombs, hurricanes and tornadoes.

A January 9, 1989, *Boston Globe* article entitled "Going Right to the Heart of a Winter Storm," described an effort to track a bomb on January 3, 1989, that was even more powerful than the 1978 blizzard. The storm's barometric (atmospheric) pressure dipped even lower than the reading recorded during the 1978 blizzard. The storm fortunately stayed out at sea.

Six scientists from several Canadian and American universities and government agencies flew into the storm to examine firsthand the dynamics of one of New England's most ferocious storms. The scientists were part of a three-month project (December 1988 to February 1989) called Experiment on Rapidly Intensifying Cyclones over the Atlantic (ERICA). The $8 million program sponsored by the Office of Naval Research used aircraft belonging to the National Oceanic and Atmospheric Administration (NOAA) and the Office of Naval Research.

During an August 3, 1990, telephone interview, Dr. Carl Kreitzberg, a professor of physics and atmospheric science at Drexel University, a renowned meteorologist and ERICA's chief scientist, explained that ships' crews have

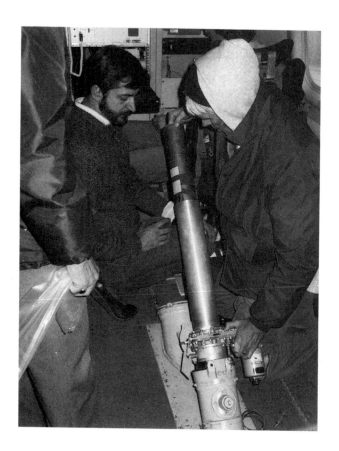

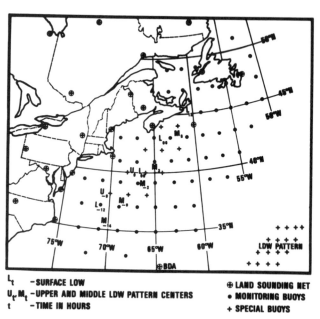

To gather data for Project ERICA, scientists dropped instrument canisters into storms to measure humidity, temperature, and wind speed and direction. Above is a map of various data-gathering instrument positions.

reported bombs for years, but ERICA was the first project to go out and examine them while they were happening.

The project observed eight storms over the Gulf Stream and North America. The scientists used five research aircraft designed to fly in storms. Special depth buoys dropped in the ocean were fitted with instruments to report conditions during the storms. The aircraft used are normally based in Miami for hurricane research, but for the duration of the ERICA project, they were stationed in Brunswick, Maine. The aircraft flew nine-hour tours, often several flights simultaneously, through storms that met ERICA's criteria.

Dr. Kreitzberg said the bombs developed far more rapidly than they had anticipated. The three months of experiments will not be repeated for about five years. The scientists expect that it will take that long to analyze the enormous quantity of data collected in the December 1988 to February 1989 experiments and to prepare for another expedition.

Only the Broad Outlines of Bombs Are Understood

The storm reported in the *Boston Globe* recorded winds that had increased over a four-hour period from light and variable to 70 miles per hour. The storm also exhibited thunderbooming squall lines and a barometric pressure that had dropped almost twice the minimum rate to meet ERICA criteria.

Measurements of barometric pressure are important in predicting a storm. Barometric pressure, also known as atmospheric pressure, refers to the pressure at any point in the atmosphere due solely to the weight of the atmospheric gases above that height. In areas of low pressure, the air tends to rise and be accompanied by clouds and precipitation. Winds flow from areas of high pressure to areas of low pressure. The greater the difference between the two, the faster the flow.

The Jet Stream

In general terms, scientists can explain why the East Coast of the United States spawns an average of five bombs each year. A bomb is set off by the presence of a strong jet stream, a large quantity of unstable moist air from the Gulf of Mexico, cold Canadian air and tropical waters carried north by the Gulf Stream (a river of water that flows northeast from the Straits of Florida up the Atlantic to east of Newfoundland, where it splinters into rivulets). These ingredients coming together cause temperature variations. While scientists know a considerable amount about the separate phenomena that come together to produce a bomb, they do not know how the constantly fluctuating wanderings

of the upper air and the ocean currents affect the track the storm will take, nor do they know what mixture of ingredients creates this powerful storm.

Scientists are still learning about the jet stream, which is a relatively narrow band (perhaps a couple of hundred miles in breadth) of high-flying, fast-moving winds that circle the globe in varying corridors in the middle latitudes, flanked by more slowly moving currents. The winds define the boundary between polar and tropical air and thus dictate the routes taken by violent storms.

The position of the jet stream plays an important role in where major precipitation falls on the North American continent. Since the jet stream divides the great air masses of the world's weather into warm and cold regions, it varies in strength and position. Depending upon the season, the jet stream, traveling from west to east, guides the great tempests of winter and early spring across the United States in an unrelenting pattern of blizzards and tornadoes, but in summer, the jet stream flows meekly across the Canadian prairie, steering weak storms of minor consequence.

The jet stream is most powerful and influential between November and April. Traveling through the United States, storms usually follow the jet stream eastward, deriving strength from the differences in temperature that exist on the north and south sides of the jet stream.

In the fall, decreasing heat from the sun leads to dropping temperatures and, as a consequence, the jet stream slips southward bringing with it the pathways of the major continental storms. Over the winter months, the jet stream slips further south. Usually in the month of January, it reaches its most southerly position along the shores of the Gulf of Mexico.

When the jet stream dips low into the South, storms entering the United States from the Pacific cross the Continental Divide (the ridge of the Rocky Mountains that separates rivers flowing toward the Atlantic from rivers flowing toward the Pacific). Once past the Continental Divide, the storms turn southward to skim the southern Plains and the Gulf States and either head out to sea or reorganize into an Atlantic coastal storm. As the winter continues, the increasingly direct rays of the sun warm the South and the jet stream moves northward once again.

The Gulf Stream

The Gulf Stream exerts considerable impact on the global climate. Food production in Europe is dependent on the warmth the Gulf Stream carries from the equator. For the quantity of water it transports, the Gulf Stream is the world's fastest major ocean current. Considering the importance of this river of waters, a surprising amount remains unknown about it.

Beneath the Gulf Stream runs a gigantic flow of highly saline (salty) water that flows in the opposite direction. The northerly flow of the Gulf Stream is tied to the deep return of the saline river beneath it. The Coriolis effect (the influence of the earth's rotation and tilt on moving bodies) exerts force on the northward flow of the Gulf Stream and the southward flow of the saline river to keep them hugging the western edge of the Atlantic Basin.

As it flows northward along the Atlantic Coast, the Gulf Stream is trapped between the "north slope water" on the left and the Sargasso Sea on the right. The north slope water is the ocean area between the eastern seashore and the Continental Shelf (the submerged land that slopes to the point where the steep descent to the ocean bottom begins). The Sargasso Sea is a large tract of still water in the North Atlantic. The tug of the Sargasso Sea, which is about 3 feet higher than the north slope water, creates a gravity pull northward, and the earth's rotation pushes water in the Northern Hemisphere in an easterly direction. As a consequence of the competing forces, the Gulf Stream begins to meander.

Some loops of the Gulf Stream circle back on themselves creating wells of water as much as a 100 miles wide. A loop on the north side isolates cold northern water to spin off clockwise. A loop on the south side captures warm Sargasso Sea water to spin counterclockwise. The eddies travel in a direction opposite to the Gulf Stream. Large eddies 200 miles southeast off Nantucket are suspected of creating thermal convections (upward flows of heat) that create the sudden winter storms that pummel New England.

Fronts

When two air masses of different type meet one another, they do not mix easily. The colder one slides under the warmer one and a transition zone called a front develops between them. They are called fronts because they were first described by a Norwegian meteorologist during World War I when "fronts" was a common military term that signified battle lines.

Meteorologists classify fronts on the basis of which of the air masses is advancing. When the cold air is advancing and pushing the warm air before it, the transition zone is called a cold front. When warm air is advancing and pushing the cold air before it, the transition zone is called a warm front.

When the warm air is moist and unstable, showers and thunderstorms often form in the warm air rising over a cold front's leading edge. The cold air gliding up a warm front on occasion may contain widespread clouds, rain and snow. If the boundary between warm and cold air does not move, it is called a stationary front.

When a cold front overtakes a warm front and runs under it, the fronts are said to be occluding (blocking each other). A zone separating cold air under the front from warm air above the front is called an isothermal or inversion layer

Naval planes used for Project ERICA. A report on the project was scheduled to be presented in New Orleans, at the First International Winter Storm Symposium, sponsored by the American Meteorological Society, January 1991.

(which implies that the air mingles and becomes approximately the same temperature). The stability of the inversion layer acts to reduce mixing of cold and warm air.

Fronts can result in a dramatic shift in wind, temperature, level of humidity and barometric pressure over a brief period. The front may be only 20 to 50 miles wide and its passage can be completed in less than an hour, or it may be 200 to 300 miles of cloud deck (upper surface of clouds) and take a day or more to pass.

A strong cold front barreling into unseasonably warm air can drop the temperature 20 to 40 degrees overnight. A summer thundershower associated with a cold front can drop temperatures 20 degrees or more in only minutes.

Cyclones: A Conflict Between Fronts

A cyclone is any violent, circular storm with heavy rainfall and winds rotating about a calm center of low atmospheric pressure. Bombs, hurricanes and tornadoes are cyclones with special characteristics. A cyclonic storm moves at a rate of anywhere from 2 to 40 miles per hour.

Once a storm assumes a cyclonic flow, it quickly becomes divided into different sectors with distinctive properties. Well in advance of the main storm center, as warm air climbs over cold air, clouds form and precipitation begins. Sometimes signaling the arrival of the storm by more than a thousand miles, high cirrus clouds (filmy clouds at an average level of 33,000 feet) spread out ahead of the storm's movement.

In the early part of the 19th century, it was recognized in England that there was a connection between large storm systems and passing regions of low pressure. For about a century, various scientists theorized about the characteristics of cyclonic storms. Unfortunately, there was an absence of reliable observations taken over a large enough region to draw conclusions.

Toward the end of World War I, major advances in understanding cyclones were made by the Norwegian meteorologists Vilhelm Bjerknes, his son Jakob and their associates. They collected sufficient observations to be able to study the structure of several cyclones over Europe. From their analyses they developed the "frontal theory of cyclones."

They speculated that a cyclone forms along a nearly stationary front. A disturbance develops on the front when cold air is deflected southward and warm air is deflected northward. In this process, potential energy (the ability to do work) is converted to kinetic energy (energy of motion) when cold, heavy air behind the front sinks while warm, humid air rises.

As the cold air continues to sink and the warm air continues to rise, in a movement similar to a wave, condensation takes place in the warm ascending air, clouds form, and there may be precipitation. At the top of the wave, there is a fall in pressure. The cold front advances faster than the warm, and the sector of warm air becomes increasingly smaller. The air motion turns in a spiral (counterclockwise in the Northern Hemisphere, clockwise in the Southern Hemisphere). Wind speeds in the warm sector exceed the speed of the overall warm front.

Along the leading edge of the advancing cold front, warm, humid air rises rapidly, producing cloudiness. If the air is sufficiently unstable, there will be thunderstorms. While the cyclone continues to develop, the advancing cold front catches up with the warm front and occlusion takes place. Beneath the occluded front, there is a mixture of cold air that is below both the warm and cold fronts. With continued occlusion, there is dissipation of the temperature differences. In the final stages, the cyclone is a weakened vortex, a whirl of winds around a center, made up of uniformly cold air.

The actual behavior of cyclones often differs in significant details from the theory. A cyclone may last only a day or as long as a week. The first stages may occur in hours. In a typical pattern, many small wave disturbances may occur along a long stationary front, with only a small number of them developing into mature cyclones. When a mature cyclone does develop, another is likely to follow along the same stationary front, in a pattern known as a cyclone family.

Favorite Targets

In the United States, particular regions encourage the development of cyclonic storms. The eastern slopes of the Rocky Mountains, the Gulf Coast, the waters east of North Carolina's Outer Banks, and the northern, central and southern Plains of the United States are fertile breeding areas of cyclonic development. They are regions where unlike air masses—polar and tropical—may intermingle before they undergo any dramatic modification. In other words, southward-moving, dry, cold polar air freely mixes with northward-moving, moisture-ladened, warm, tropical air.

Hurricanes

Like all other cyclones, hurricanes are storms with winds rotating around a calm center with low atmospheric pressure. However, with some justification, hurricanes have been called the greatest storms on earth. No other storm phenomenon gathers together so much atmospheric power or delivers so much destruction over so large an area in so short a time.

When air is diverging (high pressure), the result is generally fine weather. When air is converging (low pressure), a mass of air may turn on itself, accelerate the up and down movement of air, form a vortex and possibly reach hurricane strength. As the storm generates, clouds build to heights of 30,000 feet or more, convective (upward flowing) winds increase and great quantities of moisture are sucked into the atmosphere, thereby releasing heat to further fuel the storm.

The development of a storm begins when the air is unstable, convection currents are strong, and a band of cumulus clouds (dense, dome shaped clouds, with flat bases) becomes heated. Quickly the cumulus clouds grow into cumulonimbus formations (clouds of towering vertical height of as much as 60,000 feet) and thunderstorms occur. Water vapor from the ocean condenses and releases energy into the atmosphere, setting the stage for more stormy weather.

As a storm intensifies, gathering more moisture and organizing clouds and bands of precipitation, atmospheric pressures fall over a large area, producing the lowest pressure in the center of the storm. Rising air produces lower density in the lower atmosphere, hence the term "low pressure system."

When a low pressure system nears its peak of intensity as the boundary zone between warm and cold air narrows, enormous amounts of energy are released into the atmosphere accounting for the kinetic energy of the system and strong winds.

When a tropical storm's winds exceed 73 miles per hour (mph), the storm officially becomes a hurricane. A fully developed hurricane can have an impact over a million cubic miles (a cubic mile is a mile long, times a mile wide, times a mile deep) of the atmosphere. Hurricane winds reach out in all directions for nearly a hundred miles. The steeper the rate of change in atmospheric pressure with distance, the stronger the winds blow in that sector of the storm. Wind velocities are highest at the inner wall of the hurricane.

However, in the center of the hurricane, the so-called eye, the skies may be sunny and the winds calm or blowing at no more than 15 mph. The eye of the storm acts as a chimney where warm currents fuel the storm by sucking up vast amounts of oceanic moisture that produces energy as it vaporizes.

Below the storm center, the ocean is pulled upward like water in a straw to form a mound of water a foot or higher. This small ripple becomes coastal surges of 10 to 25 feet high as the hurricane center comes ashore. The force of the storm wave as it pounds the coast is far more destructive than either the hurricane-force winds, which may reach 200 mph, or the flooding rains that accompany a hurricane.

Influences on North American Hurricanes

There are semipermanent high and low pressure areas present year-round in particular locations. A high-pressure cell that has a strong influence on the weather in North America resides over the North Pacific, off the California coast. Another strong influence known as the Bermuda high is anchored in the Atlantic, with a center near Bermuda. The regions are so stable that storms usually have to traverse around their outer fringes because they are unable to penetrate the subsiding air.

In contrast to the semipermanent stretches of high pressure are two lesser, though very significant to North America, areas of low pressure. One area is centered near the Gulf of Alaska and extends into the Sea of Japan. The other, the Icelandic low, covers the continent of Greenland and Iceland.

A persistent zone of stormy weather can emanate from the Alaskan low and control North America's weather for weeks at a time. The storms are apt to follow a typical pattern. Particularly during cold winter months, a "family" of storms will proceed across the Pacific. As many as five or six storms will line up two or three days apart and assault the Canadian and American west coasts for a couple of weeks. Each successive storm in the family will come ashore further southward. Following the last storm, polar air will invade and calm will prevail before the next family lines up.

Storms coming from the West Coast lose strength as they cross the Sierras and Rockies and redevelop on the other side of the mountains. Once redeveloped, they generally head northeastward for the Great Lakes and the St. Lawrence Valley or through the Ohio Valley. Sometimes a storm on this course transfers its energy to a low over the mid-Atlantic, which then becomes the primary storm.

A major area of storm development for North America is in the Gulf of Mexico or along the Florida panhandle. These storms usually track north and north eastward. In winter, they supply copious amounts of snow in the form of "nor'easters." In spring and fall, they provide rain along the Atlantic coastal plain.

Another source of a number of North American hurricanes lies off the northern coast of Africa. Hot desert winds streaming off the African continent carry sand and dust, which serve as seeds to pick up moisture as the winds cross the ocean.

Initially, these storms are apparent only as a line of thunderstorms imbedded in the northeast trade winds, relatively permanent circulations of wind over the major oceans, located at approximately 30 degrees north latitude and 20 degrees south latitude, also known as "easterlies." The African-spawned storms travel over the expanse of the Atlantic gathering strength and moisture.

Occasionally, the storms grow into a hurricane. In most cases, they remain rain-bearing depressions (areas of lower atmospheric pressure), known to mariners and

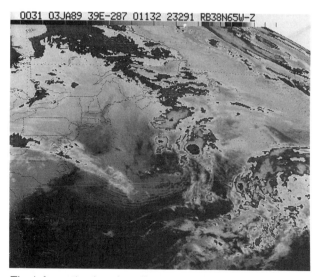 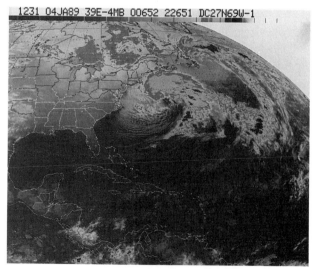

The information bands at the top of the satellite photographs above indicate that the one on the left was taken at 00:31 on January 3, 1989, and the one on the right 12:31 on January 4, 1989. The photographs show the movement of a coastal storm from over the mid-Atlantic states out to sea.

meteorologists as "easterly waves." An easterly wave is an elongated area of low pressure that fills a relatively deep vertical level throughout the atmosphere. As an easterly wave crosses the Atlantic, it stimulates a variety of weather.

From time to time, particularly when the Bermuda high is weak and south of its normal position, a trough of low pressure from the north, known as the polar trough, pushes into the tropics, shoved by a polar front embedded in the mid-latitude winds, the westerlies. Once in the tropics, the polar trough becomes trapped in the prevailing winds, the easterly trade winds. This causes a shearing effect (winds moving in opposed directions) basic to hurricane development. If a hurricane does not develop immediately from the conflict, an easterly wave forms.

Over the course of summer and fall, there are more than 100 easterly waves. Perhaps, 10 or 12 per season develop into tropical storms and only 6 or 7 become full-fledged hurricanes.

The exact trigger that converts an eddy (a current of air moving against the main current) in the atmosphere, such as an easterly wave, into a full-blown hurricane is not understood. Scientists do know that there is an accompanying drop in atmospheric pressure, unlike any known in an ordinary thunderstorm.

Hurricanes develop as a consequence of several seasonal factors. They demand vast amounts of oceanic moisture and the energy that comes from the vaporization of the moisture. Ocean temperatures must be in excess of 80 degrees Fahrenheit to provide a suitable environment. Hurricanes appear to get an assist from the counterclockwise wind system around the earth slightly north and south of the equator. This vicinity, known as the "intertropical convergence zone (ITCZ)," receives maximum energy from the sun. In the absence of centrifugal force (which makes a rotating body move away from the center of rotation), winds in the zone are basically calm.

The position of the sun also has a role to play in hurricane development. The sun moves north and south with the seasons. The sun's maximum northern position, from July to September, coincides with the North Atlantic's hurricane season. The sun's position allows the influence of the Coriolis effect to generate sufficient "swing" to set up a tight circulation around a tropical eddy, which can evolve into a tropical storm.

The influence of the Coriolis effect is strongest in the area between 7 degrees and 15 degrees north of the equator. The time of the strongest Coriolis effect coincides with the time when the Bermuda high is also at its strongest, therefore weather disturbances are forced to skirt the southerly perimeter of the Bermuda high's region of generally fair weather and follow the northeast trade winds.

The Progress of a Hurricane

Shortly after the eye of a hurricane passes, the winds shift 180 degrees and blow with equal ferocity from the south or southwest. Along the Gulf Coast and other landmasses whose coast is east-west oriented, the northerly component of a hurricane's winds acts to hold back the damaging waves, but when the winds shift and blow from the south they drive the already high ocean waters inland with great force.

In the early stages of growth, a hurricane's forward movement drifts in an easterly direction at a rate less than 23 mph. As long as the temperature of the ocean is greater than 80 degrees Fahrenheit, and other conditions support it, the slow pace permits the storm to intensify. Once a hurricane enters the middle latitudes, it encounters strengthening westerly winds and its forward speed is accelerated; however, environmental conditions no longer foster its growth. Most hurricanes break up over cooler northern waters or when they encounter land.

Hurricanes have struck the United States during every month of the year; however, the period of greatest frequency extends from the first of June to the end of November. The height of the season is the last week in August through the first week of October.

Tornadoes

Like other cyclonic storms, tornadoes (often called twisters) have whirling winds around a calm center. What make tornadoes unique is the violence of the whirling winds, accompanied by a rapidly rotating, funnel-shaped cloud. Tornadoes are perhaps nature's most frightening spectacles. They may destroy property on one side of town and not touch the other. On an annual basis in the United States, tornado sightings number at least 700. Few pass through major population centers and few cover much territory.

On August 29, 1990, a lethal tornado dropped from an overcast sky to churn an 8-mile course through cornfields and subdivisions of Will County, Illinois, an area 25 miles southwest of Chicago. The storm killed at least 25 people, injured more than 350, and demolished 50 homes and 500 apartments. Some victims were killed when they were sucked up from an apartment complex and tossed into a nearby cornfield.

Fred Ostby, director of the National Severe Storm Forecast Center in Kansas City, Missouri, explained that one reason that the tornado was not detected was because current weather radar at Chicago and most other cities in the United States is outdated.

A new Doppler radar system better able to detect tornadoes is scheduled to be installed in Chicago within the next two years. Doppler radar uses echoes. The echoes are changes in frequency of sound waves or light waves that vary with the movement of the target in relationship to the observer. As the target and the observer draw closer together the frequency increases. However, Ostby could not be sure whether even the newer system would have been able to pick up the August 29th storm. In the absence of radar and reports of funnel clouds from ground observers, forecasters had not suspected that the storm cells crossing Illinois on the night before the storm were powerful enough to produce tornadoes

The National Severe Storms Center keeps track of the development of severe thunderstorms and tornadoes in the United States by using a combination of satellite photographs, weather balloon recordings, ground reports, and Doppler radar soundings.

Because Doppler radar can detect precipitation in the form of rain and hail, as well keep track of wind shifts and speeds, it is an excellent form of tornado detector. Sometimes Doppler can detect a storm that has the capacity to spawn a tornado a half hour or more before the actual funnel cloud forms.

Like a tropical storm, tornadoes need specific conditions in order to form. The conditions include the presence of a warm, moist, unstable atmosphere capable of producing violent updrafts and condensation, such as those found in most thunderstorms. Tornadoes also require a strong temperature inversion in the upper levels of the atmosphere to help concentrate substantial amounts of moisture in the lower levels. Wind shear (movement of air in opposed directions) common in the early stages of a tropical storm is also critical to tornado formation. Development of the tornado's cyclonic circulation is aided by a warm, dry level in the atmosphere, with strong winds from the southwest.

Converging surface winds (winds close to ground or ocean level) produce the rotary motion of a tornado. Most tornadoes are associated with surface temperatures between 65 degrees and 84 degrees Fahrenheit and with a dew point that is greater than 50 degrees Fahrenheit. Dew point is the temperature at which dew begins to form or vapor to condense into a liquid.

Tornadoes are generally associated with unseasonably warm air. They develop in response to stark contrasts of temperature and humidity in two unlike air masses. Atmospheric contraction whips the funnel cloud into a tighter and tighter circle. Within the circle, in response to the rapidly falling atmospheric pressure, the winds blow at rates of as much as 300 mph.

From a fully developed cumulonimbus cloud, a tornado can drop to the ground in shapes that vary from a dangling rope to a mile-wide black column of spinning debris. The visible funnel is made up of water vapor from the cloud that spawned it. The funnel assumes a dark or black appearance after it has touched the ground and picked up dust and rubbish. Once fully formed, a tornado sets off on a voyage that may be only a few hundred yards or may be hundreds of miles. The average tornado trip is 6 miles, however a tornado in May 1917 traveled 293 miles through parts of Illinois and Indiana.

Guiding surface winds encourage nine out of ten tornadoes to approach from the southwest. Most of the rest are from the southeast. Some tornadoes remain stationary, for as long as 45 minutes. Some make U-turns or circles, others zig-zag or are erratic. The average speed is 35 mph, but some move much faster.

A narrow strip of the United States between 97–98 degrees W. meridian from the Texas panhandle to the Dakotas is the nation's most vulnerable locale for tornadoes. It has been dubbed "tornado alley." Tornadoes are comparatively rare in the rest of the world. Tornadoes at sea are generally smaller in diameter and are known as waterspouts.

The season for tornadoes travels with the sun. During winter and early spring, they occur with the greatest frequency in the Gulf states. By April, tornado activity has shifted to the central Plains and middle Mississippi Valley. By June, tornadoes have migrated to the Great Lakes and northern Plains states for the reminder of the summer. By the first of December, tornadoes have moved back south to the Gulf.

On occasion, tornadoes develop in families or swarms. On April 3 and 4, 1974, 148 tornadoes touched down in 12 states from Illinois to Virginia. The cause of a swarm of tornadoes is usually an intense, migratory spring storm. A storm that spawns tornado swarms is loaded with moisture and is created from extreme contrasts in temperature. In a warm sector of the atmosphere, temperatures may be in the 60s and 70s, while in a cold sector, blizzard conditions may prevail. Squalls (brief violent windstorms, usually accompanied by rain or snow) set up along the air mass boundary lines and tornadoes can break out along or ahead of the fronts. As a consequence of solar heating that increases the contrast in temperature between the ground and the cold, unstable middle layers of the troposphere, tornado swarms are more likely in the late afternoon.

The passing of a hurricane can also prompt a swarm of tornadoes. Such an outbreak is apparently due to frictional drag as the hurricane passes over the land, particularly in the northeast sector of the storm.

Given their tight funnel of winds spinning at rates up to 300 mph, tornadoes have enormous destructive power. Fortunately they are usually limited in geographic area.

Storm Research Goes On

Storms play a critical role in distributing heat, cold and moisture around the world. Unfortunately, they sometimes leave destruction of people, animals and property in their wake. Being able to predict their arrival helps to avoid some of the destruction. A clear understanding of the mechanisms involved in a storm must precede improvements in prediction. Scientists regularly risk their lives to fly into severe storms to unlock the puzzles of how they form, perpetuate themselves and die.

8

The Stars and the Universe

THE SEARCH FOR EXTRATERRESTRIAL INTELLIGENCE (SETI)

A Technically Sophisticated Hunt for Signals from Extraterrestrial Civilizations

The contention that intelligent beings might exist elsewhere in the universe, and that they might be capable of contacting Earth, inspires a growing number of scientists. They have been encouraged by recent discoveries, such as the detection of organic molecules, the basic building blocks of life, in interstellar space, and evidence that several stars besides the earth's sun may have planetary systems. The most important advance is the development of new detectors and data-analysis technologies that have made possible fast, efficient and large-scale searches for signals of intelligence coming from the cosmos. Over the past three decades, approximately 60 separate, active searches for signs of extraterrestrial life have been carried out using radio astronomy techniques, logging in more than 200,000 search hours. (Radio astronomy studies celestial objects by using their emitted electromagnetic radiation.)

Whether Earth is unique or whether other planets like Earth circle stars elsewhere in the Milky Way (a broad band of faintly luminous stars seen across the night time sky) is a continuing unanswered question. In spite of the fact that many scientists have believed that other stars, like our sun, could have planetary systems, observational data to support their view are still scant.

In 1988, the first convincing evidence of a planet circling a star other than the planets circling the star (the sun) of this solar system was secured by Smithsonian scientists using a painstaking technique intended to discover tiny variations

in a star's motion. The variations in motion are caused by the gravitational pull of a companion body.

The dim sun-like star studied by the Smithsonian scientists is named HD 114762 and is located at a distance of approximately 90 light-years (a light-year is the distance that light travels in a vacuum for the period of a year, approximately 3.67 trillion miles). HD 114762 was found to have a slight periodic (occurring from time to time) wobble due to a large body in orbit around it, 10 to 20 times more massive than Jupiter, the largest planet in this solar system. (HD 114762 is not really a planet. It is a brown dwarf, a star whose mass is less than 0.08 times that of the sun and whose core temperature does not become high enough to start hydrogen-burning nuclear reactions.)

Scientists interested in the possibility of extraterrestrial life don't just search the heavens for answers to their questions. They also look on Earth.

Terrestrial life first appeared on Earth approximately 3.5 billion years ago as simple cells. To biologists, this early appearance of life on Earth suggests that, if environmental conditions are right, the probability of chemical evolution leading to biogenesis (the generation of living organisms from other living organisms) is high.

Most of Earth's biological history has been a record of microorganisms, with evidence of large plants and animals not appearing until the last 15% of existence of life on Earth, and intelligent life-forms appearing only very recently.

From left to right: Edward Purcell, Phillip Morrison, Carl Sagan, Michael Papagiannis, Frank Drake. They share an interest in research into the new field of bioastronomy. This picture was taken at an IAU symposium on the Search for Extraterrestrial Life held at Boston University in 1984 under Professor Papagiannis.

Complicating a quest for universal principles that would pertain to life throughout the universe is the fact that the evolution of life on Earth seems to have been dictated by the planet's particular qualities.

The Search Begins in Earnest

After decades of dreaming and living on minuscule budgets, a small band of about 20 scientists received funding in 1990 to embark on a $100 million, 10-year project to search for life in the universe. The search for extraterrestrial life, SETI (pronounced see tee), will scan the sky systematically, listening for faint signals from advanced civilizations.

In an interview for a February 6, 1990, *New York Times* article entitled "Hunt for Aliens in Space: The Next Generation," Dr. Frank Drake of the University of California at Santa Cruz, one of the founders of the modern field of extraterrestrial searches, said, "This is the big step. It will allow us to do very sophisticated searching."

On the way to respectability, the scientists interested in SETI were attacked, ignored, ridiculed and threatened with professional excommunication by traditional astronomers and astrophysicists. Nevertheless, they persisted. During the course of their struggle, they had to learn how funds are allocated in Washington.

After ridicule by Senator William Proxmire, the program's funding was dropped for a year and restored only after the National Academy of Science and an array of eminent scientists mobilized a campaign for restoration of funding. Dr. Drake described the recurring problem by saying, "SETI is always burdened with the threat of being declared flaky or fringe or pseudo-science. So you have to be very careful that very qualified, right-thinking people are involved." Throughout the 1980s, funding ranged between $1.5 and $2 million. With the money, the scientists worked mostly on devising strategies and testing equipment for the big search.

Many of the early searches were done by individuals or small teams borrowing time on large radio telescopes used primarily in astrophysical studies (the branch of astronomy that deals with the physics of celestial bodies). The challenge for proponents no longer is borrowing time or trying to interest others in the validity of their work. Instead,

Above is the late Karl G. Jansky of Bell Telephone Laboratories with the rotating antenna he used to discover radio waves coming from space. His discovery in the 1930s came about as he searched for the source of strange noise in telephone equipment.

it is searching for powerful ways to distinguish between a genuine transmission sent by another civilization and cosmic background noise or Earth-generated static. Scientists frequently use the analogy of finding a needle in a cosmic haystack.

The major focus of the newly launched federal project will be to build a radio receiver that will simultaneously scan 14 million channels of radio waves collected by existing radio-telescopes around the world. The receiving apparatus is scheduled to be turned on in October 1992, the 500th anniversary of Columbus's discovery of America.

While there is no guarantee that Congress will continue to fund the program for its planned 10-year duration, the funding in 1990 made it possible to begin construction at NASA Ames Research Center in California of instruments the scientists hope will be turned on in 1992.

Tools for the Search

The radio telescope receivers are designed to divide incoming signals into separate frequency (number of cycles per unit of time) bands, each only 1 hertz (one cycle per second) wide, and then analyze each one for extraterrestrial clues. They will scan for either continuous radio waves or for pulsed signals (comparable to rotating lighthouse beacons.)

The receivers are designed to weed out: signals from natural sources, such as pulsars (celestial bodies in the Milky Way that emit radio pulses at regular intervals); artificial signals produced on Earth (radio-frequency interference and hoaxes); and any other "false alarms" that filters or computer algorithms (special methods for solving certain kinds of problems) can eliminate.

No one will sit in front of a screen becoming bleary-eyed. The search will be entirely computerized. Among the many telescopes that will be used will be the world's largest, the 1,000-foot radio telescope at Arecibo, Puerto Rico.

An August 23, 1988, *New York Times* article entitled "New Proposals Bolster Search for Life in Space," noted that most SETI searching equipment will operate in or around a slice of the radio spectrum called the "water hole," named after the building blocks of water. The frequency is bounded at one end by the natural radio emission of the hydrogen atom, which functions as a tiny transmitter as it flips between its two energy levels and, at the other end, by the emission of hydroxyl, which consists of one atom of hydrogen and one atom of oxygen. If the hydrogen atom and the hydroxyl were joined, they would make water, H_2O. As early as 1959, scientists suggested that this "magic frequency range" would be the most likely choice of an extraterrestrial civilization for communicating across space.

The water hole is nearly free of disruption from radar and cosmic noise; however, scientists are worried that growing interference from satellites and terrestrial microwave transmitters might drown out any signals. Radio interference on the ground and from orbiting satellites is increasing so fast that the 1990s may be the last opportunity for Earth-based searches.

Search Plan

The NASA effort will have two parts. Based on the premise that there may be Earth-like planets with civilizations, one segment will be aimed at specific targets, including about 770 sun-like stars at distances of up to 80 light-years (293 trillion miles) from Earth. The radio telescopes will focus on a star for 5 to 15 minutes. In time, the targeted search will swing out to more distant stars.

The other segment, an undertaking called the Sky Survey, will slowly scan the entire sky, including the Milky Way and its 400 billion stars, a small section at a time over a much wider frequency range, from about 1 GHz to 10 GHz. (GHz means gigahertz, a unit of frequency equal to 10^9 herz.) Besides widening the search, the survey will use the opportunity to catalog all known and new radio sources and will serve as a resource for studying naturally produced emissions.

During the survey, no area of the sky will be observed for very long, but signals from an unexpected direction might be picked up. If any signal exceeds a pre-established level, the antenna will be pointed back at the spot for closer listening. The computer will interrupt the routine sequence of operations and order a series of checks (for example, for the passage of spacecraft overhead). Following the checks, the antenna will be moved slightly off target, and then back again to see if the signal reappears, and a scan will be made around the area to determine whether the signal remains constant. If the unexpected signal passes all the tests, the computer will alert the scientists and they will ask other observatories to check as well.

Opponents and Proponents

Scientists involved with SETI believe that their equipment is sensitive enough to pick up beacon signals sent out by advanced civilizations broadcasting their presence. Moreover, they think that some routine transmissions, not intended for communication into space, could also leak out.

The main criticism of SETI among astronomers and astrophysicists who are skeptical is that there is no firm basis for a belief in extraterrestrial life.

Criticism centers on the assumptions that SETI scientists make in order to conclude that advanced civilizations in space exist. Opponents argue that SETI scientists presume that such civilizations would not want to travel across vast empty spaces from star to star, but would instead opt for powerful radio communication that could be overheard.

Skeptics assert that an advanced civilization might choose to build large, self-sustaining colonies on spacecraft, which would do away with the need for giant transmitters that could be heard on Earth.

Critics frequently ask: "If biological evolution is as universal as SETI advocates claim, and if feats of interstellar travel are possible, given the vastness of the Milky Way and the 15-billion-year-old age of the universe, why have aliens not already visited this solar system by now?"

Advocates respond to critics by pointing out that their equipment does not depend upon another civilization having powerful beacons. It is sensitive enough to eavesdrop. Moreover, they stress that they base their program on conservative assumptions. They do not assume a capacity for interstellar travel or other exotic possibilities. Instead, they work with known entities such as planets, radio transmissions, biological evolution and technological feats feasible on Earth.

In his interview with the *New York Times* in February 1990, Frank Drake said, "You can theorize forever. But intelligent life is so complicated in its activities and philosophies, as we know from ourselves, that it's quite impossible to psych out the extraterrestrials and deduce by logic how they might behave. The only way we can really learn the truth is to search."

Dr. Drake has developed an equation for estimating the likelihood that advanced civilizations exist elsewhere in the universe. With explanations of its variables below, Drake's equation states:

$$N = R^* f_p n_e f_l f_i f_c L$$

N, the number of civilizations in the Milky Way Galaxy whose radio emissions are detectable, is equal to

R^*, the rate of formation of stars per year suitable for the development of intelligent life, times

f_p, the fraction of those stars with planetary systems, times

n_e, the number of planets, per solar system, with an environment suitable for life, times

f_l, the fraction of suitable planets on which life actually appears, times

f_i, the fraction of life-bearing planets on which intelligent life emerges, times

f_c, the fraction of civilizations that develop a technology that releases detectable signs of their existence into space, times

L, the length of time such civilizations release detectable signals into space.

SETI scientists typically estimate that there are 10,000 to 100,000 advanced civilizations in the Milky Way alone. Their estimates use assumptions about variables that Drake has included in his equation. Many of the terms of the equation, particularly L, have great uncertainties.

Onging Searches That Have Nurtured Interest in SETI

The first modern systematic search was carried out in 1960 by Frank Drake at the National Radio Astronomy Observatory in Greenback, West Virginia. He began with a modest program that observed two nearby stars of the hydrogen line using the Observatory's 85-foot antenna. The hydrogen line is a range of wavelengths emitted by neutral hydrogen that is used to study the velocity of hydrogen in the galaxy.

Since Drake's beginning, a number of ongoing searches have been conducted for several years; many are currently in operation. SETI enthusiasts at Ohio State University, in 1973, began using their radio telescope to listen for extraterrestrials. In 1977, an Ohio State team member found an indicator of a strong artificial signal on a printout and wrote "Wow!" next to it. Wow has never been repeated, but it inspired SETI enthusiast Bob Gray, in 1980, to begin scanning the skies from the backyard of his Chicago home with a 12-foot commercial telecommunications dish.

The most elaborate search has been conducted at the Harvard-Smithsonian Oak Ridge Observatory in Harvard, Massachusetts, outside of Boston. The Harvard physicist Paul Horowitz has conducted Project META using megachannel spectrum (million-channel range of frequencies) analyses. His instrumentation has scanned the northern skies by listening to 8 million channels.

At the Nançay radio observatory in France, Dr. Jill Tarter, a scientist at NASA Ames and, for a time, the acting director of NASA's SETI program, has collaborated with French colleague Francois Biraud. Since 1980, they have looked intermittently for intelligent signals from the vicinity of solar-type stars, which they assume are most likely to have habitable Earth-like planets.

Nikola Telsa, the American physicist and engineer (born in Croatia), was an early user of radio signals. In 1899 he thought he picked up radio transmissions from extraterrestrials.

The Italian inventor Guglielmo Marconi, who developed wireless telegraphy. Marconi thought he detected radio signals from Mars, while on his boat the Elettra.

Some of SETI's Intellectual Ancestors

The consideration that there might be life in other solar systems is a concept referred to as "the plurality of worlds." At least since the time of Classical Greece, a belief in the existence of extraterrestrial life has persisted.

The ancient Greek philosopher Anaxagoras, who lived about 450 B.C., said that the most important experience in this world was to see the starry sky and to comprehend the order of the universe. Metrodorus of Chios, 400 B.C., who wrote a book on nature, said, in effect, to consider the earth as the only world with life in all of space is as absurd as to believe that in an entire field sown with grain only one plant will grow.

About 50 B.C., a Roman poet-philosopher said, "Nothing in the universe is unique and alone, therefore in other regions there must be other earths inhabited by different tribes of men and breeds of beasts."

Around 1820, the famous mathematician Carl Fredrich Gaus of Germany suggested that a triangle about 10 miles in size ought to be planted with wheat in Siberia. Along each of the triangle's three sides, squares of pines would be planted. His signal, which might have appealed to extraterrestrial mathematicians, was never planted, but the idea of communication with extraterrestrials did take hold.

In 1840, Joseph Von Littrow, who was director of the Vienna Observatory, recommended that a signal be stationed in the Sahara Desert. He proposed to build a large circular ditch filled with water and covered with kerosene. The lighted circle would perhaps intrigue extraterrestrial engineers.

In 1869, Charles Cross proposed the use of a shallow but very large mirror to focus light on the surface of Mars so that those on Mars would know that the people on Earth were trying to reach them.

On July 14, 1890, at the Boston Museum of Science, Dr. Michael Papagiannis, a professor of astronomy at Boston University and the first president of the Bioastronomy Commission of the International Astronomical Union (IAU), gave a lecture on the highlights of the history of SETI. Bioastronomy is the name under which IAU has been willing to consider the search for extraterrestrial life. Papagiannis invented the term and was largely responsible for its acceptance.

Papagiannis began his lecture by showing the audience the flag of the earth, which includes a blue earth, a yellow sun, and a white moon, on a black background. The flag hangs in every observatory around the globe that has undertaken searches for extraterrestrial intelligence. The flag has a unifying effect and reminds the scientists that it is researchers from many parts of the earth who are collectively working on SETI.

The 20th century, in Papagiannis view, is a century of miracles. The Wright brothers first flew in 1903. By 1957, the first satellite, *Sputnik*, was launched into space. Twelve years later, Neil Armstrong set foot on the moon. Perhaps, Papagiannis proposes, the century might end with the discovery of extraterrestrial life.

A Shift from Clever Schemes to Workable Tools

In Papagiannis's view, the many earlier proposals contributed to the development of the idea of SETI but produced no results. Toward the turn of the 20th century, prospects changed when radio waves were discovered by Heinrich Hertz in 1887.

One of the early users of radio signals was Nikola Tesla, a physicist, engineer and inventor. At his home in Colorado Springs, in 1899, Tesla thought he had received radio disturbances from extraterrestrials. He wrote in his notebook,

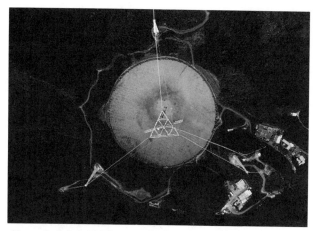

Above is the 1,000-foot radio dish at Arecibo, Puerto Rico. The National Astronomy and Ionosphere Center (NAIC) is negotiating for $22.8 million to refurbish the facility. NAIC wants to install a 60-foot-high radio noise shield around the 20-acre dish, a Gregorian subreflector to channel the faint radio waves to the telescope's receivers, and a 1 million watt radar transmitter to replace the current 450,000 watt system.

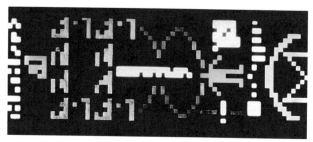

Above is the coded message sent out from Arecibo in the 1970s. Comprised of primary numbers, it translates into various shapes, such as a radio dishs.

"The feeling continues to grow in me that I was the first to hear a message of greetings from one planet to another."

The famous Italian radio engineer Guglielmo Marconi, who in 1901 pioneered transatlantic telecommunications and received the Nobel Prize in physics in 1909 for his work, also thought that he had received radio signals from Mars while on his boat *Elettra*, which was equipped with colossal radio antennas. The signals had much lower frequencies than those used by the Marconi Company for Wireless Communications.

During World War II, there was great progress in radio communications because of the desire to build radar to detect the approach of aircraft attack. When the war ended, the new knowledge was immediately put to other uses.

One of the greatest post–World War II achievements was the discovery of a radio frequency that was characteristic of hydrogen atoms, the most abundant element in the universe. The discovery of the hydrogen line was made in 1951 by Harvard professor Edward Purcell and his thesis student, H. Ewen.

A spectral line refers to discrete frequencies at which an atom or molecule emits. The hydrogen line is a spectral line emitted by natural hydrogen at a frequency of 1420 megahertz, which is the equivalent of a wavelength of 21 centimeters (cm). With this discovery, Purcell and Ewen launched the field of radio astronomy. (Later, Professor Purcell shared the Nobel Prize in physics with Felix Bloch of Stanford University, for the discovery of nuclear magnetic resonance.) Radiation from the hydrogen line is used in radio astronomy to examine the abundance, temperature and velocities of hydrogen in the galaxy. Hydrogen consists of one heavier particle, a proton in the center, orbited by a much lighter particle, an electron. Both particles tend to spin. If both spin in the same direction, the frequency is different than if they spin in opposite directions. If there is a shift in spin directions, the change can be detected by the release of a small bit of energy, a phenomenon called radio transition.

The hydrogen line inspired two scientists, Phillip Morrison and Giuseppe Cocconi, to write a paper in 1959 that was published in the journal *Nature*. The authors suggested that the hydrogen line should be used to carry out the first radio SETI. The possibility for success was difficult to predict, they said, but if no one ever searched, the probability was zero.

The efforts started with Frank Drake's work, in the spring of 1960, at the Radio Astronomy Observatory at Greenback, West Virginia.

Universal Conditions Suited to SETI

During his lecture, in addition to a review of the historical roots of SETI, Papagiannis also presented other reasons why scientists believe in the effort. He pointed out that the chemistry of the universe is made of the following:

hydrogen,	75%,	an active chemical element,
helium,	23%	an inert element,
oxygen,	0.9%,	
carbon,	0.4%,	
neon,	0.2%,	an inert element
nitrogen,	0.15%.	

Thus, the four most common chemically active elements in the universe are hydrogen, oxygen, carbon and nitrogen. Chemically active elements interact with other elements, while inert elements under normal circumstances do not interact with much of anything. An examination of the biomass (all living organisms on Earth) reveals that its composition is also about 98% oxygen, carbon, hydrogen and nitrogen. Therefore, the chemical composition of life on Earth is in harmony with the composition of the universe.

The number of galaxies in the universe is also pertinent to an assumption of a potential for extraterrestrial life. There are roughly 10 billion galaxies. Every galaxy has about 100 billion stars. Of those stars, roughly one in a thousand looks like the earth's sun. Taken together, these quantities mean that the whole universe has 1 billion × 1 billion suns comparable to the sun in this solar system.

In Papagiannis's view, it is difficult to believe that in the whole universe, which is made of the same chemical elements as those on Earth, and a multitude of solar systems with stars similar to our sun, that life managed to begin only on Earth.

Moreover, Papagiannis believes that the universe has created a "very smart combination." It has stars like the earth's sun with hot temperatures, about 6,000 degrees Kelvin (11,329 degrees Fahrenheit). It has planets with intermediate temperatures, about 300 degrees Kelvin (1,069 degrees Fahrenheit). And it has a background of very low temperatures of only 3 degrees Kelvin (–454 degrees Fahrenheit).

He explained his idea of a smart combination by saying, "The planets are the lucky ones to be in the middle. They take good quality energy from their star. They use it to build up complexity in their own environment, and then they dump the no-good low temperature they produce into the background." Thus, they become the places where complexity can keep increasing.

Studies with radio telescopes and other means have collected a tremendous number of different organic compounds that exist in the universe. Given the variety of organic compounds, the whole universe has the mechanism to also build complex organic compounds.

As an example of organic complexity, Papagiannis pointed to small, very black rocks that fall to the ground and are called carbonaceous chondrites. A laboratory analysis of carbonaceous chondrites reveals that they have complex organic compounds, including amino acids, such as those that make up the proteins of all living organisms.

In summing up his view of the presence of universal conditions that would support extraterrestrial life, Papagiannis said, "It is fair to say that the universe is favorably predisposed to the origin of life and its long evolution to an advanced civilization."

Gaining Acceptance

In 1971, a conference on SETI was held in the Soviet Union, cosponsored by the national academies of the United States and the Soviet Union. MIT Press published the proceedings, edited by Carl Sagan. In 1979, the International Astronomical Union (IAU), asked Papagiannis to propose a topic for one of its triennial assemblies that was to be held in Montreal. He proposed a day's meeting on extraterrestrial life. A report that summarized the meeting was attended by more than 1,000 astronomers.

At the 1979 IAU meeting, an effort was launched to establish a SETI commission of the IAU. Much behind the scenes activity led to the acceptance of the idea in 1982 when the general assembly of IAU decided to establish a Bioastronomy Commission, with Papagiannis as its first president. The new commission held its first meeting at Boston University in 1984. A 600-page volume was published subsequently to document the meeting. According to the IAU, the volume sold more copies than any previous volume.

In 1985, the general assembly of the IAU was held in India and Frank Drake took over as president of the commission. It was also the 25th anniversary of Drake's SETI project at Greenback, West Virginia.

In 1991, a SETI facility will begin operation in Argentina. The project will cover the southern skies, which will mean that the whole celestial sphere will be included in the searches. That same year, the IAU's general assembly will meet in Argentina, and their meeting will coincide with the dedication of the SETI project.

In 1992, NASA's major two-part effort, the targeted search and the sky survey, will begin.

What If the Search Turns Up a Message?

Should a message be received, a host of immediate questions would arise, including, "Who gets told and when?"

For some time, the possibility of getting such a message has been the preoccupation of a working group of several dozen scientists and lawyers, as well as representatives from NASA, the U.S. State Department and a variety of groups from the United States, Europe and the Soviet Union.

The group has put together a set of guidelines, called the "Declaration of Principles Concerning Activities Following the Detection of Extraterrestrial Intelligence." The declaration acknowledges that "any initial detection may be incomplete or ambiguous and thus require careful examination as well as confirmation."

The declaration is not just for NASA. It is essentially a manual for any astronomer, spacecraft engineer, policymaker, diplomat or anyone else who might play a role in a possible SETI success.

The topic of SETI is fraught with a potential for misunderstanding. Anyone who received a false alarm and read too much into it could create public turmoil. The SETI guidelines seek to minimize a panicky public reaction by disseminating accurate information at least as promptly as rumors. The protocol was also written to avoid government censorship and to avoid the appearance of censorship.

A further issue is what constitutes credible evidence. Jill Tarter of NASA's Ames Research Center, NASA's SETI project scientist, during an interview for a May 19, 1989, *Science News* article entitled "Listening for ET: What If a Message Comes?" said, "What constitutes 'credible evidence' is being unable to explain a signal—which you also can't make go away—by any known astrophysics or technology."

A touchy matter still to be resolved is whether to answer such a signal. As it stands, no response is to be made until appropriate international consultations have taken place. The declaration left the details of the procedures for such consultations to be worked out in a separate agreement. The search for an agreement about what to do in response to a extraterrestrial signal may turn out to be as complex as the search for extraterrestrial intelligence itself.

THE HUBBLE SPACE TELESCOPE

A 44-Year-Old Idea Finally Lifted Off in the Spring of 1990

The initial proposal to put a telescope in space was made by Lyman Spitzer, Jr., now a professor emeritus of astrophysics at Princeton University, in an addendum entitled "Astronomical Advantages of an Extraterrestrial Observatory" attached to a 1946 Rand Corporation study of artificial Earth satellites. Spitzer predicted that a telescope with a 200-inch mirror could measure the extent of the universe, determine the structure of the galaxies, resolve the images of individual stars hidden in the hazes of globular clusters and reveal the nature of other planets. Spitzer's 44-year-old dream materialized in 1990 when the Hubble Space Telescope, named for Edwin Hubble, an American astronomer (1889–1953), who provided proof that galaxies lie far beyond the Milky Way, was launched.

Telescope Design

Although no one is sure who actually invented the first telescope, known as a refracting telescope, it is thought to have been created by Hans Lippershey, an obscure Dutch lens maker, who applied for a patent for his device in 1608. In the refracting telescope, a lens gathers light and forms a direct image of the object. Early in the 17th century, a few natural philosophers used the new instrument to study the heavens. In 1609, the Italian astronomer Galileo aimed his telescope at the sky and, by 1610, he had made the remarkable discovery that four moons revolved around Jupiter.

A telescope with a different design, known as a reflecting telescope, was invented in 1669 by Isaac Newton and was destined to become the primary research tool of astronomers. Newton's telescope was essentially a tube 6 inches long, with mirrors at both ends. The front end of Newton's tube was open to admit light. At the back end, a concave mirror, called the primary mirror, collected light from astronomical objects. The primary mirror, which Newton had ground by hand, was about 2 inches in diameter. (A concave surface bulges inward, like the inside of a ball sliced in half, in contrast to a convex surface, which bulges outward like the outside of a cut ball.)

From the primary mirror, the light was reflected back toward the open end of the tube to a much smaller, secondary convex mirror. The task of the secondary mirror was to divert the reflected light to the eyepiece (a lens system) in the side of the tube. When Newton looked through the eyepiece and adjusted the distance between the primary and secondary mirrors, using a screw behind the primary mirror, he could see images of distant objects toward which he directed his telescope.

The Space Telescope's Design

Like Newton's reflecting telescope, the 12-ton Hubble Space Telescope is basically a tube with a mirror at each end. Light from an astronomical object enters the open front end, travels to a concave, highly polished, primary mirror, 96 inches in diameter, and is reflected back to a convex secondary mirror, 12 inches across. To keep the telescope's image in focus, the distance between the primary and secondary mirrors of the Space Telescope must be maintained at 193 inches, without a change of more than a ten-thousandth of an inch.

To ensure that the mirrors will not move out of position, despite being alternately warmed by the sun and cooled by the vacuum of space, they were built with composite materials that suffer virtually no thermal expansion or contraction.

Unlike Newton's telescope, the Space Telescope's light is not diverted to the side of the tube. Instead, it is bounced back through a hole in the primary mirror. (This type of telescope is called a "Cassegrain reflector" after its French inventor.) When light passes through the hole in the primary mirror, it becomes available to a variety of scientific instruments.

The Space Telescope is a completely automated observatory, whose scientific data is radioed back to Earth. On board the Space Telescope is an electronic version of a photographic plate, the so-called Charge Coupled Devices (arrayed so that the electric charge at the output of one provides the input stimulus to the next.) It also carries the Faint Object Camera (FOC), which is basically a kind of television tube. In addition, the Space Telescope has a High Speed Photometer, an instrument for measuring very rapid fluctuations in the light output of stars and galaxies. The telescope's guidance system is designed to accurately measure the positions of astronomical bodies.

The Space Telescope's equipment also includes two spectrographs, instruments that split the light from astronomical objects into constituent wavelengths for analysis. The Goddard High Resolution Spectrograph observes brighter objects, whose light can be widely dispersed, and the Faint Object Spectrograph, examines in less detail the light from dimmer objects.

Saturn's rings were not discovered until the invention of the telescope. Galileo thought he detected a large satellite. In 1656 Christian Huggens observed an actual ring, which he thought was thin, flat and solid. In 1675 Jean Cassini saw two separate rings of swarming satellites. This photo was taken by the Hubble Space Telescope, launched in 1990.

The Lure of Space

In his 1989 book, *The Space Telescope: A Study of NASA, Science, Technology, and Politics*, Robert Smith describes some of the reasons that a number of astronomers have labored so long to send a telescope into space, where it will orbit a few hundred miles above Earth. A significant reason is the limitations on what even the largest and best optical telescopes on the ground can achieve. Although most of the world's largest Earth-bound telescopes are generally located several thousand feet above sea level, they still rest at the bottom of an ocean of air.

The ocean of air, the atmosphere, is seldom steady or tranquil. While traveling through the atmosphere, starlight is bent, thus making a star look as if it is located at a certain position when it is actually located somewhere else. Moreover, the atmosphere is composed of blobs known as "seeing cells," which change position and make a star's image appear to jiggle around in the sky.

With large telescopes, the diameter of the primary mirror is usually greater than the size of the seeing cells, which results in an image made up of many small images, each a faint and moving speckle. Time exposures take an average of the speckles (comparable to the blur of a runner on a photograph), resulting in a smeared image known as a "seeing disk," which is much larger than any single speckle. The worse the atmospheric conditions, the larger the seeing disk.

Although the Space Telescope was not planned to be particularly large by the standards of ground-based telescopes, its position in space was expected to make up for whatever it lacked in size. The Space Telescope was designed to detect stars about fifty times fainter than the faintest stars observable from the ground. With this greater capacity, the Space Telescope was expected to observe stars at distances approximately seven times further away than ground-based telescopes.

The Space Telescope's Significance for Astronomical Research

One of the major lessons that astronomers have learned from astronomy's history is that larger and more penetrating telescopes have led to new discoveries and raised new questions. New discoveries spawn new theories.

A major interest of astronomers in having a telescope in space is to answer questions in cosmology, the study of the large-scale structure and evolution of the universe. For more than 50 years, scientists have speculated about the big bang, the theory that the universe began with a densely packed accumulation of matter that exploded, spewing matter in all directions, and that continues to expand outward. Astronomers want to know how much time has elapsed since the big bang occurred and whether the expansion will go on forever or reverse itself and contract.

One source of difficulty in answering questions about the big bang is errors in measuring the distances between astronomical bodies. Even measurements of the distance to nearby stars are imprecise. To calculate the distance of more remote objects, astronomers climb a wobbly "distance ladder." Cumulative errors of the various techniques used are so large that actual distances compared to calculated distances may be half or twice as large.

The Cepheid stars in the Virgo cluster of galaxies, 65 million light-years away, may serve as a tool to help astronomers measure distances to galaxies. Cepheids are very bright, pulsating stars whose emissions of light vary in a precise, regular manner. Cepheids alternately expand and contract, changing in size by as much as 30%. When a Cepheid is at its most dim, its surface temperature is at its lowest.

A Cepheid's rhythmic cycle, accompanied by changes in luminosity, usually takes no longer than seven days. The period of light change is related to the average luminosity of the star and the absolute magnitude (brightness) of Cepheid can be found by measuring the period of the light cycle. Once three values, the period of change, the absolute magnitude, and the apparent magnitude, are known, it becomes possible to calculate the distance to the star. The apparent magnitude is an index of the star's brightness relative to other stars without taking into account difference in distance between stars.

The Space Telescope was expected to make possible better detection and measurement of the light output of the Cepheids. Fixing the Virgo cluster of galaxies to an extraordinary level of accuracy could establish a critical rung on the distance ladder.

Another intended use for the Space Telescope was to analyze astronomical objects that fluctuate rapidly. So-called pulsars (sources of short bursts of radio emission) at the heart of the Crab nebula (the remnant of a supernova, the explosive death of a star, observed 900 years ago) beam out flashes of radiation 30 times per second. The Space Telescope's High Speed Photometer has the capacity to make 100,000 measurements per second.

The designers and builders of the Space Telescope hoped that the High Speed Photometer could also help in the study of "black holes," collapsed stars so dense that even light cannot escape their gravitational pull. Although black holes can not be seen directly, as material falls into a black hole, rapid changes in light output occur.

Four Decades to Launch

Although German-Romanian scientist Hermann Oberth first suggested the possibility of space telescopes in the 1920s, it was not until 1946 that Dr. Lyman Spitzer at Yale expanded the concept with specific plans and research goals. The four-decade-long struggle to launch the Hubble Telescope was recounted in an interview with Spitzer for an April 10, 1990, *New York Times* article entitled "For a Space Visionary, Persistence Nears Payoff."

During the first decade, Spitzer worked mostly alone. In 1947, he left Yale to become the head of astrophysics at Princeton, on the condition that he be permitted to pursue his vision of a space telescope. In 1957, working with Dr. Martin Schwarzschild at Princeton on Project Stratoscope, Spitzer sent a 12-inch telescope aloft by balloon to 80,000 feet to make revealing studies of the sun recorded by spectographs. Project Stratoscope took place a few months

before the Soviet Union launched *Sputnik*, the first Earth satellite, in October 1957.

Sputnik spurred the second decade of Dr. Spitzer's crusade on behalf of the telescope. The U.S. Air Force approached Spitzer for ideas about how satellites could be used in astronomy.

When NASA, the National Aeronautics and Space Administration was created in 1958, one of the first programs inspired by Dr. Spitzer was the Orbiting Astronomical Observatory. Two successful observatories launched in the late 1960s and early 1970s included 30-inch telescopes to measure ultraviolet wavelengths. The telescopes were able for the first time to examine interstellar dust and gases, leftovers from exploded stars and the spawning grounds for new stars.

In the early 1960s, Spitzer was able to convince the National Academy of Sciences to form study groups to investigate the idea of a large space telescope. In his book *The Space Telescope*, Robert Smith quoted one of Spitzer's colleagues: "Lyman is a master of listening to everybody and doing in the end what he wants to do."

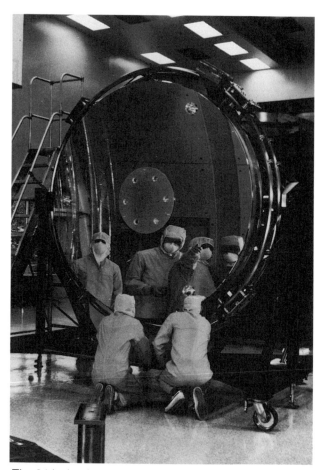

The 94-inch primary mirror is less than half the diameter of the world's leading ground telescope, Mt. Palomar on Mount Wilson in California. Here the mirror is being inspected soon after it was coated with a special relfective surface.

Following a conference of astronomers in 1964, a board of the academy recommended that NASA proceed with a project to be known as the Large Space Telescope (LST). During the third decade, the project came close to foundering. In 1975, faced with congressional resistance, NASA scaled back the size of the telescope mirror from 120 inches to 94.5 inches.

Budget cuts in 1975 and 1976 threatened to end the project. Spitzer and astronomer John Bahcall, with the help of other astronomers, lobbied key people in Congress on behalf of the program. In 1977, NASA received approval to start the project, estimated to cost $435 million. Astronauts began training in 1979, launch was scheduled for 1983 and the mirror was completed in 1981.

The fourth decade was even more turbulent than the third. Technical problems held up completion of LST. The Government Accounting Office (GAO), the investigative agency for Congress, found serious flaws in the project's management. The consequence was a reorganization of NASA and the private contractors, Lockheed Missiles and Space Company, builder of the spacecraft, and Perkin-Elmer Corporation, producer of the mirror and major telescope components.

Launch was rescheduled for 1986. The 1986 launch was canceled, however, when the space shuttle *Challenger* exploded in January and all NASA missions were grounded indefinitely.

Flaws Known About Before Launch

The delay of the 1986 launch made it possible to increase the Space Telescope's power supply. New batteries were designed to last the projected 15-year span of the project. Had the Space Telescope been launched with its original power supply, some astronomers believe that it would have been dead within a couple of years.

While most astronomers recognized that the launch of the Space Telescope would be a milestone in the history of astronomy, many felt that the project's difficulties needed to be addressed to ensure the future well-being of space science. In a January 6, 1990, *Science News* article entitled "Space Telescope: A Saga of Setbacks," author Ron Cowen reported a lengthy list of anxiety-provoking issues concerning the Hubble raised by a variety of experts.

Robert Brown of the Space Telescope Science Institute (STSci) in Baltimore, a university cooperative that coordinates software and research aspects of the mammoth project, explained his concern by saying, "We're launching a telescope with 1970s technology." In Brown's opinion, advances in observatory design, temperature control and optics have significantly narrowed the technology gap between the space telescope and its counterparts on Earth since the telescope's initial planning. He felt that the Space Telescope could have benefited from those advances. Eric

Chaisson of STSci proposed that the NASA philosophy that "big is beautiful" had complicated and slowed the project.

Robert Bless of the University of Wisconsin-Madison, the principal investigator working with the telescope's high-speed photometer, remained convinced that NASA would have been wiser to send up observational equipment on simpler, single-instrument missions. Bless cited as an example the photometer and spectrographs to be included on board the Space Telescope, which did not require a complex, costly high-resolution mirror to achieve most of their goals.

Science was the loser, Bless contended, because NASA put all its eggs in one basket. The weight of the instrument-ladened Space Telescope restricted it to a low orbit. A single-instrument satellite could have reached geo-synchronous orbit (maintaining a constant position relative to the Earth) approximately 22,300 mile above Earth. At that height, continuous observations could have been made 85% to 90% of the orbiting time. By contrast, the low-orbiting Space Telescope is partially blocked by the Earth 40% of the time.

Many management problems arose from distributing the responsibility for manufacturing and installing equipment between two main contractors. Another major source of management difficulty can be attributed to the development of the ground-based computer software known as SOGS (science operations ground system). SOGS was designed to both schedule and record telescope observations during the mission. SOGS standards, formulated without consultation with the researchers who would use the instruments, failed to take into account all the details and quirks of the telescope's five light-detecting instruments.

SOGS can be used to schedule astronomical observations, but trouble develops when it plans too far ahead. To compensate, NASA developed a second ground-based system called SPIKE to feed segments of a master plan to SOGS. Nevertheless, Rodger Doxsey, chief of computer operations at STSci, claimed that SOGS was simply "not smart enough." Experts predicted that SOGS would leave the telescope idle for several precious minutes between observations, instead of arranging for continuous viewing.

Delays in scheduling observation times are upsetting to astronomers because the mechanical functions of the telescope's detectors and the restrictions caused by the low orbit already reduce large amounts of viewing time. With all the restrictions, at best, the Space Telescope was expected to detect starlight only 35% of its time in orbit. Critics anticipated that during the first six months, while the software was being debugged and scientists were becoming accustomed to operating the telescope in space, the detecting time might drop to 20%.

Besides consuming observation time, limitations inherent in SOGS and other ground-based software were expected to hamper the use of specific instrument features and prevent observations of variable stars and the structural details of planets. For example, the high-resolution spectrograph can adjust its exposure according to the light intensity of the star or galaxy under examination; however, the software cannot adjust for a shorter or longer exposure than the one that is preset.

Another expected source of problems was the communication system used to convey messages back and forth between groundbased scientists and the telescope. NASA uses the Tracking and Data Relay Satellite System (TDRSS) to transmit messages to and from low-orbit satellites. But the military and other satellites also use TDRSS. Telescope scientists could reasonably expect to gain access only about 15% to 20% of the time. This would force the satellite to store some data on tape. However, storage capacity is so limited that the telescope's computers can hold only about one-sixth the data storable in a typical personal computer.

A major source of anxiety for everyone prior to launch was maintenance of elaborate and aging equipment. The equipment was originally designed with the assumption that shuttle crews would replace, repair or readjust telescope components every 18 months. In the wake of the *Challenger* explosion, NASA drastically reduced the number of shuttle launches. The first mission to the telescope is scheduled for late 1993, close to four years after launch.

Launch and Aftermath

On April 24, 1990, the space shuttle *Discovery* lifted off carrying the Hubble Space Telescope, which weighed 12 tons on Earth and was the size of a railroad car. The telescope was safely released into its 380-mile-high orbit and the *Discovery* returned to Earth on April 29th. Several difficulties became evident soon after the telescope's launch. They were not the problems that had worried scientists before launch.

Ground controllers learned that the telescope was unable to communicate through one of its vital antennas. Early on April 29th, ground controllers were able to get the telescope to send back detailed data about the antenna that had been stored in an on-board tape recorder. Controllers learned that a cable had become snagged in a joint that allows the antenna dish to track a communications satellite. Scientists feared that they might have to permanently restrict the antenna's motions to prevent it from being caught again.

The worst was yet to come. Sometime in the weeks immediately following the April 24th launch, with a sequence of signals from the ground, the scientists tilted one of the telescope's mirrors and reoriented a lens on one of its cameras, only to find that the image of a distant galactic cluster continued to look like cotton balls. The scientists reassured themselves that with some fine-tuning all would be well.

In early June, they had another try at focusing. With another sequence of signals from the ground, the scientists adjusted the telescope's other mirror again and again. The image of the bright star Iota Carina remained blurred. By early July, the scientists had to accept the fact that the blurred images were not going to be improved upon. The mirrors were in some way flawed.

The focusing problem was too large to be corrected from the ground and chances for an easy solution were minimal. Even though a backup primary mirror had been made for the telescope by Kodak, it was too unwieldy for astronauts to juggle into place in space. Risks of contamination by atmospheric debris precluded bringing the mirrors back to Earth.

Two days after the shattering news about the mirror, there was more bad news from NASA. Hydrogen leaks in the fuel lines, which could have caused another Challenger-type disaster, prompted NASA to ground the space-shuttle fleet indefinitely. The grounding ruled out any hope of ferrying up replacement parts on a shuttle.

Scientists across the United States speculated about what could have gone wrong. NASA quickly set up an investigating committee, chaired by Jet Propulsion Laboratory General Lew Allen, that began by looking at records on the mirrors impounded from the contractor and from NASA's own labs. The investigation was expected to center on the design, fabrication and testing of the telescope's primary mirror, a 94.5-inch, 1,800-pound ring shaped like a shiny Life Saver, and its 12.2-inch secondary mirror shaped like a solid disc.

Some scientists were inclined to believe that the mirrors' flaws came from the contractor's basic design. NASA had issued only broad guidelines, leaving it to the contractor to create a design to achieve them. However, the well-respected manufacturer, Hughes Danbury Optical Systems (formerly known as Perkin-Elmer), a subsidiary of General Motors, had improved upon NASA's manufacturing specifications. NASA had specified that the primary mirror might not deviate from a concave shape by more that one–sixty-fourth the wavelength of neon light (.000005 inch). Hughes had come 21.9% closer to perfection.

Whatever the source of the flaw, the real mystery to many was expressed by astronomer Marcia Rieke of the Steward Observatory in Arizona, during an interview for a July 9, 1990, *Newsweek* article entitled "Heaven Can Wait," who wondered "how this level of trouble was not caught well in advance of launch." One source of the problem might have been budget cutbacks in the early 1980s when NASA was forced to scale back its budget for quality control by 70% and to reduce the number of tests that the agency ran.

Robert Smith, the author of *Space Telescope*, suggested that national security reasons might have been another factor. He noted that the Pentagon did not want too many NASA people "crawling around" at Perkin-Elmer, one of its contractors.

The crew members of the space shuttle Discovery, *responsible for deploying the Hubble, were Commander Loren Shriver, Pilot Charles Bolden, Jr. and Mission Specialists Kathryn Sullivan, Steven Hawley and Bruce McCandless II. To maintain the Hubble dust-free and in flight-ready condition during delays in its launching cost $7 million a month.*

One astronomer told *Newsweek* that with Perkin-Elmer's experience in building spy satellites, telescopes that look down instead of up, the company could easily have tested the mirrors in one of the Defense Department's superior facilities and possibly caught the focal defect. NASA officials insisted that they were unaware of the availability of such mirror-testing equipment. Some observers suspected that NASA might have resisted help from the military because of fear in the early 1980s that the military was trying to take over the space program.

The two mirrors had been tested separately because NASA officials contended that it would have cost hundreds of millions of dollars to test the mirrors together. Many optics experts disagreed. Any flaw, if found, in their opinions, could have been remedied simply by repolishing the mirror. Some observers proposed that NASA had skimped on testing because they had envisioned the Space Telescope as something as serviceable as a vacuum cleaner to which regular shuttle flights could haul up new equipment and astronauts with tools.

Losses and Partial Remedies

In mid-July, experts felt that it was too early to view the cameras as irrevocably lost. They pointed out that the Space Telescope had modular components that slide in and out like tape decks. Replacement instruments could be designed to take the error into account and be installed during a June 1993 maintenance trip to the telescope, when astronauts were scheduled to lift out the wide-field camera and replace

it with a new model. Scientists speculated that the addition of a quarter-size mirror could correct the smeared images.

Not everyone was convinced. In some astronomers' opinion, the Wide Field and Planetary Camera (WFPC, or wiff-pic), intended to capture great vistas of the universe and details about planets, was, under the circumstances, not much better than the best Earth-bound telescopes. The Faint Object Camera (FOC) had 60 or more planned projects, but 10 of the FOC experiments could not be done at all and 40 could be only partially completed.

Instruments without scheduled replacements, such as the high-speed photometers, were expected to accomplish only half to three-quarters of their goals. By analyzing light pulses emitted by black holes as they swallowed up light, Robert Bless, the principal investigator, and his colleagues, had hoped to discover how much black holes weigh.

Learning to Cope with the Wobble

During the first three weeks of testing after launch, a problem with the European-built solar panels became evident. Whenever sunlight initially struck the spacecraft or stopped striking the spacecraft, the vehicle wobbled. In order to lock onto a guide star, a critical step in alignment for scientific observations, the spacecraft needed to remain steady. Scientists had to learn to work between the 10- to 20-minute periods of wobbles during every 90-minute orbit.

Engineers spent months working on a "software patch," a remedial computer program for the vibrations. Unfortunately, it didn't work. The Space Telescope

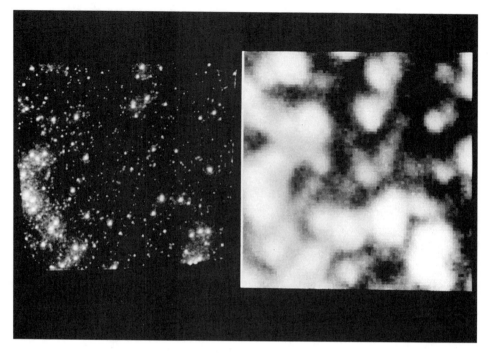

Both of these images are of a region in the globular star cluster M14. The photo at right was taken from the ground with the 4-meter telescope at Cerro Tololo Inter-America Observatory in Chile. The photo on the left was taken from the Hubble with the European Space Agency's Faint Object Camera (FOC). The FOC picture reveals hundreds of separate stars in a tiny reigon of the cluster where only dozens are distinguishable on the ground-based image.

continues to oscillate on several different frequencies—primarily at 0.1 hertz, but also at 0.4 hertz and 0.8 hertz. When the remedial software quelled the 0.1-hertz jitters, it made the guidance system overly sensitive to the higher frequency vibrations. Engineers had to return to the old software and renew their search for a solution.

The Challenge of Finding the Flaw and with It a Solution

Scientists like nothing better than solving a scientific puzzle. A July 31, 1990, *New York Times* article entitled "Sleuths Zero in on Cause of Telescope Flaw," described the relish with which many scientists fell to the task of solving the Space Telescope's woes by saying, "Armed with solid clues, intriguing rumors, and even tips from amateur astronomers, a small army of scientific sleuths is slowly closing in on the cause of the flawed mirrors in the $1.5 million Hubble Space telescope . . . 'It's fun,' said Dr. John Trauger, an astronomer at NASA's Jet Propulsion Laboratory in Pasadena, Calif., who works on one of Hubble's prime instruments. It's remarkable how many people have jumped into this because finding the problem is a fascinating thing to do."

The flawed mirrors create a symmetrical distortion that blurs the telescope's focus so that instead of starlight falling on a single point it spreads over an area. Such an aberration should have been discovered by the test equipment, therefore scientists reasoned that the testing process itself must have been faulty.

By late July, a prime suspect had emerged. Because the 94.5-inch mirror is shaped in a complex curve known as a hyperbola, which makes it more difficult to test than a spherical surface, the testing process was elaborate. Unlike testing a sphere, where a light can be bounced uniformly off its surface, a hyperbola requires a complex optic device known as a null corrector, which must be interposed between the mirror and the light source, in order to get an accurate reflection. An error in the manufacture of the test device could have led the mirror's manufacturer to produce a mirror slightly off the mark, but the manufacturer of the null corrector used in the Hubble primary mirror's testing was a highly respected leader in the field.

Surprisingly, General Lew Allen, head of the investigating panel, in testimony before the House of Representative's Science Committee, reported that, in the early 1980s, Perkin-Elmer scientists had ignored a clue that the primary null corrector they were using, which was a reflective corrector equipped with mirrors, was flawed. A second null corrector, a refractive corrector equipped with lenses rather than mirrors, had failed to agree with the primary null corrector.

Algorithms to the Rescue

NASA announced in late August that they had been able to substantially restore the Space Telescope's images with a computer program. A NASA Fact Sheet provided at a press conference said, "The unprocessed HST images presented here today are significantly better than images from ground-based telescopes. Image processing methods promise to generate images which are, for many purposes, even better than the raw images."

The tiny, bright cores of the stars had made it possible to improve the images using computer algorithm image restoration techniques. The approach is based on the fact that every star has a halo. By measuring the position and brightness of each star and then subtracting the halo, a cleaner image of the star is produced and faint stars partially obscured by the haze are revealed.

Two factors limit the accuracy of removing the stellar halos. First, the scientists do not know exactly what the halo ought to look like, therefore they cannot be sure of subtracting perfectly. They expect to improve their accuracy with additional observations.

Second, and more fundamental, is a limitation set by noise (interference) in the images. The observation of very faint stars is made by counting the individual particles of light, or photons, collected by the telescope. For the faintest of stars, only a few photons can be counted. To detect the presence of faint stars amidst the glare created by overlapping halos may be virtually impossible.

Nevertheless, NASA scientists were buoyed by the fact that even the unprocessed images were unrivaled by those made by ground-based telescopes, particularly since they included images in the ultraviolet range, a range that is absorbed by the atmosphere.

Some Grounds for Optimism

NASA had other good news to report in August. Observations using the European Space Agency's Faint Object Camera provided a view of Supernova 1987A and its surrounding shell with a sharpness and clarity down to .1 arc second. (A unit for measuring angles. A circle contains 360 arc degrees; a degree contains 60 arc minutes; a minute contains 60 arc seconds.) The image provided details only previously suggested by ground-based observations and from data collected by the International Ultraviolet Explorer satellite.

In addition, a detailed view of the core of a galaxy 40 million light-years away was now possible. The results suggested that astronomers would be able to probe the mysterious centers of the galaxies in search of black holes. Astronomers were surprised to find that the stars in the nucleus of NGC 7457 are crowded together at least 30,000 times more densely than those stars seen within our own galactic neighborhood. The stellar density exceeds earlier estimates from ground-based observation of NGC 7457 by a factor of 400. NASA's news release said, "The image, taken with the Wide Field and Planetary Camera on August 17, reveals that stars are much more tightly concentrated at the center of the galaxy than was previously expected. Since the galaxy, cataloged as NGC 7457, is assumed to be a 'typical' galaxy, these preliminary findings suggest that the nuclei of normal galaxies may be more densely packed with stars than previously thought."

A Proposal for a More Fundamental Correction in 1993

A November 19, 1990, *Boston Globe* article entitled "A New Fix proposed for Hubble," reported that a novel scheme for repairing Hubble had emerged in October 1990 from a series of meetings of the Space Telescope Science Institute, a 17-member panel of engineers and astronomers. The group had looked at 60 possible remedies. Astronomer Robert Brown, co-chairman of the panel, told the Globe in an interview, "It turned out to be a wonderful solution that applied to all the instruments, except for one camera for which a solution had already been worked out."

The solution, a device dubbed SmartSTAR, involves the replacement of one of the telephone-booth-size instruments at the base of the telescope. The replacement would contain a boom with five pairs of small mirrors. Once in place, built-in motors would extend the boom carrying the mirrors into the two-foot space between the main mirror and the instruments. Additional small motors would swing the mirrors into position so that each pair would intercept the light traveling to the three remaining instruments. Two of the instruments have two separate openings for light, which would require an additional pair of corrective mirrors for each opening.

A group of engineers at Goddard Space Flight Center was put to work doing a detailed analysis of how to build the device, how long it would take, and how much it would cost. They were scheduled to report their findings in mid-December 1990.

The instrument to be displaced in 1993 by SmartSTAR is expected to have accomplished most of its observations by then. Astronomers working with the Faint Object Camera were particularly pleased with the proposed solution. Most earlier proposals had concentrated only on adding a corrective mirror for the Wide Field and Planetary Camera.

The concept of introducing corrective mirrors just above the instrument openings was advanced by Murk Bottema, an optical expert at Ball Aerospace. The idea received widespread acceptance, but the question of how to get the mirrors in place in a fairly inaccessible part of the Space Telescope appeared formidable. James Crocker, an engineer of the Space Telescope Science Institute, suggested a possible answer.

Crocker pointed out that NASA had built and tested a dummy replacement for one of the instruments, called STAR (space telescope axial replacement), to be used in case an instrument had to be removed for repair and there was no available replacement. (Leaving an instrument bay empty would unbalance the Space Telescope.) Crocker suggested that the dummy instrument could serve as a platform to support the corrective mirrors and their mounting brackets, thereby providing a simple, reliable method of installation.

The question left unanswered was whether the SmartSTAR could be developed quickly enough to be ready for the planned shuttle mission to the telescope in June 1993. On that trip, astronauts are also scheduled to replace the solar panels that give the telescope the jitters during every orbit.

Some Scientists Remain Unconvinced

Without detracting from the wondrous qualities of the new views from space, some scientists continued to question the expense, particularly given the fact that the W.M. Keck Observatory, on top of Hawaii's Mauna Kea, will be completed in 1991. The Space Telescope's mirror is less than one-quarter the effective diameter of the Keck telescope's mosaic of 36 hexagonal mirrors, which together produce a surface 10 meters (32.81 feet) in diameter. Like the Hubble, the Keck is expected to be able to scrutinize galaxies billions of light-years from Earth, providing clues about how the Earth evolved. The Keck cannot do everything the Hubble can, but it can do some things better at a fraction of the cost.

Unswerving Commitment

Whatever the final outcome of the mission of the Hubble Space Telescope, a lot of people put forth enormous effort to make it possible. An April 29, 1990, *New York Times* article entitled "The Space Telescope: A Sign of Intelligent Life," described that effort. The author, Timothy Ferris, said, "Like other missions hammered out by a space agency notorious for tacking an unsteady course with one eye on the stars and the other on the budget, Hubble is a mass of compromises. Its size was reduced to make it fit in the space shuttle's cargo bay, its orbit is lower than many astronomers would prefer (because the shuttle can fly no higher), and the amount of power produced by its recalcitrant solar panels is barely sufficient to keep it running . . . But whatever the future may hold, the Hubble boosters cannot be faulted for any lack of personal commitment; seldom have so many scientists gambled so much of their time for so chancy a payoff."

A closeup of Supernova 1987A taken with the FOC appears in the upper left-hand frame, and an unresolved comparison star from the same exposure can be seen at the upper right. This image shows the exploding outer envelope of SN1987A and provides a fairly clear view of the structure of its luminescent ring. A second, less magnified image of SN1987A appears in the lower frame.

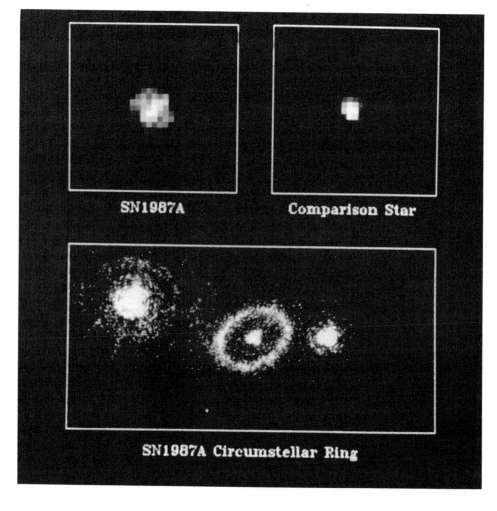

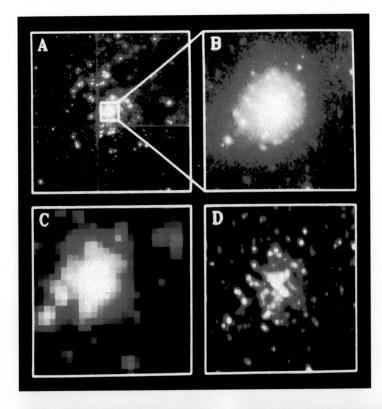

To the left are four images of the cluster of tightly packed young stars in the 30 Doradus Nebula in the Large Magellanic Cloud Galaxy. In Panel A appears a mosaic of four adjoining sky regions photographed simultaneously by Hubble's Wide Field/Planetary Camera (WFPC). Panel B is an enlargement of the central portion of the photograph illustrating the very hot, massive young stars of cluster R136. Panel C is a ground-based image taken by the Max Planck telescope of the European Southern Observatory in Chile of the same region as Panel B. And Panel D shows Panel B after computer processing.

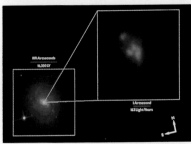

The barred spiral galaxy NGC 1068, taken with the WFPC, reveals a bright nucleus. The inset shows a cloud of ionized gas in the center of the galaxy.

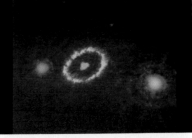

SN1987A's ring, taken with the FOC, illustrates a remnant of stellar material ejected by the progenitor star before the February 1987 explosion. The remnant will disappear within a century as expanding debris overtakes and disintegrates the ring.

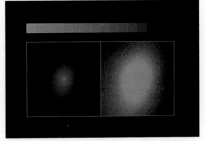

These images, taken by the WFPC, show the Galaxy NGC 7457. On the right is the central portion of the galaxy. On the left the contrast has been adjusted to reveal a high concentration of stars pinpointed exactly at the galaxy's core.

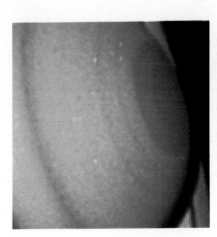

This enlargement of an image of Saturn taken by the WFPC reveals unprecedented detail in atmospheric features at the northern polar hood.

This FOC photo shows a very distant quasar. The light of the quasar was bent by the gravitational field of a nearby galaxy to produce the four bright outer images. The diffuse central object is the bright core of the invervening galaxy.

9

The Earth in the Past

ANTARCTICA

Threatened by Both Politics and Science

Antarctica's 5.4 million square miles, the world's driest desert (an arrid, barren place), is beautiful to behold, but one of the harshest and most forbidding lands on the planet in which to live. Nevertheless, a close look at the seemingly lifeless land and sea of Antarctica reveals an astonishing abundance of life. Most of the coastal waters around the continent teem with 35 species of penguins and other birds, 12 kinds of whales, six varieties of seals, and almost 200 types of fish, as well as squid, sponges and great quantities of smaller organisms. Weddell seals perforate the thick ice with their breathing holes at the site of the major U.S. research station on McMurdo Sound, and at nearby Cape Royds, Adelie penguins hatch their eggs in the world's southernmost rookery.

Research Unique to Antarctica

Much of the important research done on the "white continent" cannot be carried out elsewhere. As long as Antarctica remains pristine, scientists can study ecosystems there that are found nowhere else. Even the ice supports on the order of 10 billion bacteria per liter, as well as hundreds of millions of algal cells and protozoans.

The continent has a significant, not completely understood, effect on global weather. The reflection of the sun's heat from the area back into space results in an overlying mass of frigid air that rushes out to the sea, where it is turned by the earth's rotation into the violent winds that dominate the planet's oceans between 40 degrees and 60 degrees south latitude. Understanding how these winds, the so-called furious forties and fifties, affect the world's weather would improve the science of weather prediction.

Because most of the Antarctica's small amount of annual snowfall never melts, it has accumulated for centuries. Although the sun shines continuously in the summer months, the angle of the sun is too sharp to melt the ice. As a consequence, 98% of Antarctica is permanently covered by a sheet of ice with an average thickness of 2,155 meters (7,090 feet), representing 90% of the world's ice.

One result of the constant cold is that Antarctica has the best-preserved fossil record on earth. About 200 million years ago, Antarctica formed the core of an ancient supercontinent known as Gondwanaland, a name taken from a region in India where geological evidence of the existence of the supercontinent was found. Before the breakup of Gondwanaland, the area now known as Antarctica was located in the temperate latitudes. The climate was near tropical, and the area was covered by forests and filled with birds, reptiles and primitive mammals.

The supercontinent began to break up about 160 million years ago. After the breakup, most of the separate pieces of Gondwanaland remained in warm latitudes. The exception

Antarctica presents a cold, empty-looking panorama to the world that is deceptive. The Waddell seal in the foreground of this photo of Mount Erebus on Ross Island, Antarctica, is barely noticeable. Yet Antarctica and its waters are home to great quantities of living creatures from algae and bacteria to seals, penguins and whales.

was Antarctica, which drifted to the cold latitudes of the South Pole, where the average temperature of – 49 degrees Celsius (–56.2 degrees Fahrenheit) helped to preserve its past.

Critical Ozone Hole Research Is Best Done in Antarctica

For many years, industrial nations have released into the atmosphere chlorofluorocarbons that destroy the ozone layer, a shield that guards the earth against harmful ultraviolet radiation. The eccentricities of air currents have made ozone depletion most severe over Antarctica, although scientists also look for similar ozone depletion holes over more populated areas.

The formation of a hole in the ozone layer over Antarctica began some time in the 1970s but was not noted by scientists until the mid-1980s. (The actual beginnings were documented through retrospective analysis of satellite photographs.) Observations of the hole, which forms in the Antarctic spring in September and closes again in December, is an ongoing research effort that is critical to the well-being of the entire planet.

Antarctica's Lures: Exploitation, Exploration, and Territoriality

Throughout Antarctica's history, science has not been the primary attraction that has brought outsiders to the continent. When English explorer James Cook first circled Antarctica between 1772 and 1775, he saw a multitude of

seals on the surrounding islands. By the early 1900s, after a century of hunting, Antarctica's elephant and fur seals neared extinction.

In the wake of the hunters, came explorers seeking glory, personal and national, as well as scientific knowledge. Among them was Richard Byrd, an American, who, in 1929, was the first person to fly to the South Pole.

During the 1930s, German flyers claimed part of the continent for the Third Reich. The postwar German government did not pursue the Nazi government's claim; however, seven nations with histories of Antarctic exploration—Argentina, Chile, France, New Zealand, the United Kingdom, Australia and Norway—have declared possession of parts of the continent. The United States has made no such claim and has refused to recognize the claims of others. However, the United States has made its presence felt with several expeditions, including the largest ever mounted, Operation Highjump, in 1946, which included 13 ships, 50 helicopters, and 5,000 personnel.

A Lull in the Territorial Jockeying

The international claim-staking in Antarctica came to a halt during an agreed-upon span extending from July 1957 through December 1958, a time designated as the International Geophysical Year (IGY). This was a period predicted to have peak sunspot activity. These dark areas on the sun's surface are due to lowered temperatures in the sun's photosphere (an intensely bright shell between the sun's dense inner gases and the cooler outer layer of gases). During IGY, geophysical exploration involved a significant level of international scientific cooperation that served to dampen territorial conflicts. The intensive study involved 67 countries and much of the research was done in Antarctica.

After IGY ended, President Dwight Eisenhower, impressed by how well the Antarctic component of the IGY had worked, invited 11 other nations that had built bases in Antarctica to join the United States in an agreement to govern activities on and around the continent. The result was the Antarctic Treaty ratified in 1961. The Treaty bans military activity, nuclear explosions, radioactive waste disposal, and mandates international cooperation and freedom of scientific inquiry. While the treaty remains in force, the signatories have agreed not to press their claims for territory. Although the treaty did not completely eliminate jostling for power, no nation has actively asserted sovereignty since the 1950s.

Environmental Impact of Current Research

Given the climate of international cooperation following IGY, research in Antarctica boomed. The number of people who have traveled to Antarctica during the intervening years has been relatively small, yet they have had a disproportionately large impact on the area.

Animals, plants and research stations in Antarctica tend to be confined to the 2% of the continent that is ice-free for part of the year. The Antarctica Peninsula, a finger-like projection that stretches to within 965 kilometers (600 miles) of South America, is the locale of 13 stations. King George Island, one of the South Shetland Islands, has an

additional eight stations. From November through February each year, hundreds of scientists from a score of nations arrive in Antarctica to do research.

Throughout the Antarctic summer, planes, helicopters, snowmobiles, trucks and bulldozers are in constant operation. Almost every base has its own helipad, landing strip, harbor and waste dump.

The carelessness of the base residents' disposal of their trash went largely unnoticed until January 1987 when the environmental organization Greenpeace became the first nongovernmental organization to establish a permanent Antarctic base. The Greenpeace base is located approximately 24 kilometers (15 miles) from the U.S. McMurdo station.

Greenpeace publicized the McMurdo Station's dumping of untreated sewage into the sea, burning of trash in an open-air pit, and pollution of waters adjacent to the station with heavy metals and PCBs, highly toxic polychlorinated biphenyls. Greenpeace also documented that an airstrip under construction at France's Dumont d'Urville base had leveled part of an Adelie-penguin rookery. They also called attention to reckless dumping and burning of trash at the Soviet, Uruguayan, Argentine, Chilean and Chinese bases.

In a January 15, 1990, *Time* article entitled "Antarctica," author Michael Lemonick contrasted the public's immaculate image of the continent, often referred to as "The Ice," with the actual scene. He said,

There is another sort of life as well. All around Antarctica the coast is dotted with corrugated-metal buildings, oil-storage tanks and garbage dumps—unmistakable signs of man. No fewer than

Antarctica is uniquely available to scientific research, particularly in the areas of biology, geology, astronomy, meteorology and fossil records. Yet the scientists and their support personnel have polluted and littered the continent with the abandon of small children. Enraged outcries from environmentalists have forced the human inhabitants to reform their habits and start to clear away decades worth of accumulated debris. Here Greenpeace employees sample a cadmium discharge pipe at McMurdo Base, prior to a cleanup of scrap metal waste on shore.

16 nations have established permanent bases on the only continent that belongs to the whole world. They were set up mainly to conduct scientific research, but they have become magnets for boatloads of tourists, who come to gawk at the peaks and the penguins. Environmentalists fear that miners and oil drillers may not be far behind. Already the human invaders have created an awful mess in what was only recently the world's cleanest spot.

The fragility of the Antarctic was made obvious in January 1989 when *Bahia Paraiso*, an Argentine supply and tourist ship, ran aground off Palmer Station, a U.S. research station, spilling more than 643,450 liters (169,983 gallons) of jet and diesel fuel. The accident killed countless krill (tiny organisms that are a vital component of the food chain) and hundreds of newly hatched penguin and skua (a seagull-like bird). Moreover, the spill threatened 25 years of continuous animal studies run by scientists at Palmer.

Shortly after the *Bahia* incident, gale-force winds blew the Peruvian research and supply ship *Humboldt* onto rocks near King George Island, resulting in a half-mile-long oil slick. And in the fall of 1989, at McMurdo Station, 196,820 liters (51,995 gallons) of fuel was discovered to have leaked out of a rubber storage "bladder" onto the ice shelf.

Implicit in the press coverage in 1989 and 1990 was criticism of the scientists stationed in Antarctica. Although most scientists hoped to keep Antarctica their own unspoiled laboratory, they did share much of the responsibility for the pollution in the area. Over the past three or four years, many bases have established more stringent guidelines for their scientists and have launched extensive cleanup campaigns. Nevertheless, a balance between research and preservation has not been easy to achieve.

The Tourist Threat

While scientists have been trying to mend their ways, tourists are becoming an increasing threat to Antarctica's fragile ecosystems. Tourists' flights from Chile began in 1956 and ended only after an Air Zealand flight crashed in 1979, killing 257. Luxury cruises began in the mid-1960s and each year bring about 3,500 tourists, mostly Americans, who have paid anywhere from $5,000 to $16,000 to sail over from South America to stay four or five days in Antarctica. Chile even opened a tourist hotel near its base.

The proximity of even the most unobtrusive humans can interrupt a seabird's feeding and reproductive habits. Unfortunately, the more intrusive visitors are apt to tramp through penguin rookeries and other wildlife habitats. There was some expectation that tourism might be on the agenda at a fall 1990 meeting in Chile to discuss renegotiating the Antarctic Treaty, but most experts expected the major attention to be directed toward the future of oil and mineral development.

Emperor penguins and a chick on Coulman Island, Victoria Land, Antarctica.

The Scott-Amundsen Station at the South Pole.

One of Antarctica's elephant seals relaxing.

National Commitments to Science in Antarctica Questioned

Many observers view Antarctica as the planet's last frontier. As with other frontiers, the explorers' motives are not always pure. While there is obviously much for scientists to study in the "ice-covered continent," some critics view the science currently being conducted in Antarctic as an expensive subterfuge. As a consequence, they question the commitment of governments to science and the quality of much of the research being conducted there.

Concerns about the purposes for being in Antarctica were explored in a television program entitled "Antarctica/ Frozen Ambitions," which was broadcast on WGBH, Boston's educational channel, on November 20, 1990. The broadcast reported that most nations who have scientists in Antarctica claim that they are there for three reasons: science, peace and international cooperation. However, the broadcast suggested that the governments' actions lend credence to the idea that the actual reason is mainly to have a presence in the area, should they ever desire to pursue a territorial claim. Two scientists, an American and a Soviet, who were interviewed during the broadcast, each explained why they considered their government's support of science as having an entirely different motive.

The American scientist interviewed, Professor Al Erickson of the University of Washington in Seattle, has a worldwide reputation as a mammalogist and spent eight seasons in Antarctica working under the auspices of the National Science Foundation (NSF). (NSF is the U.S. government agency that runs all the U.S. programs in Antarctica.) Professor Erickson complained that the scientific work in Antarctica has emphasized field exposure and the accumulation of data, but a substantial portion of the data has never been turned into published knowledge. "It seems to me," he said, "the cost-effectiveness of the scientific effort is rather poor, in fact, I would say it is abysmal."

The allocation of U.S. funds spent in Antarctica suggests that Erickson's assertions have some validity. The National Science Foundation spends more than $150 million a year on its Antarctica program. About $17 million goes directly to science, in the form of grants, and another $28 million is used to provide clothing, transportation and equipment for the scientists. The remaining $105 million is mostly spent on supporting McMurdo Station, the largest on the continent.

The Soviet scientist interviewed for the broadcast, N. Kaup, an Estonian biologist, whose scientific specialty is the ecology of lakes, claimed that among the Soviets too, much routine work was done and that the opportunities for original research were not used to advantage. He said, "The main aim of the Soviet Union and other nations is to be present in Antarctica."

The Soviet Union's allocation of effort and personnel in Antarctica provide some confirmation for Kaup's assessment. The bulk of the 450 Soviet personnel are engineers and technicians, rather than scientists. Kaup is the only scientist who routinely leaves the base for field work.

Most of the Soviet effort appears to be devoted to routine weather and communications work. Twice an hour, every hour for 17 years, the Soviets have sent out radio signals from their main base to be picked up by their other stations. A second station receives signals put out by the same network of stations. In another fixed Soviet routine, for 22 years, at the same time every Wednesday, a rocket is launched into the atmosphere to probe conditions 50 miles above the earth's surface.

Antarctica's Future Dangles as Political Conflicts Continue

After the 1973 oil crisis, environmentalists became concerned that pressure to dig for petroleum might extend even to the harsh environment of the Antarctic. In time, the Antarctica Treaty nations agreed that before such an event might happen it would be wise to have rules in place. The result of that decision was the Wellington Convention, which was agreed to in New Zealand's capital in June 1988 and submitted for signature and ratification.

The document forbids any mineral exploration or development, unless agreed to by all treaty participants. The convention would allow even large-scale extraction, if it were deemed to have no "significant adverse effect." Since its passage, environmentalists have been deeply disturbed that the possibility of oil drilling is even suggested by the accord.

The chances are uncertain that commercially valuable minerals even exist in Antarctica. Moreover, the extremely harsh climate discourages exploration because of the danger and extreme expense. Nevertheless, opponents of mining fear that some nations might be tempted. In an interview for the *Time* article, Jim Barnes, the founder of the Antarctic and Southern Ocean Coalition, an alliance of more than 200 environmental groups, said, "Some nations are awash in cash and technology and have no domestic oil supply. I think Japan would be down there as soon as the continent opened up."

In support of their opposition to mining, environmentalists pointed out that the Antarctic Treaty already has established guidelines on solid waste disposal, air and water pollution, and the protection of fragile wildlife habitats. But the guidelines have been violated regularly.

The Antarctica Treaty nations meet at least once every two years to share information, resolve disputes and establish what activities will be allowed or banned. Despite the often conflicting interests of the members, decisions must be made by consensus. Reaching agreement is never easy.

There has been enormous opposition to construction of the Dumont D'Urville airstrip by the French. Apparently, no thought was given to the position of the airstrip with respect to the local wildlife.

The focus of contention in 1989 and 1990 was whether the adopted Wellington Convention would be signed and ratified. Proponents of the convention, drafted over six years of negotiations, claimed that it contained stringent environmental safeguards. Opponents of the convention, mostly environmentalists, claimed that the proposed agreement was the first step toward the dangerous exploitation of Antarctica's store of minerals. They argued that the continent ought to be turned into a "world park," in which only scientific research and limited tourism would be permitted.

The environmentalists' position did not have much support until the spring of 1989, when France and Australia, two countries with a major presence in Antarctica, announced that they supported the idea of a world park and would not sign the Wellington Convention. In the United States, Senator Albert Gore of Tennessee led a fight in Congress to get the United States to withdraw its support for the accord.

A November 19, 1990, *Boston Globe* article entitled "Antarctica 'Reserve' Idea Gains Support" reported the opening of a three-week meeting of 24 nations in Vina del Mar, Chile, which could determine the future of Antarctica. Support for the idea of a world park had grown to include five nations. France and Australia had been joined by Belgium, Italy and New Zealand.

The issue of mining remained the main obstacle to proposals for a world park. The United States, Great Britain and several other countries opposed a permanent ban on mining. The U.S. position softened somewhat, following the passage in Congress of the Antarctic Protection Act, which barred any U.S. national from mining in Antarctica and urged the Bush administration to negotiate an international prohibition. President Bush signed the bill on November 16, 1990.

Although the United States no longer backed the idea of the Wellington Convention, it was not ready to endorse a world park. E.U. Curtis Bohlen, the head of the U.S. delegation in Chile, told the *Globe* that the United States was seriously considering a long-term (25 years or longer) moratorium on mineral activities. Such a moratorium would be replaced by highly regulated mining, like that originally envisioned under the Wellington Convention.

R. Tucker Scully of the U.S. State Department, a delegate at the Chile meeting, said that environmentalists were kidding themselves if they thought they could suppress interest in Antarctica mining forever. John Heap, head of the British delegation, argued that it would be foolhardy to lock up the riches of Antarctica as natural resources elsewhere became exhausted and populations continued to grow.

Environmentalists proposed that an international body, comparable to the U.S. Environmental Protection Agency, should be established to enforce environmental rules. While there was some disagreement among environmentalists about how such an agency would work, there was unanimity that mining should be banned.

In an interview with the *Globe*, French explorer Jacques Cousteau, an early supporter of the park concept, said that mining "would automatically bring about dozens of ships bringing oil, bringing equipment, running aground, having terrible consequences. We can put people on the moon, but we are totally unable to transport oil safely."

The Middle East conflict begun in the summer of 1990, when Saddam Hussein seized Kuwait, raised the issue of an oil crisis once again. The Persian Gulf region alone accounts for 65% of the world's proven oil reserves. Some observers speculated that the potential for renewed interest in oil drilling in Antarctica might result in some changes in attitude toward the Wellington Convention. Opponents of the convention might adopt the position that some protection from the convention was better than no protection, while opponents to the convention's strictures on mineral development, such as Great Britain, might fear an oil shortage and turn against the convention.

If the convention were to be voted down, without the concept of a world park being put in place, the informal moratorium on exploration and mining, adopted in 1977 until a convention could be ratified, would end. Antarctica would be opened to unregulated mining.

Dreams of a World-Class Research Center in Antarctica

Global political changes in 1989 and 1990 in Eastern Europe and the Soviet Union could also have a profound effect on Antarctica. In a December 17, 1989, *New York Times* article entitled "Cold War's Thaw Might Reach Clear to South Pole," the author Malcolm Browne said, "For the first time in the two centuries since human beings set foot on the continent, Antarctica is poised to become a world center for scientific research."

To take advantage of Antarctica's vast scientific potential is too costly for one nation to bear alone. In the past, scientists and support staff have had to put so much energy into surviving in the world's most hostile environment that resources have been drained from research. Because it was easier to explore, the coast and its unusual wild life have been the focus of much of the scientific effort.

With what they consider a foothold on the continent, some scientists believe that the time has come for more than "survival science." They propose that the new political climate in the Soviet Union makes possible a full-scale scientific collaboration. Dr. John Lynch, NSF science director of the U.S. South Pole Station, believes that the time has come for a change in the kind of installation used for polar research. In an interview for the *New York Times* article, Dr. Lynch said, "We need to

start planning now for the continent's first truly international station, which we could build at high altitude on the East Antarctic ice sheet."

Lynch envisions a new station on the polar plateau at about 82 degrees south latitude and 45 degrees east longitude, about equidistant from the United States' South Pole Station and the Soviet Union's Vostok Station. The new station would be the highest in the Antarctic and would be ideal for astronomical research because atmospheric obstruction would be minimized. Because of the altitude and the cold, such a station would have to be pressurized, a factor that would add immensely to the cost, which is one reason that sharing the expense with other nations would be so attractive.

Since seven nations lay claim to such large and overlapping parts of the continent, few observers believe that all of the 39 nations subscribing to the Antarctic Treaty are likely to ever agree to such a collaboration. In an interview with the *New York Times*, David Geddes, Australia's senior representative in Antarctica, discounted the possibility of an international station. He said, "Coordinating staffing would be difficult, and before we could get that far, the Antarctic Treaty nations would have to organize a permanent secretariat."

Before discussions of a costly expansion of scientific research in Antarctica can begin, two fundamental issues need to be addressed: The feeling among respected scientists who have spent lengthy periods working in Antarctica that the quality of research being done there is not adequate, and the concern over environmental damage being done by the current level of research, argues against further expansion until the current level of harmful impact can be reduced.

An Uncertain Future

Some of the harm already done has far-reaching impact and will not be easily repaired. The issue of how to further protect Antarctica, which remains the only largely pristine, wild continent on earth, has engendered fierce debate from Washington to Wellington, with limited results. Until some resolution is achieved, the damage is likely to continue.

FREE-FLOWING RIVERS

The Colorado River moves southwest out of the Rocky Mountains and then west across the Colorado plateau, falls to the desert border of Arizona and heads south to the Gulf of California. In order to descend approximately 6,000 feet from the plateau to the desert, the river cut its own 280-mile-long channel, known as the Grand Canyon. In some places more than a mile deep, the canyon varies from 4 to 18 miles in width. Within the main canyon, there are other, smaller peaks and canyons.

Comparatively free of mountains, the Colorado plateau extends from Arizona north into Utah, and west into Colorado and New Mexico. The plateau is a succession of slightly sloping platforms that rise above sea level from a level of 5,000 feet in Arizona to a level of 10,000 feet in some areas at the base of the Rocky Mountains to the northeast.

The current flow of the Colorado River begins in the snow-covered mountains in Colorado. The flow begins as rivulets of frigid water, streaming from beneath steep, pebbly slopes and granite boulders. Traveling southwest, the Colorado River meets and joins with the Green River, a larger river that begins in Wyoming's Wind River Mountains. The two rivers, together with many smaller tributaries, drain a 500-mile-long division of the western side of the Rocky Mountains.

The Grand Canyon continues to awe visitors who see it for the first time. Major John Wesley Powell, adventurer and geologist, who led the first recorded boat trip down the Colorado River in 1869 described the Grand Canyon by saying, "If a hundred mountains, each as large as Mount Washington, were tumbled into this canyon, they would scarcely fill it."

Among the Native American tribes of the Southwest, there are several legends to explain the creation of the Grand Canyon and the Colorado River. Scientists have spun some of their own explanations about the great abyss and its river.

There is no question that the river carved the canyon. Other details of the creation are less clear and have served as points of continuing debate. Among the questions left unanswered are the age of the river and the circumstances of its original development.

The canyon is such a gigantic example of the impact of erosion (the act of wearing away) that early geologists

The Grand Canyon is overwhelming viewed from almost any angle, but never more so than from the base of the canyon when sitting on the Colorado River.

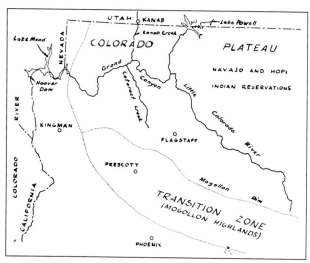

Mature tributaries that flow northwest, such as Cataract Creek and the Little Colorado River, are evidence that the ancestral Colorado ran to the northwest before the time of the canyon. The dotted line denotes the edge of the Colorado plateau. On the western side, the Grand Wash Cliffs form a sharp border between the plateau and the lower basin and range province. The transition between these two zones is less distinct in the south, where the zones are separated by intermediate highlands.

believed that the canyon must represent 50 million years of carving. Major John Wesley Powell and geologists who followed him over the ensuing years believed that all parts of the Colorado River were the same age. They believed that whatever pertained to one part of the river was true for all parts.

Scientists in the 1930s and 1940s who were studying the western canyon and the lower Colorado River concluded that the Colorado River was no older than 6 million years. However, scientists studying the upper section of the river in the 1960s found evidence that the river was at least 20 to 30 million years old. Puzzled by the contradictory findings and forced more than once to change their minds, scientists have begun to view the river as an evolving system that developed in a manner similar to that of a biological system.

The Grand Canyon and the Colorado River have a way of regularly demolishing scientists' assumptions. For about 20 years, scientists had a theory that the ancient Upper Colorado River flowed southwest, traveling out along the Little Colorado River and possibly continuing on to the Rio Grande, which empties into the Gulf of Mexico. An article in the December 19 & 26, 1987, issues of *Science News* entitled "What's New in the Ol' Grand? Geology's Great Monument Continues to Baffle and Amaze" described the two-decade-old theory about the pattern the modern Colorado takes. Scientists theorized that the Colorado River formed nearly 5 ½ million years ago when, near the west coast of Mexico, a huge rift (a narrow opening caused by cracking) was created in the earth by plate tectonics (a theory of the earth as being made up of semi-rigid plates adrift on still molten rock).

The theory held that the rift separated Baja California from the rest of the continent. As the rift grew, the Pacific Ocean flowed into the opening basin, creating the Gulf of California. The tectonic rearrangement would have shifted drainage patterns in northern Arizona, causing the ancestral Colorado River to take a southwestward course toward the new gulf.

This theory of a southwestward flow has recently been forced into revision. Ivo Lucchitta of the United States Geological Survey (USGS) in Flagstaff, Arizona, who has studied the Grand Canyon for more than a quarter of a century, reported to *Science News* that new evidence undermines the old theory. Lucchitta and others suggest that the ancestral river flowed *northwest* along the course of the Little Colorado.

While exploring in the area north of the present canyon, Lucchitta found ancient gravel that could not have come from nearby rocks. Researchers traced the out-of-place gravel to deposits that lie to the south of the canyon, raising the question of how the gravel could have leaped from one side of the canyon to the other. Lucchitta proposed that the streams that deposited the gravel existed long before the time of the canyon. Flowing to the northwest, the ancient streams would have fed into the ancestral Colorado River, which would also have run northwest.

Other factors have helped convince the scientists of the correctness of Luchitta's view about how the gravel came to be in an unexpected place. Tectonic movement is continually shoving up mountains in one region and creating basins and chasms in another. The tectonic rearrangements alter the gradients of rivers, thereby changing drainage patterns. (Drainages are geographic areas drained, as by a river.)

During an interview with the *Science News*, Lucchitta said, "All the better-developed drainages in the Grand Canyon region—ones that are clearly not short, stubby and immature—have this trend. The Little Colorado is a good example. Cataract Creek is another example. They all trend northwest." The drainage patterns suggest to scientists that the oldest, more mature (undergone maximum development of form) rivers ran toward the northwest, before there was an uplift of the ground and the canyon was cut. The latest theory revision was just another reminder to geologists that rivers continually evolve.

The evolution of the Colorado is a part of the continual change in the surface of the earth, which reflects constant tectonic activity. Mountains are regularly being pushed up in some areas, while basins and troughs are being created in others. Geologists in their discussions about the Grand Canyon frequently use cakes to make analogies. The canyon was formed as if a knife (the river) had sliced through a cake, except that the cake (the plateau) had not remained stationary; it had risen around the river. The pushing up of the plateau rather than the river's action had carved the canyon.

The canyon's strata (horizontal layers) of sedimentary rocks (compressed remains of life) bear the record of changing environments. Long before the canyon was carved, even before the era of the ancient Colorado River, the area was located at sea level and, at times, even lower. For billions of years, the region that would eventually become the canyon was periodically overrun, then left to dry, by seas that appeared and retreated. Fossils embedded in the strata of sediment, together with lava from ancient volcanic eruptions, help to date the many incursions of the sea, a phenomenon called transgressions.

There are many gaps in the canyon's sedimentary record corresponding to times when the land was above sea level and subject to erosion. Geologic evidence from some periods of time is totally absent or appears only in selected parts of the canyon.

George Billingsley of the USGS in Flagstaff, Arizona, during the 1980s, found a missing piece of sedimentary record in an area called Surprise Canyon. Along the walls of the canyon, Billingsley located cross-sections of ancient river valleys that coursed through the area during the Carboniferous period, approximately 340 million years ago, long before the existence of the Grand Canyon. The rock's strata include a distinct 20 million-year period not present in most of the other parts of the canyon.

The Surprise Canyon walls hold a wider variety of fossils than any other formation in the Grand Canyon. They reveal that the sea transgressed twice during the 20-million-year period. The bones and teeth of a multitude of ancient sea creatures, including sharks and starfish, remain embedded in the rocks of the Surprise Canyon formation. Subsequently, Billingsley found rocks from the Surprise

Canyon Formation in other areas of the Grand Canyon, including ancient caves.

While ordinary visitors to the canyon are filled with a sense of wonder when they stand along the rim and view the breathtaking precipices, geologists are awed by the information the canyon yields. Much remains to be studied. The oldest rocks at the bottom of the canyon, in the inner gorge, have not been examined in detail. Left from the Precambrian time, they formed the base of 2-billion-year-old mountains that eroded away long before the time of the Surprise Canyon formation.

At the opposite end of the geologic time scale, geologists have yet to determine the canyon's most recent history. It is generally acknowledged that the Colorado River, in its present form, is less than 5.5 million years old; however, geologists hope to narrow down the estimate of the 3 to 4 million years that they think the river took to carve the canyon.

Geologists also continue to have questions about the processes that widened the canyon. While the river carves the vertical dimension of the canyon, avalanches and landslides carve the sides, thereby widening the canyon. Why landslides occurred in particular locations is not yet clear.

Air pollution is a problem for the Grand Canyon just as it is for cities. A recent study, conducted by the National Research Council, lent support to an earlier National Park Service study that one source of the pollution is a huge coal-burning power plant, 16 miles away, that emits sulfur dioxide.

Wild and Scenic Rivers

While the Colorado River is likely to continue for some time to play its role as inspiration for visitors and teacher of geologists, many other scenic rivers have less secure futures. The year 1988 was the 20th anniversary of the federal Wild and Scenic Rivers Act. Though original passage of the act did not produce the wide protection that its proponents had hoped for, more recently the rivers, long overshadowed by wider concerns for the wilderness, seem to have gained a following.

During an interview for a January 12, 1988, *Christian Science Monitor* article entitled "Preserving Free-Flowing Rivers: Public Support Grows for Protection of Wilderness Waters," Steven Whitney of the Wilderness Society said, "The public today understands we've got to be much more careful about managing our lands and waters. As a result there's a big constituency for rivers and it's a vocal one."

A focus among activists has shifted from simply cleaning up rivers to preserving their free-flowing waters to be enjoyed, rather than allowing them to be contained for industrial or municipal use. In January 1988, Oregon Senator Mark Hatfield introduced a bill to bring 27 more Oregon rivers under the protection of the federal Wild and Scenic Rivers Act. Oregon congressmen Peter De Fazio and Les AuCoin introduced similar legislation in the House of Representatives. The bill was ultimately signed into law by President Bush in November 1989.

During an interview with the *Christian Science Monitor*, Congressman De Fazio said, "We need to study the cumulative effects of all our management decisions, particularly hydroelectric projects, waste water treatment, clear-cutting [removing all the trees in a forest area] for timber, and road building in sensitive watersheds. The present system of management does not allow us to look at the sum total of the decisions we make affecting our rivers."

A systemic approach has become characteristic of the river movement in the West. Ron Stork of the Sacramento-based organization Friends of the River reported to the *Christian Science Monitor* that his group was no longer content to fight for rivers mile-by-mile and stretch-by-stretch. Friends of the River was instrumental in gaining substantial protection for three major California rivers, the Kings, Merced and Kern, which drain the High Sierra.

In Oregon, the Oregon Rivers Council launched an Oregon Rivers Comeback Campaign intended to protect, enhance and restore every river mile in Oregon. Oregon industrial interests had thwarted comprehensive legislation to protect the rivers, but 1987 saw the enactment of key bills that curbed hydroelectric development.

In Washington, the Northwest Rivers Council brought together outdoor guides, environmentalists and Indian tribes to push for less hydroelectric development and omnibus legislation for river protection. In Colorado, House representative Hank Brown helped environmentalists, industrial advocates and outdoor users carve out a management plan for Colorado's Powder River, a designated "wild and scenic river."

A 1988 landmark study in resource economics by Richard Walsh and his colleagues at Colorado State University demolished the myth that the only people who care about rivers are an elite with the financial resources and leisure to enjoy water-based recreation. The study revealed that support was widespread among the general public as well.

Different strata of the Bright Angel Canyon as visible when viewed from Yavapai, Arizona.

The Columbia River, looking upstream from Beacon Rock.

The study found that favorable opinions toward resource protection reflected three characteristic attitudes. One attitude favored preserving the rivers for future generations. A "bequest value" was placed on the resource. A second attitude favored protection of the rivers in order to be assured that the rivers continued to exist, giving them an "existence value." A third attitude favored protection of the rivers in order to keep them available for some future recreational, scenic or contemplative use, their "option value."

Stephen Whitney of the Wilderness Society explained the public's growing support of the rivers movement by saying, "In economic terms, rivers have always been the lifeblood of our nation. But a lot of people have had very positive, personal experiences with rivers from early childhood, whether it is swimming or it's fishing with a grandparent. As a result, rivers are a major focus in this country for recreational as well as contemplative experiences, and that is translating into direct action."

Riverkeepers

At the same time, wild and scenic rivers were the object of increasing organized attention, a traditional occupation was revived in a new form in the United States. An English feudal practice among the wealthy was to hire "riverkeepers" to protect their private trout and salmon streams against poachers. Riverkeeping continues to be an occupation in England.

Robert Boyle, the president of the Hudson River Fisherman's Association (HRFA), created a modern American version of a riverkeeper. HRFA is an advocacy group that was formed by a group of citizens united in their concern about the Hudson River. They have an office with a staff of four that operates the Hudson Riverkeeper Fund, which pays for litigation, investigations and field work involved in environmental lawsuits. The staff includes Robert Kennedy, Jr., who runs an environmental law clinic at Pace University, and six university law students.

In 1983, Boyle hired John Cronin as the Hudson River's riverkeeper. One of Cronin's major successes came soon after he started on the job. A state trooper alerted Cronin that Exxon oil tankers regularly sailed up the Hudson to anchor off Hyde Park, where they rinsed fuel residue from their holds into the river. After Cronin began watching them, he learned that they also filled up their holds with fresh water to sell to water-poor Aruba.

Over a two-year period, Cronin collected evidence that 177 Exxon tankers flushed out their holds and removed clean water from the Hudson. Faced with the evidence, Exxon settled out of court, with $250,000 going to the Hudson Riverkeeper Fund and $1.5 million to New York State to help improve the river.

Riverkeeping on the Hudson is not an easy task. The Hudson River was dying in the mid-1960s from pollution. In response to a quarter of a century of effort by environmentalist groups, the river's rich ecosystem is reviving. Sturgeon, shad, herring, eel and blue crab are making a return. Striped bass are flourishing; however, they remain inedible due to contamination from polychlorinated biphenyls (PCBs) that were dumped in the river by General Electric for 30 years.

Cronin described his work for *People* by saying, "One aspect of my job is to be intimate with the Hudson. I'd sue my own grandmother if she were polluting the river." Talking to the *New York Times*, he described the Hudson by saying,

> Biologically, it is one of the most productive estuaries in the world, I guess. We've a lot to protect. The problem is that while we are doing well, other estuaries are declining, and we know very little about the reason why, for either one. The answer is to protect both with equal vigor. And part of my job is to start to accumulate a living memory of what the Hudson River is like in certain places. You don't know something has changed unless you've looked before it changed.

The Hudson stretches from its source, a tiny freshwater mountain lake in the Adirondack Mountains, to the salty New York Harbor, 315 miles away. One-half of the Hudson, from the Battery to Albany, is an estuary (an arm of the sea that extends inland to meet the mouth of a river), where the river bottom is below sea level and the waters are tidal. The other half of the river, from Peeksill north, is fresh water. The only major estuary on the East Coast that still has historic stocks of fish species, the Hudson River has 186 species, 73 of which are saltwater.

Knowing the Hudson's banks, currents and natural inhabitants intimately enables Cronin to perform his job as detective, scientist and public advocate. He quickly recognizes suspicious activities, landfills that release chemical runoff, companies discharging waste and municipalities exceeding their sewage limits.

Much of Cronin's time is spent on the water, taking water samples for analysis, snapping pictures and gathering other kinds of evidence to take to court. He actually spends more time in court than he does on the river. Since 1983, the Hudson River environmentalists have been successfully involved in 40 enforcement cases and lawsuits against Hudson River abusers.

Cronin's work has drawn substantial media attention, with articles in the *New York Times*, *People* and elsewhere. In addition to the newspaper coverage, Cronin was the subject of a children's book, published by Macmillan, entitled *Riverkeeper*, and Warner Brothers plans to make a movie based on his life. Cronin has made his share of enemies, who claim that he is using the river to gain publicity. Robert Kennedy, Jr., and Robert Boyle counter the charges by saying that Cronin has brought a sustained legal focus on the river.

Cronin's success has inspired others. In January 1988, the Delaware River acquired its own riverkeeper, Cynthia Poten, a writer and an environmentalist. Poten's part-time salary is paid by the American Littoral Society (the littoral zone is the area on a seacoast between the high-water and low-water marks), a nonprofit conservation group based in Sandy Hook, New Jersey. In describing her job for the *New York Times*, Poten stressed the role of others in successful preservation. "We rely on information and leads from people who are out on the river. Some are recreational, some are from environmental groups. Sometimes, water-skiers will see something and tell us about it."

The 280-mile Delaware begins as trout-filled streams in the Catskills in New York and ends alongside oil refineries in Delaware Bay. Development is a principal concern along the Delaware, not just housing tracts but also a new recreation area that could adversely affect the river.

Like Cronin, Poten has not met with universal approval. The chief engineer of the Delaware River Basin Commission said of Poten and other environmental groups, "Sometimes there are worthwhile concerns, but too often, too many of the people involved have this close-the-door-after-me syndrome." By that he meant that environmental abusers want protection rules to apply only to those who come after them. On the other hand, many state officials say that in spite of strong antipollution laws, they don't have enough staff to enforce the laws, and welcome the help of people like Poten.

In June 1988, Long Island Sound also acquired a keeper. The Connecticut Coastal Fishermen's Association hired Terry Backer, a third-generation commercial fisherman, to be the Long Island Soundkeeper. In 1972, the association,

a group of commercial and recreational fishermen, had successfully sued the Connecticut cities of Norwalk, Bridgeport and Milford for violating the Clean Water Act. Backer's full-time salary is paid from a 1987 settlement from the suit against the city of Norwalk.

Among the first concerns of the fishermen's group and their soundkeeper was a truck weigh-in station scheduled to be built in Greenwich. They objected to the prospect of rainwater running off the pavement into the Sound, carrying with it antifreeze, oil and other pollutants left behind by trucks. Another source of anxiety was a marina planned in Norwalk Harbor that would have destroyed a mud flat, an important breeding ground for organisms important to the Sound's food chain.

Like the other keepers, Backer spends substantial time in court. When he was hired, the fishermen's group was engaged in suing the cities of Stratford and New Haven for sewage-plant discharges that violated the Clean Water Act. Another suit under way involved the Remington Gun Club, a defunct Stratford association that had dumped 48 million skeet-shooting targets in the Sound over a 62-year period, fouling the water with hydrocarbon-laden petroleum pitch and lead. Hudson Riverkeeper John Cronin commented on the appointments of Poten and Backer: "We now have a person on each waterway in three main adjoining coastal areas. We share some of the same individual animals and fish, such as the striped bass that move from the Hudson to the Long Island Sound."

In 1989, Michael Herz, a respected scientist, with a doctorate in biochemistry and a long record of environmental advocacy, became the self-proclaimed San Francisco Baykeeper. Herz's environmental work had earlier prompted the Alaska governor to appoint him to the governor's 1989 task force on the Prince William Sound oil spill.

Herz fears that the public has been lulled into thinking that environmental laws passed in the 1970s, such as the Clean Water Act, have ended the worst abuses. In an interview for a July 7, 1989, *San Francisco Chronicle* article entitled "The Enforcer," Herz argued, "What good are the laws if they're not enforced? And the evidence is overwhelming that they're not. The fact is that there isn't anybody out there looking—at least not regularly. It's not enough to tell dischargers to monitor themselves and report their violations, which is basically what they do. After all, when's the last time you looked at your speedometer and saw you were doing 65 miles an hour and pulled off the road to write yourself a ticket."

An August 10, 1989, *New York Times* article entitled "One Man Organizes Pollution Patrol," described Herz's first month on the job. The author, Jon Stewart, wrote, "Armed with a knowledge of marine biology and environmental law and grants of $150,000, Mr. Herz appointed himself the 'eyes, ears, and nose' of San Francisco Bay, the West Coast's largest estuary . . . he has

Cynthia Poten, riverkeeper for the Delaware River, warns that even dedicated government inspectors may be thwarted by nay-saying directives of superiors serving economic interests.

been skimming the bay several days a week, recruiting volunteers to help him document environmental violations and forging relationships with law schools and public interest law firms to push legislation."

Even armed with cameras, videotape and electronic equipment, a single person cannot patrol 400 square miles of water and 1,000 miles of shoreline. Herz enlisted help from fishermen, windsurfers, swimmers, bird watchers and anyone else available and willing. In just a month, he had 75 volunteers, including helicopter pilots, boat owners, scientists and computer experts to whom he promised to give a short course on environmental law, rules of evidence and water-sampling techniques.

A broad goal of Herz's program is to arouse Bay area residents' awareness that its most vital ecological organ—the bay itself—is being illegally poisoned almost daily. Herz's long-range goal is to teach the public about the relationship between the mountain streams, the rivers, the deltas, the bay and the Pacific. He said, "It's all one system. Things you do in one part of the system affect other parts of the system. And this bay is where you best get a sense of the systemness."

Long-Overdue Attention

While the Colorado River has continued to receive its well-deserved share of attention, many other rivers across the country have been neglected. Laws, such as the Wild and Scenic Rivers Act, and new keeper-watchdogs, as well as the continuing efforts of environmental groups, are tools that may make a difference in halting the deterioration of the nation's rivers.

The Hudson River Fishermen's Association used money won in a lawsuit over fish kills at power plants to hire a full-time riverkeeper. When present riverkeeper John Cronin is not patrolling, he may be testifying in court.

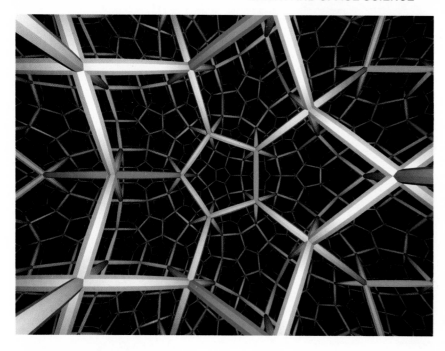

A view from within three-dimensional hyperbolic space that has been marked by a pattern of small squares tesselated (checkered) by regular dodecahedra (polyhedrons with 12 faces) with all right dihedral angles (those formed by two half planes bound by the same straight lines). The silhouettes of the beams are curved, since, unlike Euclidean space, the ideas of equidistant and parallel lines are not equilateral in hyperbolic space.

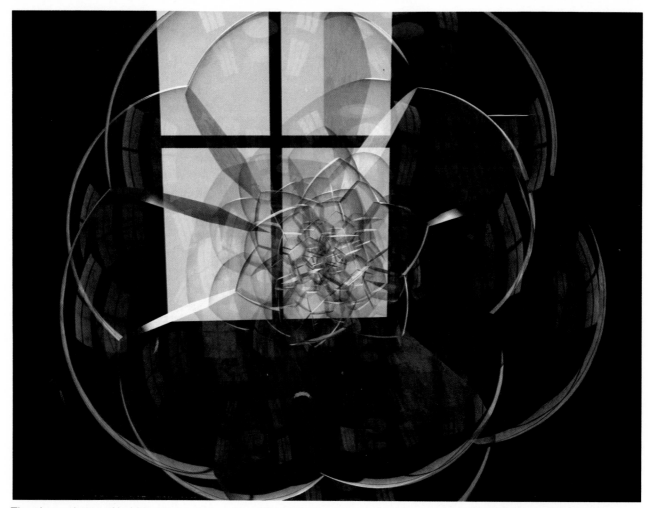

The above cluster of bubbles comes from a four-dimensional, regular polyhedron (a geometric solid figure with several plane surfaces, usually more than six). When projected as a plane, it appears as a cluster of 119 soap bubbles.

PART THREE

Physical Science and Mathematics

EVENTS AND TRENDS IN PHYSICAL SCIENCE AND MATHEMATICS

During 1990, best-selling books by two physicists, Stephen Hawkings and Roger Penrose, made their authors well known outside of the world of science. Stephen Hawkings's *A Brief History of Time* is a review of efforts to create a unified theory of the universe. Roger Penrose's *The Emperor's New Mind* contends that computers will never be able to replicate the processes of the human mind. Other scientists were thinking small in 1990. The microscale organic laboratory techniques of Ronald Pike at Merrimack College and his colleagues at Bowdoin College were changing practices in undergraduate laboratories and nanotechnologists were making machines so small they could be accidentally inhaled. And, in 1990, soap bubbles were helping mathematicians visualize geometric forms and helping physicists understand transformations of metals and ceramics.

Mathematics

For decades, futurists have been predicting that devices would soon be available that would permit telephone callers to see each other while they talked. The prediction has not come true because standard telephone lines can not carry enough information to transmit both voices and good quality pictures at the same time. Some researchers are predicting that a solution to the problem may be at hand in the form of "wavelets," a virtual toolbox of mathematical devices for solving extremely complex problems in math, science and engineering.

When information is reduced to its components, it can be transformed more efficiently. To demonstrate this underlying concept of wavelets, a July 16, 1990, *Boston Globe* article entitled "Wavelets—Wave of the Future?" used the analogy that orange juice can be kept in much greater quantity when it is reduced to concentrate. The orange concentrate becomes juice when water (the equivalent of nonessential "information") is added.

Wavelets are efficient tools for eliminating distortion from visual images. The name wavelets was coined by French researchers Jean Morlet and Alex Grossman from "ondelettes," the diminutive of "ondes," which means waves, in French.

Wavelets are not really a new technique, rather they are a reformulation of methods used by scientists and mathematicians to analyze certain problems. Wavelets are used in a technical formula called the "wavelet transform" or "wavelet transformation."

Transformations are a basic tool of engineering, science and mathematics used to analyze a wide range of complex phenomena, for example, musical or spoken sound, the behavior of a jet engine or the vagaries of economic indicators. The phenomena, referred to as functions, can be plotted on a graph as wavy lines to represent the changing position of the function over time. Many functions, such as the vibrations of a bell or the strings of a musical instrument, are periodic, that is, they repeat themselves.

Transformations break down functions into simpler units in order to: make them easier to analyze; strip them of distracting "noise"; efficiently transmit them; or store them. One of the most commonly known and used transformation tools is the Fourier Transform, named for the 19th-century mathematician Jean B.J. Fourier, who discovered that complex functions, such as the vibrations of a musical note, could be decomposed into the pure tones making up the note.

The Fourier method is indispensable in processing many kinds of information, but it has limitations when it is used to represent very complex functions or functions that stop and start erratically. Wavelets provide versatility. With wavelets, many differently shaped curves can be fitted to the graphs of complicated phenomena, and then the best fit can be chosen.

Unlike the Fourier transform, wavelets can probe a complex function at different scales of resolution—high power to look at details and low power to give an overall picture. Wavelets can capture the important details of a signal, such as the sharp attack of a trumpet note or the edge of a feature in a picture, while at the same time less important information in a picture, such as a background blank wall, can be reduced to almost nothing, to be reconstructed later if desired. With wavelets, it may be possible to reduce the information in a picture by 1,000 times.

When information has been compressed into small and simple elements, the images or sounds represented can be stored, processed, transmitted over phone lines, analyzed or altered. Following such manipulations, scientists can then expand or reconstitute the building blocks into their original form with little loss of detail. Moreover, wavelets can remove distracting detail to reveal an underlying trend.

During the past few years, researchers in a wide range of fields have recognized that the concept of wavelets can be useful. Yale University mathematician Ronald Coifman describes them as a common language and a bridge; nevertheless, he is reluctant to oversell them "because what is dreams and what is reality isn't clear yet."

Computer Science

In the late 1960s, a small group of computer scientists imagined it could be possible for scientists and engineers to share information instantly, no matter where they were located. A scientist working in Massachusetts could use a computer in California as if the computer were in the next room. The result of their efforts was ARPAnet (Advance Research Projects Agency network), the grandfather of all computer networks.

The original ARPAnet was built around small computers that handled connections with slow dial-up terminals and separate message-passing computers, known as interface message processors or IMPs. Each IMP was connected to another IMP on a leased phone line and was capable of sending and receiving messages at high speeds.

Each computer in ARPAnet was an equal partner. As the first computer network in the United States, ARPAnet set the custom of a "peer to peer" relationship, a concept that remains fundamental to networking. ARPAnet was extraordinarily successful and has now been replaced by Internet, an international web of almost 2,000 networks in 35 countries. In 1990, data traffic on Internet's main path, NSFnet (National Science Foundation network), was 3.2 billion data packets a month and was increasing at a monthly rate of 25%.

Important to the development of ARPAnet was Rand Corporation scientist Paul Baran's search for ways to make telephone networks more reliable in the event of nuclear war. He proposed that digital messages could be broken up into packages, which could each be addressed electronically and sent by whatever route was available. Also important was MIT psychologist J.C.R. Licklider's work on linking computers.

In 1968, when ARPAnet was just beginning, engineer Robert Kahn took a year off from teaching at MIT to work for Bolt Beranek & Newman, a think tank in Cambridge, Massachusetts, which brought together the ARPAnet creators' efforts. The work was funded by a contract with the Defense Department's Advanced Research Projects Agency (DARPA).

In 1972, Dr. Kahn joined the staff of DARPA, where he was in a position to authorize innovative research. However by the 1980s, at a time when many of the nation's best computer scientists resisted working on weapons, DARPA's freedom to fund pure research was increasingly limited to weapons-systems research. The strains of working for DARPA prompted Dr. Kahn to leave the agency in 1985. A year later, he founded the Corporation for National Research Initiative, a nonprofit company.

From the base in his nonprofit company, many experts believe that Dr. Kahn has put into place the early stages of a profound technological transformation. He has brought together a coalition of corporate competitors, government agencies and educational institutions. The coalition members have agreed to participate in the research needed to develop an integrated, highspeed national network of computers, perhaps by early in the 21st century.

During an interview for a September 2, 1990, *New York Times* article entitled "Creating a Giant Computer Highway," Dr. Kahn likened the information infrastructure he envisions to a national highway system for data. The system would make it possible to transport huge quantities of information at what are called "gigabit" (1 billion bits) speeds, a thousand times faster than the fastest network currently available.

Once in place, Kahn's network would provide users who needed information, such as scientists, scholars, students, economists and business executives, with immediate access to computerized libraries, comparable in size to the Library of Congress. In June 1990, the National Science Foundation awarded Dr. Kahn's corporation a small grant of $15.8 million to oversee the research needed to set up five separate networks and to experiment with new hardware and software technology. Rough estimates of corporate commitment to the effort suggest an investment of about $300 million is required.

Government officials calculate at about $200 billion the cost of building the entire network that could one day reach every American home. Economists believe that the economic and social benefits of the network will exceed the costs by a wide margin. Moreover, they claim that the costs of not building it could be much higher in the long run.

Japanese corporations have pledged $20 billion to a comparable network and France has begun work on a national digital library. Some observers do not view the Asian and European pursuit of such a network as competition but as offering the potential for information sharing on a worldwide basis.

Physics

When, despite its complexity and intellectual rigor, *The Emperor's New Mind* became a best-seller, physicist-mathematician Roger Penrose found himself under attack by artificial-intelligence (AI) researchers. Barely known outside his own field of expertise, Penrose, a shy Oxford professor with a solid reputation among his colleagues, has spent most of his career creating theories in abstruse areas of physics and mathematics. To give readers of his book the background needed to understand his ideas, Penrose delves into fractal geometry, number theory, quantum physics, entropy and cosmology.

AI researchers objected to the central conclusion of *The Emperor's New Mind*, which stated that computers will never think. An example of the AI scientists' opposition appeared in a June 25, 1990 *Time* article entitled "Those Computers Are Dummies: A Physicist's Attack Riles Artificial Intelligence Researchers." The article quoted Massachusetts Institute of Technology (MIT)'s Marvin Minsky who said, "Penrose is O.K. when he talks about mathematics, but most of his evidence is *against* his conclusions. As far as I can tell, he is just plain wrong."

To support his position that computers will never be able to think, Penrose points out that all computers operate according to algorithms, that is, by following rules that prescribe how to solve problems. Yet some problems cannot be dealt with by any set of rules, a theory explored by mathematician Kurt Godel in the 1930s.

Godel's theorem held that in any mathematical system there are certain propositions that are obviously true but that can never be proven within the rules of the system. Moreover, in the 1950s, mathematician Alan Turing used an imaginary, simple "computer" to demonstrate that there are some mathematical problems that can be solved by humans but that cannot be solved, even in principle, by computer. Penrose freely admits that a second major position of his book is much more speculative. Based on his own extensive experience in solving abstract puzzles, Penrose concludes that the human mind can reach insights that are forever inaccessible to computers. He proposes that consciousness and insight are governed by as yet undiscovered laws of physics.

Penrose believes that an explanation for consciousness and insight will be discovered when a connection between Einstein's theory of relativity, which concerns itself with gravity, and quantum theory, which governs the submicroscopic world, two theories that are mathematically incompatible, is established. Physicists are now trying to create a quantum version of the phenomenon of gravity. A consequence of such a merger would be that particles could jump from one place to another without traversing the space in between.

In Penrose's opinion, neurons making quantum jumps from one energy state to another is an act of creative thinking. Since computers do not operate by quantum rules, he believes they will never have these insights.

Penrose proposes that quantum gravity could also be behind consciousness. Human consciousness perceives time as moving forward, a peculiarity that baffles physics, since all laws of physics work equally well in reverse. When quantum gravity is finally observed, Penrose believes that it will not work in reverse, pointing out that the big bang, the phenomenon that created the universe, must have been governed by quantum gravity and can not be reversed. If quantum gravity does govern the mind it would explain why for humans time moves forward and not backward.

Essentially, Penrose theorizes that human creativity and consciousness are nothing less than the workings of the most basic laws of the universe.

Chemistry

Although scientists and engineers have made great strides in the development of alternative fuels, drastic funding cuts of the 1980s have slowed the progress. The 1990 Middle East crisis was a reminder of the vulnerability of Western nations to their dependence on oil and their need for alternative fuels. Two-thirds of all oil used in the United States is used in transportation. If alternative fuels and technologies could replace gasoline, it could eliminate much of the need for imported oil.

Environmental concerns over the last few years have brought a number of alternative approaches to powering motor vehicles close to fruition. Many of the alternatives are made with renewable resources and emit less pollution than gasoline. The alternative fuels being seriously studied are: methanol, ethanol, compressed natural gas, liquified petroleum gas and electricity. Ethanol and methanol are both alcohol fuels whose price is nearly competitive with that of gasoline.

An August 28, 1990, *Boston Globe* article entitled "Alternatives to Oil Move from the Lab to the Road," explained the difficulties in weaning Western nations from oil. The Western systems of energy consumption that are built around the use of oil are so extreme that even with an accelerated program in alternative fuels, it could take decades for alternative fuels to replace oil.

A lack of technologies is not an obstacle. American automobile manufacturers have built engines designed especially for ethanol-fueled engines and installed them extensively in cars sold in Brazil. Auto manufacturers in the United States have developed model flexible-fuel engines whose manufacture is possible. Those engines burn methanol, ethanol and gasoline interchangeably, or any mixture of all three.

The interchangeability of the flexible fuel engines could make it possible for alcohol fuels to replace gasoline use gradually, without disrupting the current economic system. California, with its stringent new policy against air pollution, is scheduled to serve as a pre-production testing ground for cars equipped with flexible fuel engines.

Some experts expect natural gas to play an interim role until the use of wood and other vegetation as feedstocks (sources of fuel) can be more fully developed. As transportation fuels, methanol and ethanol share an advantage in that they can be produced from a variety of feedstocks. Methanol can be made from natural gas, sludge or garbage. Ethanol can be made from grain. Either can be made from wood.

With some modifications, either ethanol and methanol can be used in existing cars. However, because alcohol fuels provide less energy per gallon than gasoline, to make the alcohol fuels fully competitive engines would need to be redesigned.

The major impediment to a switch to alternative fuels is the size of the energy system and the amount of capital invested in it. Changes in anything that extensive take considerable time, even when the new technology can compete with existing energy sources. The process of change may be speeded up, however, if the price of oil rises high and steadily over a long period of time.

10

Mathematics

COMPUTER GRAPHICS

A New Dimension Has Been Added to Geometric Investigation

Making a New Perspective Possible

Physical models and drawings have served a significant function in mathematics for a long time. The graphic form enables mathematicians to represent abstract ideas in concrete ways. Nineteenth-century mathematicians were able to visualize and comprehend geometric forms by creating models of wood or plaster or by drawing sketches. Their representations provided guides to help them uncover the basic principles of geometry.

To move beyond the limits of plaster, wood and pencil, mathematicians of the late 20th century have begun using computers to display on a video screen images that are animated and colorful representations of equations and mathematical structures. A hub of such activity is the Geometry Supercomputer Project at the University of Minnesota at Minneapolis/St. Paul, where an international collection of prominent mathematicians and computer scientists are linked by a high-speed telecommunications network. The staff includes 18 mathematicians and computer scientists and their associates in the United States and abroad.

The original impetus for the Geometry Supercomputer Project was described in a January 2, 1988, *Science News* article entitled "Shareware, Mathematics Style." During a lunchtime meeting several years ago a productive collaboration began between Princeton computer scientist

David Dobkin, who was fascinated by computer graphics, and Princeton mathematician William Thurston, who was drawn to the twists and turns of three-dimensional space.

To pursue this idea meant making a leap from equations jotted on the back of a napkin to graphic images representing those same equations. On the way to creating the images, Dobkin had to learn a great deal about graphics and about topology (the study of the properties of geometric figures that remain unchanged, even when under distortion, so long as no surfaces are torn).

The initial collaboration between Dobkin and Thurston eventually expanded to become the Geometry Supercomputer Project. Opportunity to proceed with the program came when the University of Minnesota established a supercomputer institute with access to a Cray-2 supercomputer. Albert Marden of the University of Minnesota, who was aware that several other mathematicians besides Thurston lacked the resources to pursue a strong interest in the potential of computer representation, grasped the chance to organize the project. Marden described what prompted him to take action: "People were running around excited about the supercomputer, without being quite sure of how to scientifically take advantage of it."

It took Marden two years to organize the group and to arrange for funding from the National Science Foundation. During an interview for a December 23 & 30 1989, *Science*

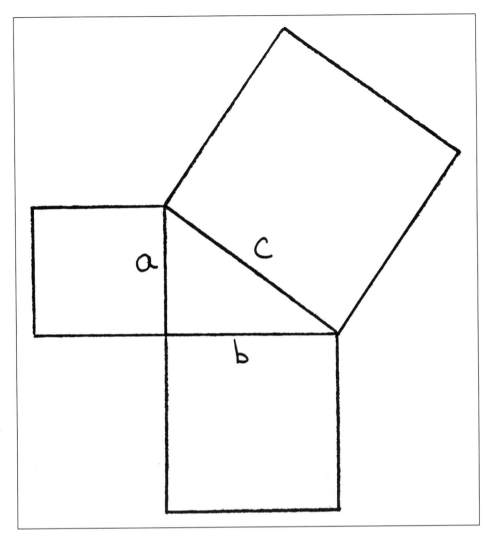

Mathematicians have long translated mathematical thoughts into visual representations, for example a formula that will always result in a triangular number. A triangular number is one in which if the number were expressed in dots, the dots could always be arranged into an equilateral triangle. Perhaps the most famous visual representation of a mathematical formula is the Pythagorean Theorem, which states that the square on the hypotenuse of a right triangle is equal to the sums of the squares of the two sides. In other words, if one used each side of the right triangle to build a square and then calculated the area of each of those squares, the area of the square built on line c would equal the sums of the square built on lines a and b. The Egyptians used this phenomenon long before the Greek Pythagoras postulated it as a theorem.

News article entitled "The Color of Geometry: Computer Graphics Adds a Vivid New Dimension to Geometric Investigations," Marden explained the value of the program. He said, "It's hard to write computer programs, and people often don't have the necessary equipment. In this project, mathematicians for the first time can participate in the world of professional graphics and learn what it has to offer."

The interests of those involved in the Geometry Supercomputer Project cover a broad array of concerns, including soapfilm surfaces, the geometry of hyperbolic space and the construction of knots. The scientists' ideas are translated into colorful mathematical images, where they can be explored.

A Few Typical Categories of Problems

Some group members use computers to follow the consequence of repeatedly evaluating algebraic expressions, a standard method called an iterative process used in solving equations that describe the dynamic behavior of materials, fluids, and other systems. For example, with an expression such as $z^2 - 1$, for various values of z, the process involves: 1) substitution of a number in the expression; 2) finding the answer for the equation; 3) plugging the answer back into the same equation; and 4) repeating the sequence. The scientists keep repeating the sequence to see where the process leads. For some starting points, the answers keep getting larger. For others, they remain around the starting values. Some translate into colorful, intricate images.

Some of the Geometry Supercomputer Project members take advantage of the computer-generated images to examine fractals, patterns repeated on ever-smaller scales. Fractals are geometrical shapes that, when magnified, resemble the original object. Like a pine tree, a fractal looks the same in its entirety as it does when a small section is magnified. Benoit Mandelbrot of Yale University, who is a project participant, is a leading authority on fractals and coined the term to describe the self-similarity he observed.

Some project members, such as Robert Tarjan of Princeton, are interested in algorithms (well-defined rules for the solution of a problem in a finite number of steps). During the course of his exploration, Tarjan has found connections between his work and the type of geometric problems with which Thurston has wrestled.

Much remains to be learned about which algorithms are most suited to solving specific geometrical problems. For example, David Mumford of Harvard University has an interest in algorithms that mimic the pathways followed by nerve signals that determine visual memory in humans.

Fractal tiling. Fractals are geometric shapes whose structures, when magnified, yield the same shape. The non-periodic (non-repeating) tiling above is made up of three shapes, any one of which will repeat infinitely. Rotated around a point where five tiles meet and expand, the small tile goes to the middle tile, the middle to the large, and the large to a union of two tiles, a quality referred to as self-similarity.

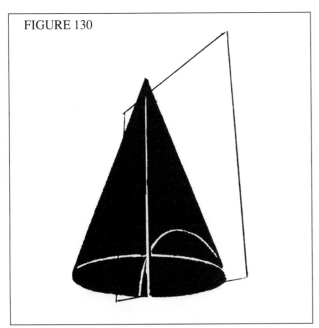

FIGURE 130

Euclidean or plane geometry is not the only type of space with which geometrists work. Often they deal with space "sliced" off from a cone. These conic sections are curves obtained by the intersection of a plane with a cone. The manner in which the cone is intersected or sliced determines the type of curve obtained. One such mathematical curve is the hyperbola formed when the angle the plane makes with the base is greater than the angle formed by the cone's side. The sonic boom of a jet traveling faster than the speed of sound is a shock wave in the shape of a hyperbola. All people within the hyperbola hear the sound at the same time. Those outside the hyperbola do not hear it at all.

A Capacity to Look at Places No One Has Seen Before

Using a hyperbolic-viewer computer program developed by David Dobkin and his colleagues at Princeton University, a mathematician can fly into a brightly lighted, fanciful landscape representing a three-dimensional mathematical structure. He or she can operate at any desired pace, from any desired point of view, stopping to look behind objects or to zoom in on areas of interest.

Different geometries function using different rules. The hyperbolic viewer makes it possible to see scenes as they would appear in several different geometries. In hyperbolic geometry, the sum of the angles within a triangle is less than 180 degrees, in contrast to Euclidean geometry, in which the sum is exactly 180 degrees. As a viewer flies toward shapes in hyperbolic space, he or she sees features in greater detail. For example, a patchwork-pleated surface of hundreds of triangles opens to reveal additional triangles. Hyperbolic space makes it possible to display substantial information in one part of a scene, without cluttering other parts.

The Geometry Supercomputer Project has another program that addresses the classical mathematical problem of packing a given volume in the least amount of space, a process frequently done using soap bubbles. The program, known as the "surface evolver," was developed by Kenneth Brakke of Susquehanna University in Selinsgrove, Pennsylvania and is available to any mathematician interested in generating and studying least-area surfaces.

The surface evolver begins with a geometric shape of a given volume and changes the figure into a new shape with the smallest possible surface area containing the same volume. Starting from suitable geometric points, the surface evolver can compute and display a broad array of minimal surfaces. The program turns a cube into a close approximation of a sphere, its least-area counterpart, by breaking up the surface into successively smaller triangles.

The minimal-surface team developed a program to replicate the action of soap bubbles. The process begins with a collection of points in space. The researcher divides up the space into compartments so that each point has all its near neighbors in its own compartment. The division creates an assortment of shapes that all have the same volume. The program next rearranges the boundaries between the shapes, while at the same time it adjusts the compartments' boundaries to keep volumes constant within all the compartments. The process continues until a minimum is reached for the total surface area of all the interfaces.

Prior to the advent of the program, mathematicians simply guessed at the existence of some forms or tried to achieve them with soap bubbles. Frequently, in the absence of an equation that describes its surface, a computer-generated picture offers evidence that a specific form exists. The researchers have used the soap bubble program to mimic crystal growth, particularly the branching patterns typical of snowflakes. They feel that at the very least the program can tell them whether they are on the right track.

While the ability to see structures in three-dimensional form can solve some problems, it can create others. Charles Peskin of the Courant Institute of Mathematical Sciences at New York University has spent more than a decade untangling the convoluted bundles of complex muscle fibers that constitute the beating heart. Some heart fibers form shells that resemble nested doughnuts; others follow complicated pathways that tie together the heart's right and left sides.

For Peskin, moving to three dimensions raised difficult geometric questions, but the move made it possible to come close to a three-dimensional anatomical model of how fibers are laid out. A particularly difficult task for Peskin was to make it possible to display a three-dimensional structure in motion, while showing the flow of fluid inside the structure. Peskin envisions ultimately being able to reduce muscle-fiber geometry to a set of numbers that can be used efficiently by a computer to allow researchers to examine normal and diseased hearts.

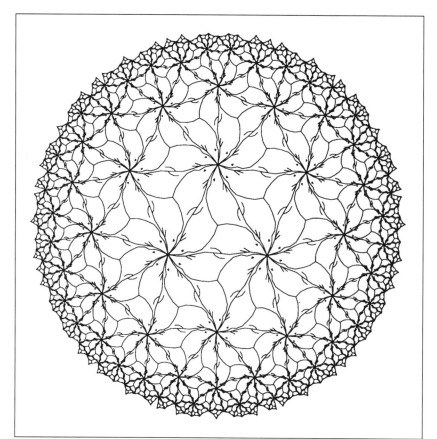

The two pictures show tilings of the hyperbolic disk, which is comparable to an ordinary disk but is measured differently. Each of the picture's tilings are congruent (of the same shape and size if placed on one another). The procedure is analygous to handling the familiar tiles on bathroom floors, which are measured using Euclidean (plane) geometry.

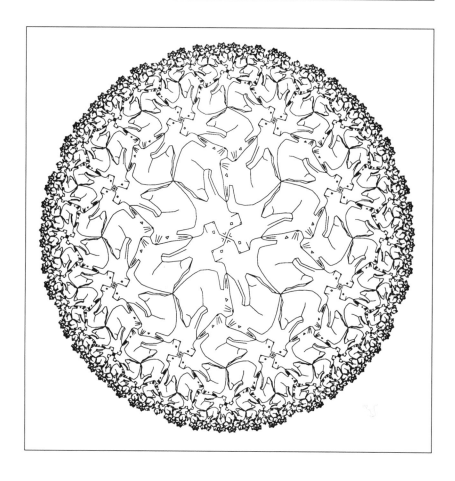

In the physical world, the sphere is the most compact arrangement of surface area to space, i.e., the greatest amount of mass can be enclosed by the least amount of surface area compared to other geometric forms. The sheer compactness of spheres has inspired interest in the problem of "wasted" gaps in a packing arrangement. To the right are the most space efficient arrrangements devised. The top figure shows a layer on a single plane with each sphere touching six others. The bottom figure shows a multiple layer arrangement where each sphere touches 12 others. Until the advent of high-tech communications, where coded information has to be packed into ever smaller spaces, sphere packing was an obscure mathematical curiosity.

Knots are another hard-to-visualize area of interest among the Geometry Supercomputer Project members. Unlike the knotted rope of a school child or a sailor, a mathematician's knot (or curve) has no free ends. It travels through space to catch its tail and form a closed loop. Nevertheless, mathematicians ask the same kinds of questions that a sailor might. What sort of knot is it? Is it really knotted? Can a second knot undo the first? How can different knots be distinguished? Molecular biologists use such knots to try to understand how DNA strands can be broken and recombined into knotted forms.

The typical representation of a mathematical knot depicts a continuous loop with breaks in the line to indicate where one piece passes beneath another. Such drawings are little more than approximations of the actual three-dimensional knots. Knot theorists often have difficulty in deciding whether apparently different diagrams can actually refer to the same knot.

Graphics specialists Charles Gunn and Matt Grayson have experimented with converting a shadow drawing of a knot into a three dimensional rendition. The program straightens out the three-dimensional knot by making the strand behave as if one piece were repelled by another. The strand spreads out and assumes a more symmetrical shape. Application of the approach to two different knot diagrams could help theorists to determine whether two images represent the same knot.

Program's Purpose

The inclusion of project members who have varied backgrounds in the Supercomputer Project is deliberate. The project builds on prior, small-scale collaborations, such as the one between Thurston and Dobkin. Marden commented on the interlocking interests of the members by saying, "There is a good reason why every single person is in the project."

Thurston, who is a central figure in the venture, has a major interest in compiling a comprehensive catalog of three-dimensional manifolds, surfaces that take on a bewildering array of shapes. The simplest mathematical spaces are known as Euclidean spaces. An infinitely long line is a one-dimensional Euclidean space; a plane with width and depth is a two-dimensional space; and a space with three coordinates, longitude, latitude and altitude, is a three-dimensional space. The term manifold refers to more complicated types of space. Manifolds locally appear Euclidean, but on a larger scale may bend and twist into exotic forms.

The complete classification of manifolds has eluded many mathematicians. Every member of the Supercomputer Project, while pursuing his or her own interests, over time will be likely to contribute, in some manner, to Thurston's manifold classification.

In addition to answering specific participant's problems, an overall goal of the project is to open up computer graphics to all mathematicians. Toward that end, the project seeks to establish compatibility standards in its programs, techniques and tools in order to enable researchers to share software and communicate results.

The quest for uniform standards raises a myriad of questions about the best way to represent or manipulate two- and three-dimensional computer shapes. It also means development of programs that can be run on a wide variety of computer makes and models.

During an interview with *Science News*, Charles Gunn, the director of the project's graphics laboratory, said, "Part of the dream is to bring graphics tools to the people who can benefit from them. We're just beginning to see how graphics can be used and how it's going to change the way we do mathematics."

The group's members expect the tools they are developing to play an important role in the education of mathematicians. In their initial proposal to the National Science Foundation, the organizers said "Computer visualization offers an ideal approach to the teaching of mathematics. Not only the images, but also thinking about how to produce the images are powerful aids to understanding."

Mandelbrot stressed the contribution of images to greater understanding by saying, "I hope this project establishes for good among mathematicians the realization that the computer is an extraordinarily useful tool for exploring conjectures and for communicating intuitions to other people."

Novel graphics techniques and large-scale computation permit mathematicians to attempt problems they would otherwise find impossible or not even bother to consider. Jean Taylor of Rutgers University said, "In some sense, mathematics is the problems you look at as well as the answers you get. This approach extends the imagination and opens up many new questions."

THE DECENNIAL CENSUS

The Science, Art and Politics of Counting American Heads

The practice of counting citizens, the U.S. census, began soon after the 13 colonies broke their ties with Great Britain. The cost of the Revolutionary War had been high. To pay for it, the new nation had to find a way to divide up the debt equitably. But first they had to know how many people were available to share the load.

The nation's new form of government, which called for the House of Representatives to be apportioned, based on the size of each state's population, also provided a compelling reason for taking a census. For the first time in history, a nation made taking a census a part of its constitution. According to the U.S. Constitution, Article I, Section 2:

> Representatives and direct Taxes shall be apportioned among the several States which may be included within this Union, according to their respective Numbers . . . The actual Enumeration shall be made within three Years after this first Meeting of the Congress of the United States, and within every subsequent Term of ten Years, in such Manner as they shall by law direct.

The framers of the Constitution reasoned that by counting people for purposes of both taxes and representation they would get a fairer and more accurate tally. However, taxation has never been linked to the census results. On the other hand, the counting of the population for representation, at least every 10 years, has been followed since 1790.

Based on the 1790 census, the original number of 65 House representatives grew to 106. Each seat represented a population of almost 4 million. When the House reached its present size of 435 in 1911, where it has remained, the collective seats represented 92 million people, who had been counted in the 1910 census. By 1980, the same 435 seats represented 226 million people.

The Constitution provides that each state must have at least one representative. Apportioning the seats to the various states would seem fairly straightforward, given the calculated population and the fixed number of seats in the House. It is not.

Whole numbers are relatively easy. The difficulty arises with fractions, since it is not possible to send a fraction of an elected official to Congress. Finding a method that would adequately solve the fraction problem remained an issue for Congress from 1792 until 1941.

The first plan to deal with the fractions was devised by Thomas Jefferson, who apportioned a representative for every 33,000 people in a state and disregarded any leftover fractions. This method stayed in effect for the next four censuses, each with progressively larger leftovers. Several methods followed, lasting for various lengths of time, each with its own flaw.

The present technique, called the equal proportions method, adopted in 1941, requires the Census Bureau to compile a priority list of the states. Priority value is determined by dividing a state's population by the geometric mean (the square root of the product of two numbers) of its current and next seats. The formula is $\frac{P}{\sqrt{N(N-1)}}$, where "P" is the state population and "N" is the number of seats a state would have, if it gained a seat. Thus each state's claim to a seat (the priority value) would be the total state population divided by the geometric means of its current and next seats $\sqrt{N(N-1)}$.

For example, following the 1980 census, each state was first awarded its required one seat out of the current 435 total. Then the 51st seat went to the California, whose priority value was 16,736,300. The next seat, number 52, went to New York, with a second-seat priority value of 12,414,877, and Texas received number 53, with a priority value of 10,060,986.

Redistricting

When setting up or changing the boundaries of congressional or legislative districts for political purposes, there are two ways to control the districts—by geography or by population. Almost from the outset, election districts took on strange shapes and population sizes to favor particular groups or parties, thereby violating the Constitution's intent of equal representation.

Tinkering with the boundaries of legislative districts is a practice called gerrymandering, a term associated with Elbridge Gerry, who was the Governor of Massachusets in 1812 when the Essex County's senatorial election districts were drawn to make sure that his party's candidate was elected. The districts resembled a salamander and were dubbed gerrymander by Gerry's critics.

In an effort to guard against gerrymandering, since 1842 Congress has tried a variety of methods to prevent this abuse. Nonetheless, redistricting has been a way to discriminate against people because of race, national origin, beliefs, income or the way they vote. By dividing them up among several districts, a group's power could be blunted.

The Return for SOUTH CAROLINA having been made fince the foregoing Schedule was originally printed, the whole Enumeration is here given complete, except for the N. Weftern Territory, of which no Return has yet been publifhed.

DISTICTS	Free white Males of 16 years and upwards, including heads of families.	Free white Males under fixteen years.	Free white Females, including heads of families.	All other free perfons.	Slaves.	Total.
Vermont	22435	22328	40505	255	16	85539
N. Hampfhire	36086	34851	70160	630	158	141885
Maine	24384	24748	46870	538	NONE	96540
Maffachufetts	95453	87289	190582	5463	NONE	378787
Rhode Ifland	16019	15799	32652	3407	948	68825
Connecticut	60523	54403	117448	2808	2764	237946
New York	83700	78122	152320	4654	21324	340120
New Jerfey	45251	41416	83287	2762	11423	184139
Pennfylvania	110788	106948	206363	6537	3737	434373
Delaware	11783	12143	22384	3899	8887	59094
Maryland	55915	51339	101395	8043	103036	319728
Virginia	110936	116135	215046	12866	292627	747610
Kentucky	15154	17057	28922	114	12430	73677
N. Carolina	69988	77506	140710	4975	100572	393751
S. Carolina	35576	37722	66880	1801	107094	249073
Georgia	13103	14044	25739	398	29264	82548
	807094	791850	1541263	59150	694280	3893635

Total number of Inhabitants of the United States exclufive of S. Weftern and N. Territory.	Free white Males of 21 years and upwards.	Free Males under 21 years of age.	Free white Females.	All other Perfons.	Slaves.	Total
S.W. territory	6271	10277	15365	361	3417	35691
N. Ditto	—	—	—	—	—	—

A page from the first census taken by the new United States in 1790. Criticisms are raised that the size and mobility of the country make the traditional head count impractical and that those groups least likely to answer the census skewer the true count. But there are counter arguments that sampling techniques to supplement or replace a head count will introduce their own biases.

In a series of decisions that began in 1962, the U.S. Supreme Court attempted to restore equality and to extend it to state and local legislative districts as well. In 1964, in *Wesberry* v. *Sanders*, the Court held that "as nearly as practicable one man's vote in a congressional election is to be worth as much as another's." That same year, in *Reynolds* v. *Sims*, the Court held that state legislative districts must be "as nearly of equal population as is practicable."

To comply with the Supreme Court decisions, states must use detailed census information in their redistricting process. To enable state and local officials to meet their deadlines in the year of a census, officials of the Bureau of the Census must get to those officials an early preliminary count of housing units by block for local review. Moreover, by December 31 of the census year, the Bureau must send an official count to the president.

Critics of the Conduct of the Census

In 1787, being counted meant equal representation in the Congress, and it continues to mean that today. Completeness and accuracy of population counts from every section of the country directly affect every citizen's voting power. However, experts are in disagreement about how to count "accurately."

The ideal census is one in which enumeration (being counted) is based on evidence that a person is physically present in a particular location or block at the time of counting, and that each tally corresponds to a particular person. The ideal is extremely difficult to achieve.

Despite the fact that staff professionals at the Census Bureau have a high reputation among demographers (analysts of vital statistics, such as birth, death and marriage of populations), scientists find much to criticize about the census process. In a July 15, 1990, *New York Times* article entitled "The Census: Why We Can't Count," author James Gleick summarized the criticism, saying: "When the last form flicks through the machine, when the last enumerator turns in the last Questionnaire Misdelivery Record Nonresponse Follow-up—when the last lawsuit is filed—the 1990 census seems certain to stand as a bleak landmark in the annals of arithmetic. The United States Census has become an institution clinging to what many statisticians consider a myth: the idea that the Government can count the nation's population the way a child counts marbles . . . The population is too large, too mobile, and too diverse to count that way."

By and large, scientists don't count one at a time any more. Supermarkets have learned that the cheapest and most accurate approach to taking inventory is to take small random samples. Auditors don't check every transaction and astronomers don't count every star, they take samples. A sample never fully represents the whole; however, sampling introduces fewer errors than having tired, bored clerks, accountants or astronomers try to count every can of fruit juice, invoice or star.

Misplaced Precision

Another area of Census Bureau practice with which the critics quarrel is the Bureau's presentation of its data. The final census count is stated in exact numbers. It might, for example, declare that "the 1990 final population tally is 250,656,379, which implies that the population is exactly that amount. Scientists would be more likely to state such a number as something like 250 million plus or minus 4 million. The plus or minus figures would indicate a range of error, using so-called error bars or confidence intervals.

Gleick quoted Kirk Wolter, a critic who has intimate knowledge of the Bureau's policies. Wolter, who was the chief of the Census Bureau's Statistical Research Division until

1988, said, "The Census Bureau takes the position that somehow the total population counts are derived from an accounting process that isn't subject to error, and that therefore error bars have little meaning. Obviously that isn't true."

A factor that bothers some scientists about the Bureau's misplaced desire for precision is that many demographers, economic researchers and public opinion pollers accept the Census Bureau's idealization of their own data as if it were true. Such users calculate the sampling errors of their own data, but they assume the census data to be without error, even though they know that the census enumeration does not correspond to the exact population of the United States. Charles Metcalf, head of Mathematics Policy Research, a New Jersey research group, characterized the census data by saying, "It is an exact statement of the number they counted."

Errors Inherent in the Process

Even the idea that the census data is an exact statement of the number counted has some flaws. Gleick described the difficulties by saying, "The estimates, the probabilities, the compromises, the fuzziness that the census publicly abhors have already become an inextricable part of its methodology."

The smoothest-running part of the census is the millions of forms properly mailed back and filled out well enough so that no follow-up interviews must be conducted. But even in that area of the census there are inevitable errors. For example, in the 1970 census, because the dot to be filled in for those born in January through March was adjacent to "Year of Birth 186_," many people chose the wrong century of birth. The number of centenarians reported by the census exceeded some estimates of the actual number by more than 20 times.

The number of centenarians in the 1980 census was also much too large. The computer had an upper limit of 112 and would reject anything that exceeded that limit; however, there was nothing in the computer to stop two 112-year-old parents from having a 109-year-old child.

Mispunching errors for properly filled out forms can establish large categories of nonexistent people. Mispunching one in a thousand in a population as large as that in the United States can create such odd categories as a large group of teenage widows.

Moreover, apart from actual errors in filling out the forms or in plugging the data into the system, the computers are forced to make statistical guesses for people about whom the census takers know little, except that they probably exist. Three million of those enumerated during the 1980 census were abstractions added to the count using a statistical procedure called "the sequential hot deck imputation." During the process of running forms through the computer, the machine keeps a record of the last 16 plausible responses to each question. When the computer happens upon an implausible answer, or no answer, it substitutes a plausible one from its stack. The Bureau staff makes guesses because field workers frequently have no way to determine whether someone is actually living in a housing unit on their list. Given the option of declaring units empty or making a statistical guess, the Bureau chooses to make the guess.

The sources of errors in the field are seemingly endless. Census takers in single-room-occupancy hotels must guess whether unnumbered doors represent housing units. Migrant workers avoid federal agents of any kind, even census takers. Enumerators (census takers) in poor urban neighborhoods are often fearful of entering some tenements or housing projects, so they probably skip them. In the absence of mailboxes or electric meters, enumerators often fail to recognize that a nonstandard unit is occupied. Families that live in their cars are not likely to be counted.

The enumerator has forms to cover housing units added or subtracted since the last census. Unfortunately, the 1990 instructions contained contradictory directions about whether to add or ignore new units.

The errors are not all undercounts. There are overcounts as well, mostly from double counting. A couple may fill out a second form at their second home, while helpful neighbors of their primary home attest to their existence there. College students are often counted at home and at school.

Most census information collected in 1990 was done via the United States mail.

Undercount Escalation

Unfortunately, the overcounts and undercounts don't balance each other out. Since mailed questionnaires and door-to-door counting are suitable for those with enough education to follow written instructions or to cooperate with an enumerator, those overcounted tend to be wealthier and more rural than those undercounted.

Undercounting is not new. Thomas Jefferson, the director of the first U.S. census, complained that the count of 3.9 million was too low. In each census since 1940, when the Bureau first began estimating the undercount, blacks have been undercounted at a rate 5% higher than whites.

Estimates of undercounts can be made from other sources of information. One way to detect undercounting is through a demographic analysis of the aggregate tally of births, deaths, immigration and emigration.

To demonstrate urban undercounting, Eugene Ericksen, a sociologist and statistician at Temple University in Philadelphia, assembled a list of New Yorkers from 10 different administrative lists, such as voter registrations, utility bills, licensed drivers and those eligible for Medicaid. He found that the Census Bureau had omitted more than 8% of those on his lists. Since all of Ericksen's list used official records, he assumed his undercount was even greater, since those who did not use those official services would have been left out of his count.

During an interview for an April 27, 1990, *New York Times* article entitled "The Census, in One Not-So-Easy Lesson," by Felicity Barringer, Ericksen said, "The hard-to-count groups are growing at a faster rate than the rest of the population. There are more undocumented aliens, more homeless people. If we multiply the cost [of taking the census] by 10, we still couldn't count all the people and have a completely accurate census. All the adjustment would do is reduce the error."

A reduction in undercounting errors could favor big cities at the expense of suburbs and rural areas, and the coasts at the expense of the middle of the country. And it could change the fate of politicians. From one to three seats in Congress and scores of state legislative seats could swing to traditionally undercounted Democratic city neighborhoods.

A great deal of effort during the 1990 census was expended on coverage improvement. Informal estimates by census experts assigned 90% of the expense of the census to the last 10% of the count.

Counting the Uncountables

Scientists in most disciplines face the task of counting hidden or obscure populations. Ecologists use a technique called "capture, mark, and recapture." To implement the technique, scientists catch a large sample of the species under study, tag or mark the specimens, and release them back into the pool. Subsequently, they take a second sample. The number of tagged and untagged specimens is noted. If one out of eight specimens in the second sample were caught in the first sample, the assumption can be made that the already tagged specimens represent one-eighth of the whole population.

The method is not without flaws. Gleick quoted Henry Horn, a Princeton ecologist, who described the hazards of the capture-mark-recapture method by saying, "This is the hairy part, making the assumption that all the individuals get a chance to mix completely, that the marking process itself has no effect, and that there's no tendency for the marked individuals to be recaptured, since they were the easiest to capture in the first place. All those assumptions have to be made, and none of them are true." Such flaws are generally referred to as selection bias.

To improve the accuracy of the capture-mark-recapture approach, scientists combine it with models designed to address selection bias. Astrophysicist John Bahcall, at Princeton's Institute for Advanced Study, explained that to count the 10 billion stars in the Milky Way, astronomers count only 100,000 or so. The counting procedure depends on the model being used. The determination of which stars to count is likely to depend on such factors as the ages and composition of the stars, their type of clustering, and the proportions of difficult-to-count blue stars compared to easy-to-count red stars. The accuracy of the model depends on the data and the data help to increase the accuracy of the model in an effective circular process.

Those who doubt the wisdom of adjusting the census using the capture-mark-recapture method suggest that it could create wild inaccuracies. David Freedman, a statistician at the University of California, Berkeley, told Gleick, "In my opinion, a lot of mischief can be done. You can't afford to have an adjustment mechanism prone to errors of 10 percent if you're trying to fix a 1 to 2 percent error."

The Rocky Road of the 1990 Undercount Adjustment Plan

Ecologists have suggested that Census Bureau demographers are uncomfortable with "wild kingdom" modeling. Despite their alleged discomfort, the Census Bureau prepared an adapted capture-mark-recapture statistical program for the 1990 census.

The Bureau's effort to use the model was a response to the storm of criticism that followed the 1980 census. The Census Bureau was confronted by 38 lawsuits filed by angry communities and states, who charged that sophisticated, statistical models should have been used to account for millions of people who had been missed. Although most of the suits were put on hold, one case filed by the state and city of New York was heard by federal judge John Sprizzo of the Southern District of New York. In December 1987, Judge Sprizzo held that an adjustment of the 1980 census might cause more error than it would correct. However, testimony during the trial had identified statistical improvements needed in the 1990 census, and the Commerce Department, the parent agency of the Census Bureau, agreed to consider adjustment as part of the settlement of the suit.

The Bureau's adaptation of the capture-mark-recapture method was developed between 1981 and 1987. Barbara Bailar, former associate director for statistical standards and methodology at the Census Bureau, headed up a team to develop statistically sound methods to account for the undercounted people. The plan for adjustment worked out by Bailar and her team was tested in a mini-census in Los Angeles in 1986.

Satisfied with the results of the Los Angeles mini-census, the Bureau planned to do a post-census survey in a sample of 300,000 households. Methods had been developed for dealing with the various selection biases. The plan called for a survey of blocks chosen to represent all the elements of a mosaic of 100 demographic neighborhood types, with extra sampling in areas that in the past have been most undercounted: inner-city residents, often minorities and the poor. The questions asked would simply be name, age, race or ethnic origin.

Using a version of the capture-mark-recapture method, addresses of the sample group would be matched with addresses collected in the census to determine those missed in the first count and picked up in the second count, and those picked up in the first count but missed in the second. By looking at each group, the statisticians could see who was undercounted and who was overcounted. The estimates derived in this way would then be used to adjust the original census count.

The plan was described in a 1987 report to President Ronald Reagan. The Bureau intended to use technical standards to make a final decision about whether the sampling data should be used to adjust the 1990 census data. In October 1987, Robert Ortner, the undersecretary for economic affairs of the Department of Commerce, ordered the Bureau to cancel its plans. He said that the adjustment would be controversial and probably would not improve the count.

Barbara Bailar resigned when the Commerce Department ruled out a statistical adjustment. In a May/June 1988 *Technology Review* article entitled "Finding Those the Census Missed," Bailar said, "While Ortner is correct about controversy, he is wrong about improvement. The Commerce Department's conclusion was a political

Census tabulators were assisted by FACT (Film and Automated Camera Technology) system. The FACT system photographs each census questionnaire onto microfilm, scans it and then transfers the data into computer files.

Census employees take an oath to protect the confidentiality of individual census responses as well as an oath to uphold the Constitution. Census enumerators in the 1990 census were used to visit housing units that did not respond to the mailed questionnaire. The rule was that all non-response addresses were to be visited three times and each phone number dialed three times. Efforts were made to avoid "double counting," such as of a student with both home and school addresses.

decision, not based on technical work. The census determines the apportionment of federal and state legislative seats, and the kind of people missed— the poor, minorities, and inner-city residents—don't vote Republican. Even more important, the census is used for dividing more than $30 billion in annual federal funds for social programs."

New York City joined together with several other large cities and organizations and sued again in 1988 to try to force the Commerce Department to adjust the results of the 1990 census. New York City officials claimed that undercounting in 1980 had cost the city $675 million in Federal aid, one seat in the House of Representatives, one seat in the State Senate, and three and a half in the State Assembly.

Peter Zimroth, the attorney representing New York City argued that the Census Bureau had used corrections before. For example, 3.3 million people were added to the final tally for 1980 using the form of estimation known as imputation, a technique the Bureau planned to use again in 1990. In an interim court settlement, the Commerce Department agreed to conduct a smaller, 150,000–household survey.

Proponents of the use of an adjustment argued that whatever its flaws, taking two measures of the same thing improves accuracy. Bailar said that the trial run in Los Angeles convinced her that the method would work. Critics claimed that the sample size of 150,000 agreed to by the Census Bureau was too small to allow accurate adjustments below the state level.

The Commerce Department made it clear that it reserved the right to rule out the use of the survey results to adjust the count if the Secretary of Commerce envisioned a "potential

disruption of the process of the orderly transfer of political representation." The Commerce Department argued that the new method is new and untried and that the old method is innocent until proven guilty.

In his *Time* article, Gleick conveyed criticism of the Commerce Department by Bruce Hoadley, a statistician at the Bell Communications Research Company. Hoadley counts defects in products coming off assembly lines and has millions of dollars in manufacturing costs relying on the accuracy of his methods. Hoadley summed up the case for such adjustments by saying, "One of our great callings in life is to continually remind people that they're making decisions under uncertainty. The people who say, 'we shouldn't screw around with adjustment because it is subjective,' are being subjective too, in the worst possible ways. They know it's wrong. If your adjustment is zero, zero is known to be just about as bad as you can do. Any reasonable methodology is going to do better than zero . . . everything is uncertain, and data is very, very expensive."

Simple Methods Could Improve the Current Census Data Collection

Increased use of the telephone could cut costs and improve data collection. Because the census counts housing units, not telephones, and because people have unlisted phones and multiple phones, the census has always sent someone to personally visit everyone who has failed to respond to the written request. Personal visits are not only getting more expensive, they getting more difficult as fewer people are home during the day. Merging the Census

Bureau's address computer file with a telephone file would permit many follow-ups to be done by phone.

Another method to cut costs and improve data collection would be a constantly updated master address list made by merging all the address lists the Census Bureau maintains on businesses and residences. The Census Bureau's master list is reinvented each time the census is taken. Every 10 years, the Census Bureau buys direct-mail lists from private vendors and supplements them by going out to look for additional housing units. Over the course of a decade, buildings are regularly being put up and torn down. A constantly updated list would preclude sending forms to buildings no longer in existence and ensure that forms were sent to the occupants of new buildings.

The most revolutionary suggestion for fixing the current census approach is to cut down on the size of the census. Over the decades, many questions have been added to the census, each question having its own advocates. For example, local governments want commuting information and the construction industry wants housing information. Eliminating any particular question would be difficult; eliminating all the additional questions and returning to basic data would save a great deal of money but, politically, would be virtually impossible.

Proposed Alternative Approaches to the Census

A variety of statistical sampling methods are under consideration for integration into the Census Bureau's methods—once the political heat of the 1990 census is past.

One suggestion to improve accuracy and reduce cost is a so-called "high-tech tap-in." For example, a driver's license of the future might become a "smart card" encoded with a variety of vital statistics. The Census Bureau could instruct everyone on April 1 to go to a local machine and stick his or her driver's license into the machine. Immediately, 90% of Americans of driving age would be counted. Such an approach would free the bulk of the funds to track down the rest of the population and the hard-to-find segment.

Leslie Kish, a statistician at the University of Michigan, asserts that the worst distortions of the census come from the fact that it is obsolete almost immediately. He is in favor of a "rolling" census created via a sequence of 520 weekly surveys taken during the course of a decade.

A more elaborate version of Kish's rolling survey proposes interim surveys done in conjunction with a slimmed-down census taken every 10 years. Except for the basic information asked in the once-a-decade census, such an approach would shift from complete enumeration to a series of sample surveys, at least one of which would be large enough to give users results on a neighborhood level.

The surveys would be taken more frequently—some monthly, some annually, some every five years. This is an approach that would not save money and might even cost more, but its advocates believe that it would make the information more useful than the current method.

One aspect of the survey technique would be a rolling sample survey of the states, which would ensure that each state had been measured by the end of the decade. But the approach is fraught with political difficulties. Since Congress allocates government spending on a year-to-year basis, states could be expected to jockey to be surveyed early in the decade for fear that Congress would find other uses for the funds later on.

The Task of the 1990 Census

The 1990 census consumed the labor of a record 350,000 workers. Forms were mailed out the last week in March 1990, with a request that they be returned by April 1, 1990, Census Day. The task of enumerators was to conduct the census in rural areas and to follow up on questionnaires that were not mailed back in more populous areas.

The rate of noncooperation in 1990 was staggering. Almost twice as many respondents to whom forms were mailed failed or refused to return the forms than in any previous census. Response rate in some large cities was below 50%. By the scheduled June 6 deadline for completion of the door-to-door phase, less than 30 of the Bureau's 487 field offices had shut down. In some typically undercounted poor urban neighborhoods, the count continued into July. The adjustment survey intended to help correct the undercount was delayed in many cities. To get the response rate back on track, the Bureau launched a massive advertising campaign, which, according to the Bureau's press office, proved effective.

Preliminary figures released on August 28, 1990, for review and possible correction by states, counties and municipalities revealed that California had grown by 5.6 million over the decade since 1980, to above 29 million, making it more populous than Canada, Australia and three-quarters of the countries in Europe. The magnitude of growth in Florida was almost as dramatic, with Florida gaining 3 million people.

As a consequence of the census, California gained seven more congressional seats, bringing the state's number to 52, 12% of the nation's total, more than any one state has ever had. Florida gained four seats while New York lost three. Among the 435 congressional seats, 19 were slated for redistribution.

The data showed sharp rural losses and enormous coastal gains. More than at any time since World War I, the population increase was largely due to immigration, legal and illegal, mostly from Asia, Latin America and the Caribbean.

A Core of Data Not to Be Dismissed Lightly

For all its sociological and statistical faults, the census remains a framework around which other data is collected, and its value tends be overlooked by most critics. An article entitled "High-Tech Head Count?" by Marcia Farnsworth Riche, in the March 9, 1990, *Census '90*, published by *The Wall Street Journal Report and American Demographic Magazine*, predicted that the 1990 census would be the last of its kind, but made a point missed by many others. Riche said, "Public cooperation is dwindling—at the same time public demand for accuracy is increasing. And users of census data are demanding more and more information."

The reason for the demands for accuracy is that there is a large body of information seekers who utilize the census data for a variety of purposes, and want more. *Census '90* carried an article entitled "Shrinking Markets: Finding a Niche May Be the Key to Survival," by Kathleen Deveny and Peter Francese, which described some of the users of the census data. Many American businesses, for example, depend heavily on census information. An entire industry has come into being to translate census data into information that marketers can use to direct their products to target groups (micromarkets), such as the elderly or Hispanics. Micromarkets have to be reached efficiently or the cost of reaching the customer can outweigh any revenues gained.

Claritas Corporation, a unit of VNU Business Information Services, based in Alexandria, Virginia, is one company that makes census data available to businesses. Specializing in geodemography, the company has combined census data with cartographic (maps and charts) data to classify 240,000 census neighborhoods in the United States into 40 different life-styles. Deveny and Francese comment that, "With the other information it now has, as well as its new analytical tools, business will be able to make those census numbers perform as never before. Nelson Craige, manager of consumer research at Heinz, U.S.A., says: 'The power of the census data is probably limited only by our imagination.'"

Predictions of the demise of the census as it is now conducted may be premature. The census has a constituency. Moreover, an institution that has remained in place for 200 years may not be scientifically graceful, but it clearly provides a needed service.

America's decision to count its entire population was a little unusual for the 18th century, although the practice of taking a census was not new. For example, in ancient Rome, "Caesar Augustus published a decree ordering a census of the whole world." But the practice was not universally embraced. Eighteenth-century Great Britain opposed the idea of a census because it did not want an enemy to know its manpower strength. Of course, neither did Britain know.

11
Computer Science

FUZZY LOGIC

A Computer Technique That Mimics Human Thinking

More than a quarter of a century ago, Russian-born professor Lotfi Zadeh of the University of California at Berkeley created fuzzy logic, a branch of mathematics, to permit computers to work with imprecise terms, such as "slightly," or "hot," or "expensive," rather than the precision that computers normally demand. His theory has found little acceptance in the United States, but has been widely adopted in Japan, where it has been incorporated into a wide variety of products and services.

The Rationale for Fuzzy Logic

Zadeh's premise for developing fuzzy logic was that the real world does not fall into neat, crisp categories defined on the basis of traditional set theory. In set theory, membership in a class or set is not a matter of degree. Someone is either left-handed or they are not. A number is either even or it is not.

The traditional in-or-out, on-or-off approach of set theory does not work well when confronted by everyday classifications, such as a set of beautiful flowers, or a set of short children, or a set of extra-warm days. Fuzzy sets have degrees of membership. Among a set of tall people, some members are very tall, some are tall and the rest are not so tall.

To cope with set variability, Zadeh determined that membership in a set would not be 0 or 1 (on or off), but

would be a value between 0 and 1. In a set of tall men, a height of 6 feet might be given a value of 0.6, while a height of 7 feet 3 inches might be given a value of 0.99.

Zadeh and his students developed precise rules to deal with vague expressions, such as "rather fast," "extremely hot" and "mostly wrong." The mathematics they developed works for controlling robots, machine tools and electronic systems.

An air conditioner is a typical electronic system that operates on or off. Using a thermostat, the air conditioner either operates at full blast or it shuts off completely. An air conditioner equipped with fuzzy logic recognizes that some room temperatures are more comfortable for humans than others. As the system approaches the comfort zone, it begins to slow down gradually, thus creating more comfort and less electrical use.

During an interview for an April 2, 1989, *New York Times* article entitled "Fuzzy Computer Theory: How to Mimic the Mind?," Zadeh explained the need for his approach by saying, "We get carried away in our quest for precision. We have to come to terms with the real world."

As an example of fuzziness, Zadeh offered a real-world example of a person trying to park a car. A driver does not think in terms of the exact instructions that a conventional computer requires, such as "Turn the wheel 20 degrees to the left and back up at 10 miles an hour." Instead, the driver is more likely to think imprecisely about turning the wheel counterclockwise, pausing, and then turning the wheel a little more in the same direction, all the while backing up slowly. The driver's imprecise thinking is the kind of problem with which fuzzy logic is intended to deal.

One of the earliest uses of fuzzy logic was in the control of industrial processes. For example, using fuzzy logic a chemical plant control mechanism for hot temperatures might assign a value of 0.95 to a temperature of 1,000 degrees and might assign a value of 0.05 to a temperature of 600 degrees. A computer program for controlling such a process could have a rule (one of many comparative rules) that stated "If the temperature is high, lower the pressure." The amount of weight given to that rule would depend upon how high the temperature was and the value assigned to that temperature. To arrive at a decision about the controls, the computer would evaluate all the rules.

In the early 1970s, fuzzy logic was teamed up with a product of artificial intelligence research called expert systems. (Like human experts, computer expert systems apply rules of thumb, such as when the oven gets very hot, turn the gas down a bit.) A Copenhagen firm, Smidth & Company, began marketing, in 1980, the first commercial fuzzy expert system, a computer program for a rotating kiln used to make cement. The fuzzy expert system controlled the fuel intake rate.

Expert systems are developed by collecting the wisdom of several masters about how to do a task. The task might be how to: paint a house; diagnose the measles; or fill a rocket fuel tank. The body of expert wisdom is distilled into a set of specific rules. For example: "If the humidity is above 60%, don't paint" or "If lightning has been reported within 10 miles of the fueling site, don't begin loading."

Opposition to Fuzzy Logic in the United States

Zadeh believes that had he not held a prestigious university position it would have been impossible for him to get financial support for his research or get his papers published. A graduate of the University of Teheran, with a Ph.D. from Colombia University, Zadeh was the chairperson of the electrical engineering and computer science department at Berkeley when he published his first paper on fuzzy logic in 1965.

Almost everywhere but in the United States, fuzzy logic has been studied intensively, including China, the Soviet Union and Europe. A great number of books and thousands of papers and reports have been devoted to fuzzy theory and its offspring, fuzzy control, fuzzy computers and fuzzy data bases.

His opposition to the conventional computer approach, Zadeh says, contributed to his research being ignored in the United States. Because computer science in other countries has lagged behind the United States, Zadeh's unorthodox perspective did not have to battle against an entrenched

Many observations in everyday life are not easily defined as on-off or in-out. In a set of bicycles, fuzzy logic could easily handle the extreme characteristics of the bicycles above.

point of view. During his interview for the *New York Times*, Zadeh described his lack of acceptance in the United States by saying, "The whole thing is orthogonal [at right angles] to the party line of the establishment."

American computer scientists critical of fuzzy logic deny that they have ignored the need for approximate information. They claim that they have responded to it by using other conventional methods, such as probability theory (the ratio of the number of times an event can be expected to randomly occur given a specified number of opportunities). Critics view Zadeh's fuzzy logic as lacking the body of research and application that has been developed for other methods. Opponents are apt to end a discussion of Zadeh's approach by saying that the Japanese enthusiasm for fuzzy logic is not the first time the Japanese have adopted a fad.

Proponents of fuzzy logic respond to criticism by pointing out that fuzzy logic is one of the latest examples of American-generated ideas that have been more vigorously pursued by foreign nations. During an interview with the *New York Times*, Ronald Yager, director of the Machine Intelligence Institute at Iona College in New Rochelle, New York, said, "It's the classic idea of the prophet not being appreciated in his own back yard."

Japanese Adoption of Fuzzy Logic

The Japanese find fuzzy logic quite appealing. In a September 25, 1989, *Time* article entitled "Time for Some

Fuzzy Thinking," the author, Philip Elmer-Dewitt, said, "The concept of fuzziness has struck a cultural chord in a society whose religions and philosophies are attuned to ambiguity and contradictions. Says Noboru Wakami, a senior researcher at Matsushita, an electronics company: 'It's like soy sauce and suchi—a perfect match.'" The author also quoted Bart Kosko, a Zadeh protege and a professor of electrical engineering at the University of Southern California, who said, "Fuzziness begins where Western logic ends."

In April 1989, the Japanese Ministry of International Trade and Industry (MITI) opened a new Laboratory for International Fuzzy Engineering (LIFE) with a budget of $36 million for six years and an affiliation with 44 member companies. Fuzzy logic is under consideration in Japan for a wide range of tasks from controlling nuclear power plants, to detecting sleepiness in drivers.

Fuzzy logic has been the subject of a number of Japanese news reports and documentaries. By the fall of 1989, the Japanese were pursuing more than 100 patent applications for fuzzy logic. Nissan had already patented a fuzzy logic auto transmission system and a fuzzy logic anti-skid braking system. Yamaichi Securities had introduced a fuzzy stock-market investment program to provide an alert on a change in stock-market trends. Matsushita had produced a fuzzy automobile traffic controller and a fuzzy shower system that adjusts water temperatures.

The most celebrated example of fuzzy logic's technology is in the city of Sendai, where the subway system developed by Hitachi Company is operated by a fuzzy logic computer. Acceleration and deceleration are so smooth that standing passengers do not need to cling to straps. The system is also 10% more energy efficient than one operated by human conductors.

Emerging American Interest

In part because of the Japanese interest, enthusiasm for fuzzy logic has been growing in the United States. Togai Infralogic, a small firm in Irvine, California, specializing in fuzzy logic, has already achieved some of the goals that Japan's MITI set for itself, including a fuzzy computer chip able to perform 28,600 fuzzy-logical inferences a second. Although the National Aeronautics and Space Administration (NASA) has shown interest in the use of fuzzy logic to help in docking spacecraft, most of Togai's customers are Japanese.

One of the most significant endorsements of fuzzy logic came from Rockwell International Corporation, an aerospace company, which asked the Pentagon's Defense Advanced Research Project's Agency to finance a fuzzy logic initiative. (An initiative is usually an agreement to explore a topic for research possibilities and/or applications.)

Even if fuzzy logic does become widely accepted in the United States, the Japanese lead in research will make it difficult for America to catch up and be competitive.

Handling less than precise estimates are a strength of fuzzy logic. Because of its decimal base the metric system makes very precise calculations easily. But in some situations, precise measurements are neither needed nor desirable. The British system of measurements, which was developed on the basis of easily visualized standards such as the king's foot, lends itself to quick, rough estimates. To measure inches, the thumb, which is about 2-inches long, can be used as a guide.

VIRTUAL REALITY

Users Can Perceptually Enter Computer-Generated Worlds

The technology of virtual reality is expected to have profound effects in science, engineering, education, medicine, game playing and sports. Also known as artificial reality or cyber space, the technology permits a viewer to look at computer-created worlds he or she needs to see, changing perspective with a shift in the position of his or her head. Instrumented gloves and instrumented bodysuits permit an inexperienced novice to accompany an experienced practitioner in a step-by-step enactment of an unfamiliar procedure.

At the forefront of this futuristic technology are four facilities based along a short stretch of California's San Francisco Bay area. Scientists at Ames Research Center in Mountain View, part of the National Aeronautics and Space Administration (NASA), have been working on artificial reality for several years. NASA's purpose, in part, was to develop a tool for scientists to study other worlds up close and, also, to train astronauts to deal with settings never before encountered.

A second facility, the Sausalito software company Autodesk, views artificial reality as the ultimate tool for architects and other designers while Greenleaf Medical Systems uses instrumented gloves as a diagnostic tool for the study of hand function impairments.

A fourth facility, VPL Research, Inc. of Redwood City, often viewed as the most visionary in the field and whose founder and head, Jaron Lanier, is considered a wunderkind, supplies equipment to the other organizations.

During an interview for a February 26, 1990, *Boston Globe* article entitled "Artificial Reality—It May Be Better Than the Real Thing," Lanier said to reporter David Chandler, "Here's a world I just whipped up two days ago." Chandler described this new world by saying, "Well it's not really a world; it's more like a big room, once you put on the goggles. It is a world with its own rules: You can fly with the greatest of ease, soaring toward the strange geometric shapes suspended in air just by pointing your finger where you want to go and hooking your thumb to start flying."

Donning the apparel used to step into the world of virtual reality allows an individual to interact with a computer-generated world.

The Origins of Virtual Reality

The idea of virtual reality is not new. It has been around since the 1965 conference of the International Federation of Information Processing Societies, when Ivan Sutherland, a charismatic computer pioneer, predicted a revolutionary idea that he called the ultimate display: computer images so sharp and true that they would be indistinguishable from reality. Although Sutherland did not specify how the feat would be achieved, he predicted that the ultimate display would include tactile (touch) sensations.

In 1968, Sutherland fulfilled his own predictions. He presented to his peers the first virtual reality system. A headband, from which hung two miniature monitor screens, was connected to a huge mechanical arm that looked like a sword and reached to the ceiling. The rig was so cumbersome it was dubbed "the sword of Damocles." Electronic sensors along the arm told the computer the location of the headband and the direction in which it faced. The computer responded with simple images.

Despite its crudeness, Sutherland's system remained the state-of-the-art model through the 1970s. The head-mounted 3-D display system still remains the basic display component.

VPL's Role in Development

VPL's improvement on Sutherland's invention was to make his reality flexible. The flexibility permits the creation of new environments and the modification of old ones by people without special programming skills. The company's software enables the user to "fill in the blanks" and determine the size, shape, behavior and appearance of objects in the environment.

VPL's artificial reality system consists of several components. One component is the goggles, whose trademark name is "EyePhone," which use two minuscule, flat television screens to display a distinct computer-generated image to each eye. The separate images create for the viewer a single image with a realistic illusion of depth. Built into the goggles is a magnetic device that, linked to a fixed magnetic sensor in the room, informs the computer of the position of the head. As the head turns, the scene shifts appropriately.

A third component of VPL's system is called a DataGlove, which has fiberoptic cables running along each finger to make it possible for the computer to sense the shape and position of the hand. In response to the data, a computer-generated image of the hand appears in the same position in the 3-D image. A full-bodied suit, instrumented in a manner comparable to the DataGlove, does the same for the position of the limbs and the body. High-speed computers and image-generating software permit the user to design or manipulate the environment as he or she chooses.

Lanier, who was a high school dropout, was a computer illiterate in 1980. Abandoning his efforts to support himself in New York City as a street musician he took a job designing sounds in video games. In 1987, his company received high praise for its innovations in a *Scientific American* special issue on computers. At a speech in Boston in February 1990, Lanier was introduced as someone who saw humanitarian applications for his work as well as artistic ones. Lanier suggested that a stroke patient who had difficulty recognizing faces or objects might gradually relearn them by grossly exaggerating features and gradually returning them to normal. In Lanier's opinion, the experiences that are remembered the best are those that envelop the senses.

During his interview with the *Boston Globe*, Lanier said, "Kids are into make-believe and this just harnesses that." He foresees a time when a student can learn about dinosaurs by "becoming" a Tyrannosaurus rex, engaged in surveying the jungle world of 70 million years ago, "from the predator's 18-foot-high perspective."

However, virtual reality represents much more than just a delightful teaching device. It has the potential to be a significant research, work and training tool for a variety of professions. It permits the pace of a learning process to proceed at a rate that would otherwise be impossible. Learning how to repair an engine, to juggle or to execute a perfect golf swing can be done in slow motion, under conditions of zero gravity. Gravity can be slowly "turned back on" so that the movements gradually take natural resistance into account.

Simulations

By coupling three-dimensional images with the interactive control of the DataGlove and the bodysuit, designers are able to modify a design, teachers to demonstrate a process, and any user to move at will through the simulation.

However, the system is not without flaws. The images in the goggles are grainy and the computer images sometimes lag behind the user's movement. Nevertheless, the effect is strangely realistic. Despite the fact that the technology is still relatively crude, the basic tools are in place. Developers predict that as the quality of the television image and the graphics improve, the simulations will become more astonishing.

While wearing the goggles, a sensor-lined glove permits a user to walk through a room, and to touch, pick up or rearrange nonexistent objects found in the nonexistent room. The user can be joined in the room by a companion anywhere in the world who is wearing an identical pair of goggles and is linked to the same computer.

A simulation program was used by computer scientist Frederick Brooks and his team at the University of North Carolina at Chapel Hill, in 1988, to guide tours through a planned new addition to Chapel Hill's Orange United Methodist Church before ground was ever broken. Brooks put viewers on a treadmill and "walked" them through the architects' plans for the church. Viewers changed direction by turning a set of handlebars.

A simulation of a walk through a newly designed day-care center was described in an article entitled "Grand Illusions" in the June 1990 issue of *Discover*. Author Bennett Daviss recreated the experience of a child-care administrator and an architect who used virtual reality to test a proposed building design. Daviss said, "The administrator becomes concerned that a window next to the teacher's desk doesn't afford a full view of the playground. The architect nods, grasps the edge of the window frame, then pulls the window along the wall until it provides the view the administrator wants. Later, the two adults shrink themselves so that they can see the room from the perspective of a four-year old." The dream world day-care center is the creation of Jaron Lanier.

Military Uses

Sutherland's early efforts inspired many other researchers, among them Thomas Furness, a former flight-test engineer who pioneered virtual reality for the military. Furness began working on visual display systems for the Air Force in 1966. He had what most other researchers in the field did not, an employer with a continuing interest in the concept who provided steady funding.

In 1981, Furness and his team, working at Wright-Patterson Air Force Base in Dayton, Ohio, unveiled the Visually Coupled Airborne Systems Simulator, soon to be known as the Super Cockpit, as a way to train pilots to fly the enormously complex F-16 fighter jet and other high-speed aircraft.

The original Super Cockpit model crammed a self-contained world inside a Darth Vader–style helmet. Later, the scientists replaced the headgear with a lighter helmet, similar to the one normally worn by the pilots. The virtual reality was projected for the pilot on the inside of the helmet's face shield.

Flight in Furness's virtual reality world no longer required remembering the function of scores of switches in the cockpit. The pilot could control the virtual plane with eye movements and simple voice commands. Position sensors that lined the flier's glove permitted him to simply point at buttons or instruments displayed on the inside of the shield. A pressure sensor inside the glove's fingertip permitted the control of such functions as launching an antiaircraft missile by "pushing" an artificial button. Pilots loved the Super Cockpit, and those who used it improved their performance in simulated flight well above those who used conventional controls.

Furness and his group were able to solve many of the problems that stood between people and the machine-based virtual realities. However, they did not solve the problem of cost. Furness commented, "At Wright-Patterson, we created virtual worlds that were just spellbinding. Each eye had a twelve-hundred line video display, compared with the five hundred twenty-five lines a normal television has. We were updating the video display thirty times a second—the same as commercial television. But we spent close to five million on the helmet, and it still takes eight computers to run it."

Visions for the Future

Furness, who considers himself an evangelist for the technology, has spent 20 years working in the virtual reality field, first for the Air Force and currently for the Human Interface Technology Laboratory in Seattle. He told Bennett Daviss, "Right now we can build virtual worlds for quadriplegics in which they can move and behave just as well as if they weren't handicapped. We can use whatever movement they have—finger movement, even eye movement—to give them full physical mobility control in a virtual environment. They could meet other people in virtual worlds. They could do computer-aided designs."

Like Lanier, Furness believes that virtual reality has the capacity to revolutionize education. Engineering and math students could enter three-dimensional worlds and see how the rules for diagrams and equations actually work.

Other virtual reality evangelists can be found at Autodesk in Sausalito. The company's founder, John Walker, believes that virtual reality is the next frontier for computing. Autodesk is the manufacturer of Autocad, a three-dimensional drafting software that sets the standard for the computer-aided design industry. Autodesk expects to have a generic system that can adapt to almost any kind of graphics and design work on the market by 1991.

Autodesk's director of technology, Eric Lyons, explained the lure of such a system by saying, "Research and design labs will want off-the-shelf systems that will let them create their own applications. It cost a lot of money to build a new tank or a new plane, for example. Obviously, the military would like to be able to test-drive a new piece of equipment before they order it built."

Engineer Michael McGreevy, who is in charge of developing virtual realities at NASA's Ames Research

Above is a Helmet-Mounted Display System used for manual aircraft approaches and landings. Two video cameras are mounted in the nose of NASA's Boeing 737 research aircraft. The pilot sees the video image through a binocular viewing system in his or her helmet.

Center, views virtual reality as essential to planetary exploration. A satellite sent to a planet would gather information that when sent back would permit the construction of a detailed model. McGreevy imagines computer-modeled planets, where a user, by pointing to an area on the model's surface, could "teleport" himself or herself to the spot.

In addition, virtual reality sensors could be hooked to a machine, such as a robot, so that when the user moved his or her arm in the virtual world, the robot would move its arm in the real world. Astronauts working in virtual reality aboard a spaceship could control robots in space. Through a video helmet, the astronaut could see what the robot saw and the astronaut's sensor-equipped gloves could sequence robotic movements to repair satellites or to fabricate structures.

Henry Fuchs, a computer scientist at the University of North Carolina at Chapel Hill, is a leader in an effort to synthesize the various diagnostic images of a patient's body. Fuchs would like to create digital models from the images created by X-rays, magnetic resonance and ultrasound. Such models are being explored by Fuchs in the treatment of cancer.

In some forms of cancer treatment, a radiation generator is positioned sequentially at different locations around the patient. A beam from each of the locations is focused on a tumor inside the patient to irradiate and destroy it. Many current techniques already use such an approach; however, they force the viewer to adopt the computer's point of view. The advantage offered by virtual reality is that the viewer can step back and get a wider view without stopping to tinker with the keyboard.

Using virtual reality, a radiation therapist could "walk around" the virtual patient to see if the radiation beams located the proper area. Fuchs told Bennett Daviss, "We'll be able to do it within five years. Right now, the technology isn't quite up to it."

Needed Improvements

Much of the virtual reality equipment in use by researchers is in need of further refinement. While they wait for the development of high-definition television, more efficient computer circuitry and the evolution of other technologies, artificial reality engineers continue to make incremental improvements.

Fuchs considers the quality of current graphic displays terrible. What might look crisp on a normal-size viewing screen looks crude and fuzzy when reduced to monitors small enough to mount on headgear. Most current systems refresh the video image four to eight times a second rather than the 30 times necessary to appear natural to the human eye. A factor that will improve the video image is the recent availability of graphics chips that for the same price are 50%

more powerful than they were just a year earlier. Computer speed is increasing at about the same rate.

The components most in need of improvement are the position sensors and the head-mounted displays. The signals from magnetic position sensors are weak and easily garbled, therefore researchers are working on tracking systems that use fiber optics. Fuch's group has been in the process of developing a system that uses tiny, high-speed video cameras atop a helmet that informs the computer of the wearer's position in relationship to flashing infrared lights placed strategically along the ceiling. The optical tracker, when completed some time late in 1990, is expected to permit users to abandon the use of a treadmill and to roam as they please through a 20-foot room.

Also under research are a variety of other kinds of movement, including pedaling a stationary bicycle through a virtual landscape and flying via a helicopter through manipulation of a joystick.

Other Uses of Virtual Reality

Among potential users of virtual reality, goals range widely. David Zeltzer, a computer graphics researcher at MIT, reported that a Japanese company was interested in having virtual realities available in the company's employee lounge. Because Japanese offices are so crammed with people, the company wanted to offer its workers on their lunch hours a means to escape to forests or desert islands.

For several years, VPL worked to develop a lower-cost, mass-producible glove for youngsters. Once developed, the glove was licensed to Mattel, who introduced it on the market for about $100, under the trade name "PowerGlove." The system, which is hooked into a Nintendo game machine, permits players to reach inside a game and engage in hand-to-hand combat with dragons and villains. Lanier is careful to point out that the PowerGlove is not the same as the DataGlove.

Many researchers foresee modestly priced "personal reality" simulators within little more than a decade and worry about the possible consequences. Furness explained their concerns by saying,

It's not like television or a personal computer. With those, you are still on the outside. With virtual reality, once that field surrounds you and controls everything you see, you're inside. The paradigm shift in perception is absolutely compelling. Even with the crude graphics on some very basic systems, people really get turned on. The social implications are of great concern to us. The downside is the creation of socially immature people. Virtual realities will do what people want them to do and that's not the way the world works.

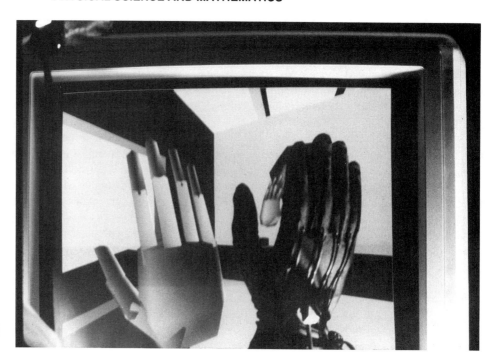

The DataGlove is an input device comparable to a keyboard. The gloves convert hand motion into a signal the computer can read and translate to the screen.

Furness worries that virtual "entertainment" realities would permit users to virtually "murder" someone and continue such deviant behavior in real life. McGreevy is more sanguine. He believes that a little fantasy is useful. Lanier is even more optimistic. He comments, "In the virtual world all possible objects are in infinite supply since they're all made of imaginary stuff. So the distinction between things—different forms, different histories—really breaks down and isn't very important. And in terms of creativity—the human point of view, the human experience—those things start to stand out . . . That contrasts markedly with the physical world where novelty is everything."

Price Remains a Controlling Factor

The price of the virtual reality equipment is still too prohibitive for widespread use. VPL's basic setup for two people, which includes two pairs of gloves, the necessary computers and the software, lists for $430,000.

In 1984, NASA thought they would begin their research by buying into the state of the art, so they purchased a Super Cockpit helmet from Furness and were shocked to be presented with a bill for $1 million. McGreevy and his team then scavenged parts from pocket-sized televisions and other handy sources and assembled what they called a "personal simulator" for about $2,000. When the video-game industry slumped, a gamemaker from Atari joined the NASA team and assisted in the development of a better system.

The price of the equipment used in most virtual reality labs ranges anywhere from $20,000 to $250,000. Most systems use the $8,000 DataGlove developed by Lanier's company.

As interest in and use of the technology grows, the price can be expected to come down. The concept has attracted not only small organizations like Mattel and other game companies, it is also under investigation by big companies like American Telephone and Telegraph (AT&T) and International Business Machines (IBM). Even with the current state of equipment, according to Lanier, a high level of virtual reality can be achieved over the present phone system.

Public Interest in Virtual Reality

Although virtual reality research has been going on for years, interest in the idea escalated in 1989. Frederick Brooks, Jr., a professor of Computer Science at the University of North Carolina at Chapel Hill, in a July 8, 1990, *New York Times* article entitled "'Virtual Reality' Takes Its Place in the Real World," was portrayed as unhappy with all the media and public attention because it delayed the progress of his team's research.

Even Jaron Lanier, who has been a champion of the field, felt somewhat overwhelmed at a 1989 trade show by the mobs of people who tried to get in to see his demonstration. Despite his discomfort, Lanier, in conjunction with Boston's Computer Museum, planned to have a bus called "Reality on Wheels" tour the country in 1991 to give people a chance to see the equipment up close.

At the University of Connecticut's Natural History Museum in Storrs, for some time, there has been a virtual reality display open to anyone who wants to use it. The installation is the work of Myron Krueger, a computer scientist based in Vernon, Connecticut. Although a pioneer in the field, Krueger is somewhat of a maverick.

Krueger thinks the helmets, goggles, gloves and equipment are too cumbersome. In his world, the participant interacts with objects, characters and other people on a screen in two dimensions. Although there is no actual human contact, the virtual contact between the participant and the figure on the screen creates a sense of actual contact. According to Krueger, "We are all creatures of artificial experience" through created worlds like novels and plays. The new technology "allows the symbolic world to become concrete."

Dissenters

In spite of all the excitement generated by virtual reality, few people have actually tried it, and some who have tried it were not overwhelmed. Howard Rheingold, the author of a book about virtual reality to be published by Simon and Shuster in 1991, characterized the experience as less exciting than a roller coaster ride. He described the current technology as in the Kitty Hawk stage, but predicted that in 10 years it would change the world.

Like many new technologies, virtual reality appears to have enormous potential to do good and to do harm. Because improvements must await the development of technology in other arenas, there is likely to be substantial lag time before virtual reality becomes a routine part of everyday life. The lag time will probably blunt both the good and bad effects of this intriguing new technology.

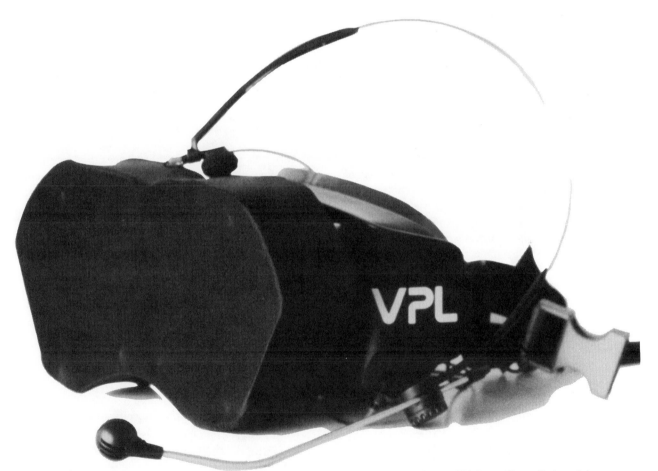

The snug-fitting goggles, the EyePhone, equipped with wide-angle binocular optics and high-quality audio headphones, allow the wearer to both "see" and "hear" the computer-generated scene that he or she has stepped into. If the wearer turns around, he or she views what is behind in this "virtual" world.

12

Physics

SMALL SCALE

Micromachines and Nanotechnology

One view of the march toward ever smaller technology was described in a brief item from *The American Chemical Society News Service* reprinted in the June 1988 issue of *Science Digest*. The item said, "First there was big, as in the Big Bang. Next came small—then portable, followed by miniature. Today there is micro, and we're headed for nano.

"In the late 1940s," it continued, "the invention of the transistor, which replaced the bulky vacuum tubes, started us on the road to *microelectronics*. The prefix micro is derived from a Greek word meaning small, and there are a million micrometers in a meter (39.37 inches). The components in today's electronics are in micrometer dimensions."

For some scientists, the microworld is still too large. Chemists at the University of Minnesota are trying to enter the realm of the nano by assembling molecule arrays that may one day be building blocks of minuscule electronic devices and chemical sensors. Nano can be traced to a Greek word meaning dwarf. A nanometer is one-billionth of a meter, an equivalent of only 10 times the diameter of a hydrogen atom.

The Prophet of Nanotechnology

For more than a decade, nanotechnology has been consistently promoted by Eric Drexler, a visionary who has lectured all over the United States on the promises and risks of this new science. Drexler traces his interest in nanotechnology back to 1976 when, as a graduate student at the Massachusetts Institute of Technology (MIT) in what he called "generic" engineering, he decided to build a biochemical computer molecule by molecule.

To discover how to build his molecular computer, Drexler read books on molecular biology written by molecular biologists, organic chemists and geneticists whose motivation was to understand the cell. As an engineer, Drexler was struck by the engineering versatility operative at the molecular level.

A November 1986 *Omni* article entitled "Tiny Tech" by Fred Hapgood explained why Drexler was impressed with this engineering potential. Hapgood said,

Atoms always perform to specification. One atom can rotate around another for the lifetime of the universe without showing wear. They don't rust, rot, get dirty or wet, or indeed require any kind of maintenance . . . Further, atoms seem to *want* to make things; they snap together like Tinkertoys in highly defined, very stable structures. For a lot of molecular structures, once tab A and B get anywhere near each other's neighborhood, they will pounce and couple automatically. And the smaller things get, the faster they move . . . Finally, when you build something atom by atom, you can build it right.

100 Microns
Accel: 19.93Kv   Mag: 0.63Kx
Width: 133.007 Microns   Test ID: YCTAI   Sample ID: SPINNING MOTOR

This tiny spinning motor actually moves and is not some decorative replica of a "real, life-size" version. With motors themselves no bigger than specks of dust, a speck of dust could completely destroy the operation.

Caught up in nanotechnology, Drexler left MIT without finishing his doctorate and wrote a book called *Engines of Creation*, published in 1986. He moved to California, where he and his chemist wife founded the Foresight Institute to publicize the latest advances in nanotechnology. At Stanford, he taught the world's first university course in this area.

A January 1989 *Omni* article entitled "Interview: Eric Drexler," by Ed Regis, mentioned that Drexler was at work on a second book entitled *Nanotechnology: Assemblers and Exploratory Engineering*, to be full of graphs, equations and diagrams intended to present the nuts-and-bolts of nanotechnological design. Drexler discussed his concept of aspirin-size pills that could, when swallowed, first diagnose a medical problem and then make the necessary surgical repairs. In reply, Drexler said, "The pills would contain large numbers of sophisticated devices, including computers and large data bases. They'd have more information available for diagnosis than does any physician today, because by then we'd understand the body structure in so much greater detail."

Molecular Production

If nanotechnology is ever to come into widespread use, its great challenge will be to gear up to mass production. A single cycle of a molecular process does very little work. Nevertheless, each day the aggregate of these single cycle processes create hundreds of thousands of tons of biomass (new organic material).

Molecular mass production is made possible by hierarchy. Molecular factories are mass-produced, and in turn mass-produce other products. For example, the body produces millions of factories known as mitochondria (slender filaments in cells that are a source of energy), which, over the course of a lifetime, generate molecular fuels that help the body to work.

Another phenomenon that permits mass production is replication. In the process of replication, molecules, such as DNA, are programmed to assemble themselves and ultimately reproduce. According to Drexler's vision, most nanotechnology manufacturing facilities will have this replicability capacity built in.

Theoretically, nanotechnology could perform astounding feats. Cell repair machines could generate enough units in a month to assess the health of every cell of every human alive. Replicative waste processors diffusing through the earth's crust and oceans could search out every toxic waste site and garbage dump in the world and detoxify them. And replicative nano-vacuum cleaners could be programmed to gobble up molecules of carbon dioxide and, in a mere few weeks, reverse the global warming effect brought about by carbon dioxide.

Small Size Distinctions

When asked to distinguish nanotechnology from other various efforts at miniaturization involving other microcomponents, Drexler replied that real nanotechnology is essentially a bottom-up process, done by arranging atoms. He said, "You can't get complete control of the structure of matter by starting with a lump and whittling away at the surface. That's the style of conventional microtechnology. There are conceivable roles for microtechnology in helping us to build a first generation of nanomachines. But those technologies aren't crucial to the development of nanotechnology."

Micromachines

Microtechnology may not be necessary to the development of nanotechnology, as Drexler suggests, but that appears to be the direction many scientists are taking. A November 30, 1987, *Newsweek* article entitled "A Small World Grows Tinier," by William Marbach, asked the reader to imagine a robot the size of a gnat, whose mission was to travel through the body's vascular system to correct a heart defect. Marbach went on to say, "Now, in a handful of laboratories around the world, scientists are crafting devices that may, one day, undertake such fantastic voyages. They are creating gears, turbines, and motors so small that 60,000 such motors would fit in a single square inch. The devices are the building blocks of a revolutionary new technology: micromachines."

To create their micromachines, scientists have used the same technology they used to spawn the microelectronics industry, the technology that shrank computers from room-sized giants to tiny computer chips. Using silicon-chip processing techniques, American Telephone and Telegraph (AT&T)'s Bell Laboratories scientists,

The tiny mechanism above, looking a little like a caboose, has a movable bar that slides in a track and visible, functional springs.

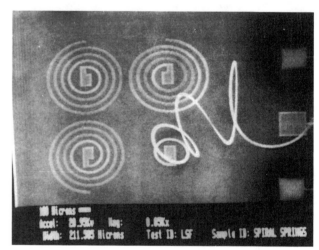

These spiral springs have as much elasticity in them as their larger counterparts.

Mehran Mehregany, Kaigham Gabriel, and William Trimmer have manufactured turbines and working gears that measured 125 microns (.0049 inch) in diameter (substantially smaller than a period printed at the end of a sentence), with gear teeth that measured 15 microns (.00058 inch) in width (less than one-fifth the thickness of a human hair).

The microworld could not work without micromotors. In a macroworld, a typical motor is made of coils of wire wound around electromagnets. In a microworld, such motors could not operate effectively, because the scaled-down models would not carry enough current. An alternative to the scaled-down motor is an electrostatic silicon motor, which is the focus of development.

At the heart of an electrostatic silicon motor is a rotating silicon disk with gearlike teeth called poles, surrounded by a ring of stationary teeth, each powered with a low-voltage charge that can be switched off and on. Given the right sequence of switching voltages, the rotor teeth are drawn toward the charged stationary teeth. To develop sufficient power, the motors have to spin at thousands of revolutions per second. Bell Labs researchers have designed a motor that weighs .013 ounce and can deliver almost a half a pound of force.

A June 24, 1990, *New York Times* brief item entitled "How Does the Micro-Motor Wear?" mentioned that researchers at MIT and the University of California at Berkeley have been working for years to develop micromotors and now are beginning to understand how the tiny engines wear and learning how bearings (around which another part revolves or slides) hold up. The most recent version of the micromotor the scientists were working on was 100 microns (.0039 inch) wide, with rotors spinning on bearings as small as 10 microns (.000039 inch) and achieving speeds of millions of rotations a minute.

At a 1987 conference on micromechanical technology in Hyannis, Massachusetts, scientists discussed a variety of proposals to make such micromoters out of silicon and other materials. The discussions focused on the fact that to make complete micromachines, scientists had to combine computer circuitry with micromotors and mechanical elements. Such machines would depend on sensors to feed them information about the outside world. Miniature sensors that can detect pressure, chemical vapors, changes in speed, and other factors have been available for some time.

A continuing drawback to laboratory work with micromachines is that their parts are so small they can be inhaled or blown off a laboratory table by a stray puff of wind. In a March 1989 *Discover* article entitled "Microrobots," author T.A. Heppenheimer commented that the Bell Laboratories scientists Mehregany, Gabriel, and Trimmer preferred to display pictures of their micromachine invention, because an accidental touch might destroy it.

Problems continue to plague Bell Labs' tiny turbine. When the blades spin at high speeds, the stress can cause the unit to fracture scattering the nearly invisible wheels. To develop something more complex than a rudimentary turbine, researchers still need to learn how friction and fluids behave on that infinitesimal scale.

Microdevice Categories

A July 1, 1989, *Science News* article entitled "Small Things Considered," by Ivan Amato, discussed two categories of microdevices—sensors and actuators. Tiny sensors, sculpted into silicon chips, for example, respond to pressure, humidity, motion and other physical conditions with an electronic signal that on-chip circuitry can then amplify, process and use. In a device called an accelerometer, researchers position a superthin, supersmall silicon strip over a micropit chemically etched into a chip. The strip responds to motion by bending, thereby initiating transient electrical currents. When activated, such circuitry can help to steer a missile or avoid a car collision.

Sensors have dominated the field, but actuators are growing in importance. Unlike sensors, which simply gather and relay information, actuators move and do work. Micromotors can spin and slide and tiny tweezers can clasp. Researchers expect that in time both sensors and actuators will share the same microchip.

Gnat Robots

While much of the laboratory work around the world has focused on ways to fabricate micromachines, other researchers have concentrated on building larger prototypes that can later be scaled down. At MIT's Artificial Intelligence Lab, scientists have worked on "gnat robots." The rationale behind the work has been that it is more cost-effective to have thousands of small, extremely simple robots do a job than to use one large, expensive robot. An often used analogy is that a swarm of locusts can harvest a field faster and more efficiently than can a farmer with a giant combine.

MIT researchers built "Tom" and "Jerry," computerized mobile robots in toy cars. Tom and Jerry are not programmed with complex instructions, but respond to environmental cues in the way a housefly navigates through a house.

Anita Flynn and her colleagues at MIT's Artificial Intelligence Laboratory have spent considerable time learning how to integrate motors, sensors, computation and power supplies onto a single, inch-square piece of silicon. The advantages of such combinations is that they would make possible mass production, lower costs, and avoid the problems inherent in combining discrete subsystems.

At a Workshop on Micro-Electro-Mechanical Systems held in Salt Lake City, Utah, in February 1989, Flynn's group introduced "Squirt," an autonomous, cubic-inch working robot "that acts like a 'bug' hiding in dark corners and venturing out only after noises are long gone." The MIT scientists said that they knew how to shrink the sensing and computing components even more, but needed the micromachining scientists to provide micromotors that could propel their flea-sized robots.

Tiny electrostatic motors have little use until their power can be used to drive moving wheels, crawling legs or whirling propellers. To reach that goal, it will be necessary to develop mini-transmissions to transform a micromotor's high-speed revolutions into the slower motion of the moving parts. Although little progress has been made in this area, Anita Flynn has developed a 10-inch robot that flies under the power of a simple rubber-band propellor. In a March 1989 *Discover* article entitled "Microrobots," Flynn said, "Remember for a swimming, crawling, or rolling robot, just about anything solid it encounters is a big obstacle. If it can fly, there's not much that can get in the way." The purpose of Flynn's prototype is not to further robot flight but to perfect navigation, sensing or artificial intelligence systems.

Understanding Nature's Micromachines

A July 25, 1989, *New York Times* article entitled "Laser 'Tweezers' Probe Nature's Tiniest Motors," described an unusual search for ever-smaller micromachines. A research team affiliated with Harvard University and Rowland Institute for Science, located in Cambridge, Massachusetts, Drs. Howard Berg, Steven Block and David Blair, used lasers to make physical measurements of microscopic features of one-celled bacteria.

In one series of experiments, the Rowland Institute scientists concentrated on the motors (known as basal structures) of bacteria and the power linkages to which they are connected. The scientists succeeded in measuring the minute force needed to twist one part of a single bacterium's propulsion system. The part under study transmits torque

(the forces that produce a twisting motion) from one of the bacterium's electric motors to its propeller-like filaments.

The motors of bacteria are true, direct current motors driven by a chemically induced flow of protons. Bacterial motors are the only examples in nature of true rotary motion. They have motors, axles and bearings, and an unloaded motor (one not at work), which in a healthy, well-fed bacterium can spin at 200 revolutions per second. To provide a sense of their size, Dr. Block compared the motor in a bacterium with a fabricated silicon electric motor used to make semiconduction chips, which is about the thickness of a human hair (about 75 microns or .0029 inch). He said, "Roughly 1,000 of them side by side would equal the diameter of the axle of one of those silicon micromotors."

Each of the bacteria motors drives a universal joint similar to the universal joints that transmit torque from automobile engines to drive shafts. (A universal joint is a joint or a coupling, as a ball and socket, that permits a swing at any angle within certain limits.) In bacterium, this joint is called a hook and it transmits rotary power to a helical (spiral) filament. When the bacterium travels forward, all of

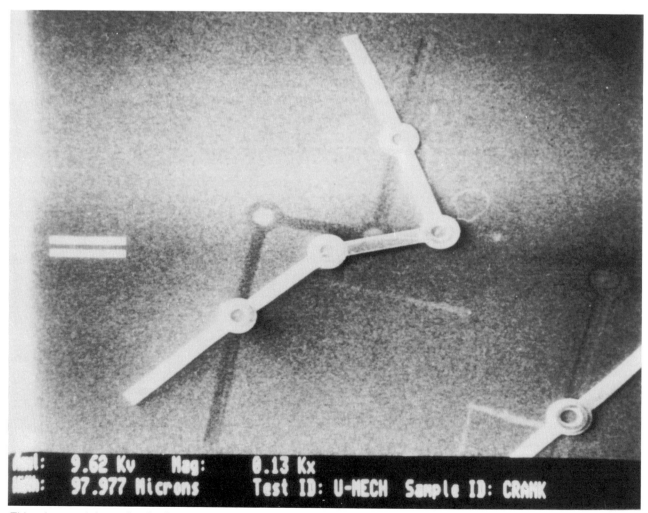

This microcrank has a fixed point at each end and two rotating joints.

its motors turn counterclockwise as viewed from the tail, and the filaments combine in bundles called flagella. The helical flagella acting together function as screw propellors moving the organism forward.

When the bacterium's motors reverse and turn clockwise, the bundles of filaments fly apart and make the bacterium tumble chaotically. Normal *E. coli* bacteria (commonly found in the intestinal tract of humans) alternately run and tumble. A run in a fairly straight line lasts for about a second and tumbling lasts about one-tenth of a second. The pattern of locomotion produces a "random walk" in which the bacterium changes direction with each tumbling phase. The walk is made even more random by the molecules of liquid through which bacteria move. Despite the randomness, the bacterium respond to environments they like or dislike. They move toward nutrients and away from poisons by extending the running time slightly and adjusting the timing of the runs and tumbles.

The bacterium's flaggellar propellers are so small they can only be seen with an electron microscope. To measure the mechanical properties of the bacterium's motor parts, Dr. Block and his colleagues devised a method for holding the subjects in position. After disabling the bacterium, the scientists applied chemicals to snap off the filaments, leaving only the flagellar nubs. A glass slide was coated with an antibody protein to which the nub of the bacterium's filament would stick, without immobilizing the entire bacterium.

To measure the motor's torque, the scientists took advantage of the fact that when an intense light, like a laser, shines through a transparent sphere and is refracted to one side, a very slight force exerted by the light tends to push the glass in the opposite direction. Scientists explain the effect as comparable to the suspension of a ping-pong ball in a rising jet of air. The ball remains centered in the jet, even if the jet moves or changes direction.

A bacterium, which is fairly transparent and spherical, when illuminated by a narrow laser beam, remains centered in the beam, even when the beam moves. Once a bacterium's filament was anchored to the glass, the laser "light trap" was focused on the body of the bacterium and rotated in a microscopic circle. By rotating the body clamped by its filament, the scientists were able to measure the resistance offered by the universal joint. They were also able to measure the springiness of the rebound when they released the body after it had been twisted.

The infrared laser the scientists used as tweezers killed some cells, but affected others so little that they went on reproducing, even while being manipulated. The capacity of bacteria to move spontaneously, their motility, varies widely. Among the ranks of disease-causing bacteria that are motile can be found the sources of such deadly scourges as typhoid, cholera, tetanus and syphilis. Ultimately, a detailed knowledge of the physiology of bacteria can be expected to aid in combatting some disease-causing organisms.

Marvel or Menace

Most scientists working in the field of nanotechnology are focused on their own projects in miniature, with little interest directed toward speculating about the future of the field. Speculation is mostly left to Eric Drexler, who points out that nanotechnology can be expected to have far-reaching consequences—some of them potentially threatening. In theory, a damaged nanomachine could reproduce itself infinitely.

FROTH PROVIDES INSIGHT INTO NEW MATERIALS

The froth made by ordinary soap bubbles has helped scientists to gain insight into the behavior of other materials. By regulating the fine structure of some grainy materials that resemble soap bubble froths, physicists have been able to make some soft metals hard and hard ceramics soft.

A March 20, 1990, *New York Times* article entitled "Humble Froth Offers Clues to Novel Materials" reported that participants at the 1990 annual meeting of the American Physical Society heard a dozen reports by scientists from major research institutions in which the authors concluded that frothiness of a fluid substance—the equivalent of graininess in solid materials—has a consequence for matter in previously unexpected ways. The 4,000 physicists were shown samples of pure unalloyed copper and silver—normally soft metals—that had been made almost as hard as iron through a restructure of the frothiness of their microscopic components.

Except for glassy materials, most solid matter is composed of crystalline grains. Within each grain is a lattice (framework) of atoms or molecules, arranged in a regular, periodic (repeating) order. The lattices in neighboring grains are not aligned with one another, therefore distinct boundaries are created between the grains.

Surface tension is what enables both drips and bubbles to form. When a drip forms on a faucet, electrically uneven water molecules adhere, forming an "elastic" surface. The drop stretches briefly, then gives way to gravity and falls. Although the surface tension of a soap bubble is less than that of a drip, the surface tension of a bubble gives way more slowly as a consequence of its lesser mass and weight.

In a metal that has been solidified from its molten form, the size of the grains depends on how fast the metal was cooled. Small grains generally are the result of rapid cooling. To make visible the grains that compose a piece of metal, the surface of the metal can be etched (acid is used to delineate the boundaries). The redistribution of atoms from large interior grains to the boundaries between small grains can sharply alter the properties of materials.

Grain Manipulation to Foster Superconductivity

Dr. Robert Siegal of the Argonne National Laboratory in Illinois told the participants at the annual meeting that in addition to metals with increased hardness, his laboratory had prepared non-brittle ceramics that alter their shape rather than break under pressure. A key use of such ceramics is in the creation of superconductive materials, able to conduct electricity without a loss of energy to resistance. (Resistance is the degree of inhibition within a material to the passage of electricity).

Conventional superconductors operate only in the super-cold temperature range of liquid helium (– 484° F), an expensive, hard-to-handle coolant. The new materials may make it possible to manufacture wires capable of carrying electric currents, without a loss of energy to resistance, at temperatures as warm as liquid nitrogen (–351° F), an inexpensive, easy-to-handle coolant.

In 1987, scientists discovered the first high-temperature superconductors, ceramic compounds in which copper oxide was the main component. While there is a diverse range of uses for superconductors, the brittleness of ceramics has been an obstacle to their exploitation, as has been the fact that the boundaries between the grains that make up the ceramic structure tend to block the superconductance of current.

Siegal believes that a way to avoid the obstacles presented by current methods may be to prepare the superconducting ceramics as solid froths of ultrafine particles under pressure. Such substances are called "nanophase materials," because the individual grains of their microscopic structure are no larger than a few nanometers, a few billionths of an inch, dimensions considerably smaller than the crystalline grains of conventional metals or ceramics.

Nanophase Material Preparation

To make the new substances, crucibles containing metals or ceramics are put into a chamber from which all the air is

No matter what other toys they have, small children generally like to blow simple bubbles. Older children (and some adults) favor making more complicated bubble arrangements—caterpillars, triangular prisms, cubes, bubbles inside bubbles etc. Scientists "study" such complex bubbles. Industry takes advantage of bubbles en masse in the form of foam.

removed, creating a vacuum. The crucibles are then heated to a temperature sufficient to vaporize (reduce to a gaseous or vapor state) their contents. The vaporized ceramic or metal condenses into a powder on a cold rod inside the chamber.

Through careful control of the conditions of condensation, the Argonne Lab scientists have been able to make powder grains that are only a few atomic thicknesses in diameter. These powders, when squeezed together under high pressure or sintered (heated without melting), have extremely fine-grained structures and properties that are remarkably different than their ordinary, coarse-grained counterparts. The nanophase form of pure copper is 500% harder than ordinary copper. A pliant, fracture-resistant ceramic composed of nanophase grains might make the development of engine blocks for high-temperature, efficient motors possible.

Soap Bubble Sandwiches

The work of several researchers who have used soap bubbles as models was described in a July 29, 1989, *Science News* article entitled "Frothy Physics," by Faye Flam. The author summed up the typical pattern of events in soap bubble research: "Through such studies, researchers are beginning to decipher the intricate dance performed by suds as they evolve toward a sort of balance between order and chaos.

"In a state of perfect order, a two-dimensional froth would exist as an array of uniform, hexagonal bubbles arranged like a honeycomb. All mechanical forces would balance, and the froth would remain stable in that pattern.

Scientists can create near-perfect froths by using a syringe to blow uniform bubbles into a soap film.

"But small imperfections—the odd five- or seven-sided bubble—inevitably creep in, upsetting the balance and sending the system on a course toward randomness. Bubbles neighboring the imperfections begin to gain or lose sides, causing areas of disorder to spread like cancer."

Smith's Contribution

An inspiration for many scientists currently working with froth is Massachusetts Institute of Technology (MIT) metallurgist Cyril Stanley Smith, who, in the 1950s, pioneered the use of soap bubble models in metallurgy (the science and technology of metals and alloys). Smith was the first scientist to study soap froth squeezed between two transparent plates.

In the bubbles' glass-encased, two-dimensional arrays, Smith noticed associations between edges, vertices (joining angles) and areas of interconnected polygons (figures with several angles and sides, usually more than four). In characterizing what he saw among his bubbles, Smith said, "The relationships describing froths are simple, beautiful equations."

In his work, Smith observed that the froth pattern coarsened over time. He noted that the average of the areas enclosed in all the two-dimensional polygons increased in a linear relationship to the time elapsed. Moreover, he discovered a similarity between the way froth bubbles change shape, as gas slowly diffuses from one bubble to another, and the way that metal crystals, or grains, change shape, as heat expands them. Smith's photographs of two-dimensional soap froths are indistinguishable from those of the etched surfaces of metals showing patterns of packed grains.

Von Neumann's Law

Smith's enthusiasm for soap bubble analysis infected mathematician John Von Neumann (1903–57), who is said to have formulated a law describing bubble coarsening while attending one of Smith's froth lectures. Von Neumann's law of bubble growth essentially states that "the rich get richer and the poor get poorer." Bubbles that have more than six sides grow larger in size. The more sides they have, the faster they grow. Bubbles with fewer than six sides shrink. The ones with the fewest sides shrink most quickly and often disappear.

In the 1970s, two scientists, David Aboav of Chorleywood, England, and Denis Weaire of Trinity College in Dublin, Ireland, working separately, but each using the same pictures taken by Smith 20 years earlier, arrived at conclusions that contradicted Smith's findings. Aboav and Weaire proposed in 1980 that rather than being proportional to the time elapsed, as Smith had found, the average area within the bubbles increased at a rate proportional to the *square* of the time elapsed.

Moreover, contrary to Smith's assertion, Aboav and Weaire found that the froth grows continually more disordered. In 1984, Weaire suggested that froths take on a fractal arrangement, a geometrical shape in which the structure of a small area is the same as of the whole (like a pyramid comprised of smaller pyramids). By fractal arrangement, Weaire meant that small bubbles filled crevices between larger ones, and still smaller bubbles filled in remaining crevices in a shrinking progression.

Vindication of Smith's Findings

A unique set of experiments conducted over the span of 1987 to 1989 by physicist James Glazier of the University of Chicago reinstated Smith's findings and refuted those of Aboav and Weaire. To conduct his experiments, Glazier blew the bubbles in a film of glycerin and "Dawn" brand dishwashing detergent, squeezed them between acrylic-plastic plates and highlighted them with a small amount of dye.

Glazier placed his slowly evolving array of bubble on the glass of an office photocopier and recorded how the 10,000 or more hand-counted bubbles changed over periods of days. To create a faster-evolving froth, Glazier stopped filling his soap bubbles with air and switched to helium.

The soap photocopies revealed that the bubbles evolved in two stages. During the first stage, which Glazier named the transient phase, the spread of disordered areas progressively compounded the disorder of the whole system. With air-filled bubbles, the transient phase lasted several days, and with helium-filled bubbles it lasted about 10 hours.

During the second phase, which Glazier called the scaling phase, the level of disorder remained constant. Although individual bubbles continued to gain or lose sides, and to grow, shrink and disappear, the overall total of bubbles with a given number of sides remained constant. For example, at the rate three-sided bubbles disappeared, new three-sided bubbles formed. The scaling phase lasted 60 days in air bubbles and 10 days in helium bubbles.

In the scaling state, the average area enclosed by the bubbles grew in an approximate linear relation to time, not to time squared as proposed by Aboav and Weaire. The relationship is only approximate, because the enclosing plates prevent the froths from expanding naturally. Glazier proposed that as the bubbles in the froth enlarged, the sum of their perimeters decreased, while the total volume of liquid separating them remained fixed. The artificially compressed bubble walls probably started to thicken, thereby slowing the diffusion of gas from one bubble to another.

Glazier speculated that Aboav and Weaire arrived at their conclusions by focusing on the transient scale of bubble evolution, when disorder increases at different rates in relationship to time, sometimes growing at a rate of time squared.

In Glazier's opinion, when the scaling phase starts, the system has reached an "equilibrium" level of disorder. He compared it to the equilibrium position of a mechanical spring.

A Balanced Disorder

In Glazier's system, the bubbles begin in a very ordered state of mostly uniform hexagonal bubbles, disorder increases beyond the equilibrium level, and then is restored, the system becoming more ordered until it reaches the scaling state. The bubble behavior is like that of a spring that is compressed, released, and then resumes its natural length at rest.

Glazier found that if he started his array closer to the disorder of the scaling state, the froth's disorder increased smoothly until it reached the final scaling state. Even an array that started out disordered beyond the equilibrium point gained order until it achieved the scaling state.

During an interview with *Science News*, Glazier explained the seeming attraction within the bubble array toward the scaling state no matter what the initial arrangement. He said, "The system is trying to find a particular disorder, and the way it starts out might not be the right disorder."

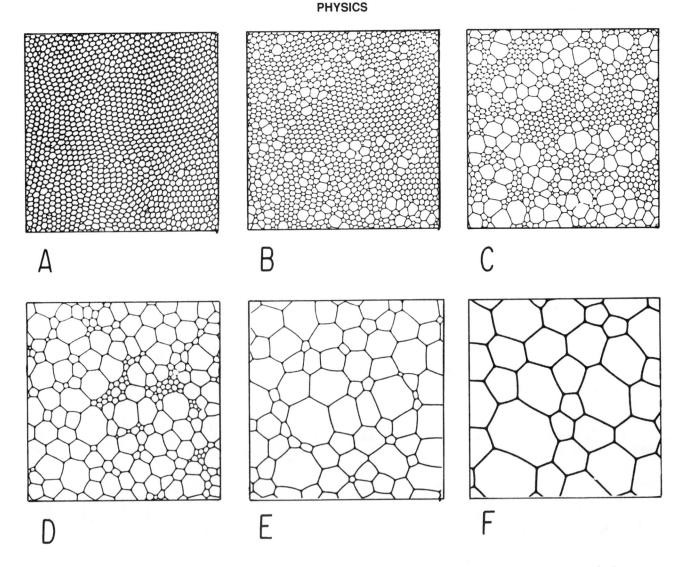

In the illustration above, James Glazier used a photocopier, over a period of several hours, to photograph soap froth sandwiched between two plates of glass. Each successive photocopy shows the progress of the deterioration of the bubbles, as those with six sides or more absorb those with fewer sides. These bubbles were initially ordered.

Physicist Nicolas Rivier of Argonne National Laboratory compared the bubble array's acceptable level of disorder to the theromodynamic equilibrium of a gas. He characterized the scaling state as a "statistical equilibrium." By that he meant that rearrangements in separate parts of the system maintain the system's overall properties. For example, the temperature of a gas remains constant, while at the same time its individual molecules engage in constant motion, some moving rapidly and others slowly. (Collisions contribute to the molecules' changes in speed.)

The laws of thermodynamics propose that gases and other phases of matter move toward a maximum state of entropy, a measure of the degree of disorder in a system: Entropy always increases and available energy decreases in a closed system. Rivier depicted the scaling state of bubbles as one in which entropy is at a maximum and the most rearrangements of individual patterns can be made within a system.

Froth Simulations

In his research, Glazier found that a real froth system differed in several ways from theoretical ideals. For example, it has long been assumed that all sides of the bubbles join in 120-degree vertices. Earlier research, including Von Neumann's law, rests on an assumption of these 120-degree angles. Glazier noticed that, while bubbles were inclined to bend their edges to approach the favored 120-degree joining angle, they did not always succeed, thus they appeared to violate and follow Von Neumann's law at the same time.

Glazier has worked with Gary Grest of Exxon Research to simulate froths on computers. The simulated froths become disordered in the same way real ones do. In the simulations, pixels (individual picture elements) on the borders of the froth, following programmed-in physical laws, vary their affiliations with neighboring bubbles.

Soap Bubble Tradition

In describing his photocopier research to his peers at the American Physical Society meeting, Glazier said, "Our apparatus may be the cheapest one around doing significant physics experiments." His enthusiasm for soap bubble research matches that of one of its early proponents, C.V. Boys.

Sir Charles Vernon Boys, scientist, inventor and professor, wrote *Soap Bubbles: And the Forces that Mould Them* with the intention that his young readers would be able to conduct his simple experiments themselves. Originally published in 1902, the book was reprinted as a paperback by Doubleday in 1959, as a part of MIT's Science Study Series monographs.

In the first chapter of his book, Boys suggests why scientists continue to be interested in and gain knowledge from the study of soap bubbles. He said, "Though there are many subjects which might seem to a beginner to be more wonderful, more brilliant, or more exciting, there are few which so directly bear upon the things which we see every day. You cannot pour water from a jug or tea from a tea-pot; you cannot even do anything with a liquid of any kind, without setting in action the forces to which I am about to direct your attention."

A'

C'

F'

Photocopies of the deterioration of soap froth sandwiched between two plates of glass that began with the bubbles initially disordered.

13

Chemistry

ALCHEMY

The Search for the Roots of Alchemy in Modern Chemistry

Modern scientists have begun to decipher some of the enigmas formerly considered mystical nonsense left by their alchemical ancestors. Alchemists theorized about, studied and practiced chemistry during the Middle Ages, from approximately the 13th to the 17th century. The height of alchemy's popularity was reached in the 16th and 17th centuries.

The alchemists' goals were to transmute (transform) baser metals into pure gold, to find a universal remedy for disease, and to discover the secret of perpetual youth. In an April 10, 1990, *New York Times* article entitled "In Alchemists' Notes, Clues to Modern Chemistry," a March 1990 discovery made among scientific archives in London by Dr. Lawrence Principe, a Johns Hopkins University chemistry professor, was reported. Principe's discovery may enable scholars to decipher some of the secret codes alchemists used in writing down chemical formulas and processes. The discovery appears to narrow the gulf between the practices of alchemy and those of modern scientific chemistry.

A typical alchemist's illustration of four centuries ago depicts a gray wolf devouring a king. In the background, a flaming pyre consumes the wolf and restores the king to life. Until recently, scholars viewed these and the many other illustrations and documents related to medieval and Renaissance alchemy as mysticism and quackery. However, in reviewing old alchemical documents, scientists and historians have discerned nuggets of genuine chemical insight that suggest that the science of chemistry may have evolved considerably earlier than had previously been believed.

A significant gulf remains between the rational observations and experimentation of modern science and the magic and witchcraft of alchemy. However, there is evidence that some of the leading alchemists stumbled on experimental techniques and chemical reactions that provided a great service to the earliest practitioners of scientific chemistry.

An examination of puzzling engravings, diagrams, formulas, and musical notations left by alchemists has led to the recognition that some of the mysterious alchemical symbols often signified genuine chemical processes. Historians have become aware that a wolf was generally the symbol for antimony sulfide, which dissolves many metals, including gold. Moreover, the traditional symbol for gold was a king.

Because antimony sulfide converts base metals into sulfide scum that can be skimmed away from melted gold, the wolf and the king picture is an allegory of the process used to refine pure gold from its alloys. The vast literature of alchemy contains hundreds of such pictures.

Alchemy's tarnished reputation is a product of its traditional association with astrology, mysticism and black magic. Many alchemists were tricksters whose frauds sometimes led to their executions. Nevertheless, the ranks of the alchemists contained some of the greatest scientists of all time, including Isaac Newton (1642–1727) and Robert Boyle (1627–1691).

Although Newton's fame rests on his discoveries in physics and mathematics, about 50% of his career was devoted to alchemy. Dr. Betty Jo Teeter Dobbs, a professor of history at Northwestern University in Evanston, Illinois, who has studied Newton's work for many years, regards alchemy as a central component to his career, rather than as an aberration.

Dobbs presented some of her views on Newton's work in a lecture given at the Smithsonian Institution, February 16, 1988, later published by the Smithsonian Institution Libraries in 1990 as *Alchemical Death and Resurrection: The Significance of Alchemy in the Age of Newton*. Dobbs commented, "Newton's underlying object was not simply to learn about nature but to discern the activity of God in all of nature. Alchemists regarded everything in nature, minerals and planets included, as animated."

During an interview with the *New York Times*, Dr. Mary Ellen Bowden of the Beckman Center for the History of Chemistry at the University of Pennsylvania said that only a handful of working chemists have ever tried to reconstruct alchemical recipes using modern chemical methods. One of the most successful, in her estimation, has been Dr. Principe of Johns Hopkins, who made the 1990 discovery.

Principe's recent research has focused on the life's work of Robert Boyle, an English philosopher who was one of the founders of modern chemistry. In the medieval and Renaissance era, a philosopher was a scholar who tried to understand nature, an activity known today as science. Among his contributions to modern chemistry, Boyle discovered the role that air plays in the process of oxidation (the union of oxygen with a substance, producing rust for example), and he demonstrated that the volume and pressure of a gas are inversely proportional.

Breaking Boyle's Code

During a periodic visit to the Royal Society in London, Principe found two torn scraps of paper in the collection of Boyle's papers. The scraps were labeled in the index as some kind of glossary. They turned out to be partial keys to a code Boyle used in recording his work.

The Latin names of chemical substances are listed on the scraps beside nonsense words of Boyle's invention. In the code that Principe broke, Boyle substituted a nonsense word starting with the letter after the first letter in the real word. For example, wherever Boyle wrote "ormunt" in a recipe, he was actually referring to potassium nitrate. When the code word is replaced by the substance referred to in Boyle's text, the chemical reaction makes sense.

Probably part of an alphabetic code, the two scraps unfortunately cover only words between C to E and F to T. To make matters more complex, Boyle used at least two other codes. Principe described his research by saying, "Boyle drops little trails of crumbs to let you know what he is doing, but finding the trails is heavy going."

Boyle's secrecy was routine among alchemists of his day. Many believed that their knowledge could be dangerous in the hands of the uninitiated, a sentiment echoed by Newton in one of his letters. In part, Boyle's subterfuge may have been motivated by the fact that some of his secrets had been stolen by rivals. Newton's caution may have been related to his job as warden of the royal mint, which gave him the capacity to send counterfeiters to the gallows, since an alchemically created gold could have debased the nation's currency.

Retracing the Chemical Reaction

Few of the records left by alchemists can be read at face value. The same author may use the same word in the same text and mean a wide variety of things that can only be identified by studying the text closely.

In a paper delivered in the Netherlands in 1989, Principe described his effort to discern the alchemist's meaning by retracing the actual laboratory steps. Boyle described a powerful solvent he called menstruum peracutum, which he said could dissolve gold, and when mixed with melted borax, would produce a tiny amount of pure silver. He apparently believed that menstruum peracutum could transmute gold into silver, a reaction the reverse of what alchemists traditionally tried to do.

Following Boyle's directions for making menstruum peracutum, Principe used "butter of antimony" (antimony trichloride) and "aqua fortis" (nitric acid). Only by experimenting with varying amounts could Principe arrive at Boyle's results, which were several pieces of white metal that resembled silver in the same shape as the gold he had originally dissolved in the menstruum peracutum.

Boyle's failure to remove an antimony impurity at a critical stage in the process yielded what he thought was silver but was actually metallic antimony, a fact that Boyle could have determined by hammering the metal but failed to do. Principe commented on Boyle's oversight by saying, "He may have merely entrusted the analysis to a student. From Boyle's account, we know that he expected to get silver, so he reported what he expected to see."

Impurities introduced into alchemical recipes by iron stirring rods and other such implements help to explain why alchemists often had results far different from those that would be obtained in modern laboratories, using pure materials and avoiding sources of contamination.

The idea of alchemy conjures visions of misguided dreamers attempting to convert lead into gold. Their work is dismissed and contemptuously relegated to the realm of folklore. Few ask why the alchemist thought it was possible to change the molecular structure of lead or what other work he did. The alchemist's themes of life, death, resurrection and restitution have only recently begun to be examined and considered.

Principe explained his purposes in seeking to unravel the alchemist's code by saying, "One of my goals is to demonstrate the importance of alchemy to the history of science and to show that alchemy cannot be dismissed out of hand as a worthless and past endeavor simply because alchemists had a world view very different than our own."

The Alchemists' Theoretical World

Just how different the alchemists' world view was when compared to that of modern chemists is laid out in Betty Jo Teeter Dobbs's published lecture about Newton. The 17th-century mechanical philosophy was based on the belief in the existence of atoms or corpuscles— discrete particles—of matter that were in constant motion. Those tiny particles of inert matter that transferred motion via pressure on, or impact with, other small particles explained all events in the natural world. But the passivity of matter described by the mechanical philosophers presented the problem of explaining how passive little inert balls could stick together and cohere into organized forms. Cohesion and development into a variety of living forms would appear to be different than the mere mechanical action of small particles of matter.

Newton was convinced that passive particles of matter could not organize themselves into living forms without divine guidance, which he viewed as an active presence that guided particles of passive matter into all the forms of plants, animals and minerals that God had ordained. Newton sometimes called this force a fermental virtue or the vegetable spirit. This was the secret of life that Newton hoped to discover through alchemy.

Dobbs explained the thinking of alchemists by saying, "Vitalism seems to belong to the very origins of alchemy. In the early Christian centuries, when alchemical ideas were taking shape, metals had not been well characterized as distinct chemical species. Metals were thought to have variable properties, somewhat like modern metallic alloys . . . Or, perhaps more frequently at that time, metals were conceived as similar to a mix of bread dough . . . perhaps a metallic mixture could also be induced to ferment, by the introduction of a suitable leaven, and then ripen into the desired form of gold."

Sometimes the alchemists thought of their metallic mixtures as similar to a maternal womb into which the injection of an active male sperm or seed might lead to the process of generation of the more perfect metal, which was gold. Confident that the vital agent was in some sense divine, Newton sought in alchemy the source of all apparently spontaneous processes of fermentation that had to do with normal life and growth, such as the assimilation of digested food into living tissue. Mechanical action by itself, in Newton's view, could never account for the process of assimilation in which foodstuffs were turned into the different forms of animals, plants and minerals. Nor could they account for the sheer variety of life forms, all of which seemed to spring from lifeless matter.

Dobbs suggests that some of 19th-century painter Vincent van Gogh's work depicts the exuberant forces of vegetation in the world that Newton had in mind. She points to Van Gogh's writhing sunflowers, rhythmic dance of stately irises and vibrant fields from which birds appear to fling themselves into the air.

Robert Boyle, an English philosopher and one of the founders of modern chemistry, was an alchemist.

The Link Between Alchemical and Theological Thought

As early as the time of Aristotle, spontaneous generation (the supposed generation of living matter from dead or inorganic matter) had been an accepted theory. Still accepted in the 16th and 17th centuries, it was thought to need a precipitation trigger, the warmth of the sun or an act of God, or both.

Creation itself was widely viewed in the 16th and 17th centuries as a chemical or alchemical process. To separate the elements of earth, air, fire and water from each other, to create plant life, to organize the heavenly bodies, to call forth the beasts of the earth, and to produce Adam and Eve, God was assumed to have used light. Alchemists compared the activation in alchemy of lifeless matter (referred to as illumination) to God's use of light at the beginning of the world. Light represented God's power to activate or reactivate lifeless matter.

Alchemists often depicted divine power as entering a chemical flask by means of the sun or moon. The alchemical use of images and symbols was similar to the religious tradition of representing divine power by using rays of light. Moreover, the style of alchemical presentation, which placed the most important figure in the highest position, was similar to devices used by medieval painters to indicate the relative importance of various figures in a composition.

In her lecture, Dobbs described a depiction of an alchemical process in which two lowly forms of earthly matter, Mercury and Sulfur, are assembled and sacrificed in a flask. They are initially dead, but they are reactivated by divine power that streams in from heaven. Thus, the chemicals reach the first crown of perfection. Next in the depiction of the process, two snakes twined about a pole reflect the alchemical symbol for Mercury, thereby signifying that the preparation of the special Mercury has reached a second level of perfection, represented by a double crown.

Above the double crown, appears the alchemical symbol for Sulfur, a triangle with a crossed stem. When the alchemist is able to prepare his perfectly pure Sulfur and join it with his perfectly pure Mercury, the process reaches a third level of perfection represented by a triple crown. Atop the final crown is a small globe with a cross that may at the same time signify Christ as the savior of the world and be emblematic of the philosopher's stone (a substance sought by alchemists in the belief that it would turn base metals into gold).

Life and Death

Thus, the alchemical world was a dynamic, cyclical interchange of death and continual rebirth or resurrection,

Isaac Newton, also an alchemist, is better remembered today for his work in physics and the formation of his famous laws.

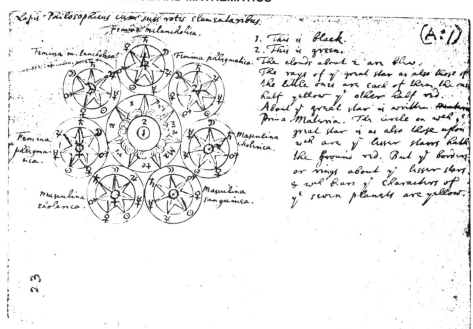

Isaac Newton's copy of a diagram of the philosopher's stone, which was sought by alchemists in the belief it would change base metals, such as lead, into precious ones.

based on a perception of the yearly seasonal cycle of the vegetable kingdom. Death was considered an essential stage early in the alchemical process. The active alchemical agent was viewed as much an agent of death and putrefaction as it was of life and vegetation.

Most of the symbols Dobbs describes are Christian symbols of death and resurrection, but they are also adaptations of ancient motifs. The cross is a Christian adaptation of the primitive world-tree, the axle pole of the world that reaches from its subterranean roots in the underworld and unites with earth and heaven. In religions much older than Christianity, the tree was an ancient symbol of fecundity. Snakes were also pre-Christian symbols of fertility, wisdom and the power to heal. Because the snake sheds its skin, it is viewed as a symbol of rebirth.

After the Reformation of the church in the 16th century, there was a strong belief that the end of time was near. The purification of the church represented by the Reformation seemed to many Protestants to signify the beginning of the end. The concept found a parallel view in alchemy, where matter was purged, cleansed and exalted. Among many early modern alchemists, there was an expectation that the end of time would bring a final redemption of matter, as it would bring a final redemption of mankind.

Alchemy's Place in the Progress of Modern Chemical Thought

In concluding her discussion of alchemists, Dobbs said,

The meaning of alchemical texts and illustrations is often obscure to modern scholars, at least partly because

of the prescientific—even archaic—assumptions that undergird alchemical thought and practice. Rather than dismiss alchemy as irrational and incomprehensible, however, one may attempt to recover alchemical meaning by historical methods, decoding its obscure symbolism by analyzing its premodern presuppositions about life, death and resurrection.

In the remarkable alchemical studies of Isaac Newton one may locate many clues that assist in that decoding. Because of the problem of explaining life under the rubric of the mechanical philosophy—the multiplicity and variety of life forms; their beauty, cohesiveness, and purposefulness—Newton turned to the study of alchemy in an attempt to find the secret of life, the divine agent of fertility, the "vegetable spirit." His analyses of the older alchemical literature often laid bare the hidden assumptions of alchemical theory regarding life and death. Although modern scientific knowledge invalidates many of those assumptions, they are nonetheless understandable in terms of ancient misconceptions.

Decoding the contributions made by these alchemists, Dobbs and others may well uncover forgotten lessons once learned by alchemists.

MICROSCALE ORGANIC LABORATORY TECHNIQUE

The Revolutionary Move to Teach Undergraduates to Use Minuscule Amounts of Chemicals

Techniques to teach undergraduate college chemistry labs had changed little in 100 years when in 1980 a student, troubled by noxious, headache-producing fumes, complained to the president of Bowdoin College, in Brunswick, Maine. It was not the first time that a student had complained or even the first time that a student had complained to the president. However, this student wasn't likely to be put off with excuses. Her father was the director of an environmental protection agency in California.

The problem in the chemistry laboratory that Bowdoin was experiencing was in no way unique. Many colleges across the country had reached a point where their undergraduate labs were serving double the number of students they had been set up for. The increased number of students had not only created crowding, it had increased the amount of chemical waste produced and worsened the air quality for students and faculty.

The Bowdoin president turned for assistance to Samuel Butcher, the chairperson of Bowdoin's chemistry department. Butcher, an air-quality specialist, advised the president that rebuilding the lab to put in the requisite number of vent hoods could cost as much as $250,000. Moreover, pumping in additional air for the new vents, given Maine's cold climate, would significantly add to the building's operating costs.

Although the president was willing to undertake the expenditure, Butcher explained that there were arguments against retrofitting (making modifications in already existing facilities) a typical lab to provide additional hood space. Expanded hood space could lead to visual obstructions and a greatly increased noise level. Butcher suggested that the president postpone his decision, while he searched for a better, less costly approach.

To help him explore possible solutions, Butcher consulted with his Bowdoin colleague Dana Mayo and with

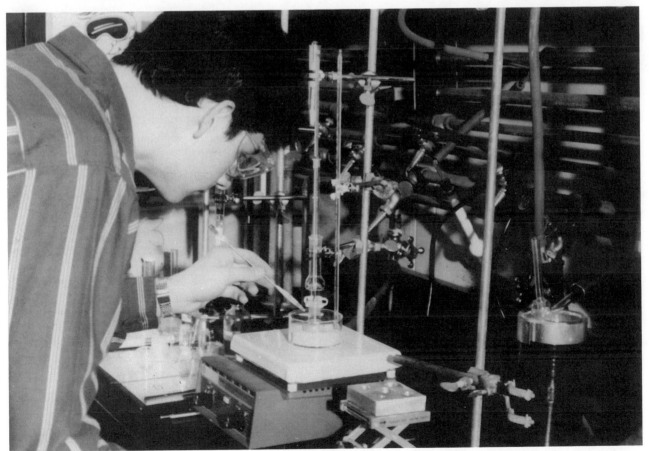

The idea that sparked a movement toward microscale chemistry on the undergraduate level, as stated by Dr. Dana Mayo, is, "If you need a pound of material in industry do you make a half-ton?"

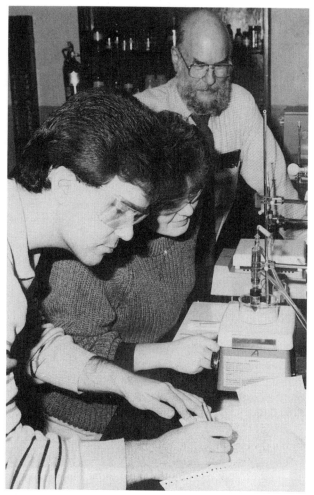

Mark Johnson and Carol Strong conduct an experiment in the microscale lab under the direction of Dr. Ronald Pike.

a visiting professor from Merrimack College (North Andover, Massachusetts), Ronald Pike. During lunch one afternoon, after a couple of days of brainstorming among the three, Mayo suggested going "micro," a laboratory method commonly used in graduate teaching labs and in industry. By micro, he meant using minute amounts, instead of the substantial amounts usually given to undergraduate students.

The basis for his suggestion was explained in the 1984 issue of *Impact*, a Merrimack College alumni magazine. Professor Mayo said,

> Clearly, it has always been accepted procedure to introduce students to organic chemical laboratory techniques at the multigram level, but, I thought, is this instructional approach relevant when one considers the scale of work commonly employed in many areas of modern industrial research where costly substances are employed? If you need a pound of material in industry do you make a half a ton? Of

course not, but this sort of distortion in experimental scale is going on in present day undergraduate laboratories.

A particularly important question to ask, it seems to me, is at what scale of introductory lab work can a student gain the greatest experience in handling organic materials in the shortest period of time?

Dr. Pike recalled the day of inspiration. He said, "We wondered, if research scientists could scale down experiments from 100 to 1000 times, then why couldn't we?"

Although undergraduates typically receive generous amounts of lab chemicals to work with, they generally only consume small amounts during the performance of their experiments. The leftovers are thrown away, creating a significant disposal hazard and expense.

Immediately, the three professors could see advantages to going micro. The annual amounts of chemicals needed would be far less and therefore costs for the lab would be dramatically reduced. Moreover, the minute amounts would give off far less fumes and the need for ventilation would be substantially alleviated.

If the advantages appeared to be all on the side of using small amounts, the troubling question was raised "Why hadn't it been done before?" The most apparent answer was a long tradition of thinking that undergraduates did not have the skill to handle more sensitive experiments. If a lack of confidence in students had ever been set aside, the next obstacle that would have discouraged change would have been logistical. To work on a smaller scale would have meant redesigning all the existing equipment.

To learn the state of the art, the professors examined existing lab manuals. To their amazement, they found that there had been few substantive changes in lab practices during the previous century.

Turning an Idea into Reality

The three professors advised Bowdoin's president that before he undertook the $250,000 lab renovation, it might be more prudent to risk $25,000 to experiment with the micro approach for undergraduates. In December of 1980, the college provided funds for an assessment. The three professors, a number of teaching and research fellows, and a tenacious research technician named Janet Hotham began the arduous work.

By the 1981–82 academic year, everyone working on the project was convinced that a complete micro-scale curriculum was feasible. A $100,000 grant from the Surdna Foundation and a $25,000 award from the Atlantic Richfield

Company provided the funding needed to carry the trials on to completion.

The effort required the complex, painstaking task of reducing the scale of traditional experiments by a factor of anywhere from 100 to 1,000. Many hours of experimentation were needed to develop procedures that could be carried out using the microscale equipment and reduced amounts of chemicals.

The enormous amount of equipment that had to be redesigned included stirrers, test tubes, beakers and fractionation distilling columns (which separate volatile components with different boiling points), to name only a few. Beakers usually the size of milk bottles became the size of shot glasses or thimbles. Some redesigned flasks had a diameter less than that of quarter, and some test tubes were no longer than a cigarette.

As Bowdoin students conducted the newly designed experiments, air quality was constantly monitored and documented. A March 6, 1984, *New York Times* article entitled "Less Expensive Chemistry," reported that Samuel Butcher conducted each of the experiments in macroscale and then in microscale in an isolation chamber, in order to determine the extent to which air pollution was reduced.

Benefits to the Students

By 1984, 30 experiments had been developed and another 15 were in progress. In the spring of 1984, 10 Merrimack College students were the first outside of Bowdoin to use the new techniques. The Merrimack students were enthusiastic. One participant commented, "Microscale makes you more skillful. You're dealing with lesser amounts of chemicals; it makes you a better chemist."

Dr. Pike agreed, saying, "Students are dealing with smaller amounts of materials. They have to be precise with their weights and their measurements. They must learn the technique and concentrate on every operation. Students are learning better than ever the fastidious techniques of experimentation."

In an April 29, 1990, *Boston Globe* article entitled "Microscience, Macrosuccess: A No-frills Path to Chemistry," Dr. Pike elaborated on the new approach. He said, "If you are going to use tiny quantities, grease, dust, dirt, any kind of contamination, even the residue of soap used to wash the equipment is a disaster. So we had to teach students how to be very precise in cleaning and preparing their experiments."

The students lost the luxury of sloshing around large quantities of chemicals. Each step in the experiment became critical because the loss of even a few milligrams could change the outcome.

Benefits to the Colleges

Although the initial cost of converting to microscale can be substantial, the cost-saving per student begins immediately. In the winter 1987 issue of *Merrimack*, Dr. Pike said, "The microscale concept reduces a college's annual cost of teaching organic chemistry by about 80%. It dramatically reduces toxic emissions and toxic wastes and virtually eliminates the danger of fire and explosions." Laboratories that once used a gallon of ether in an afternoon period, by using microscale, cut their consumption to about the contents of a shot glass.

Not only does microscale drastically reduce the danger of fire or explosion, it reduces risks in other ways. In an interview with the *New York Times*, Miles Pickering, the director of undergraduate laboratories at Princeton, said, "Twenty grams of cyanide is a serious hazard; two hundred milligrams is not likely to kill anyone."

With continued use, the advantages of microscale continue to emerge. Experiments take far less time to complete on a microscale level, because such processes as evaporation and condensation take place at a rapid rate. As a consequence, a wider variety of experiments can be undertaken during the span of the course. Reagents and starting materials can be synthesized in the laboratory, which means that expensive and hard-to-obtain chemicals are readily available. Moreover, materials, such as hormones or platinum, once too expensive to use in a college-level course, become affordable in microscale quantities.

Professional Recognition

In November 1986, the three professors were awarded the Charles A. Dana Foundation Award for Pioneering Achievement in Higher Education. During the award presentation, the Dana Foundation's board chairman said, "It is not overstating the case to say that by the 1970's, [the] entire system of laboratory education was in danger of being driven from the college campus by several problems . . . Three devoted college chemistry teachers solved the problem." The professors' textbook *Microscale Organic Laboratory*, published in 1989, has been called by Miles Pickering "a turning point in the history of laboratory education."

In addition to the Dana award, by 1990, Drs. Pike, Mayo, and Butcher had received six additional awards.

The Idea Continues to Spread

By 1990, more than 450 colleges in the United States, as well as some schools in France and Egypt, were using microscale. Moreover, Dr. Pike had completed another book, *Microscale Inorganic Laboratory*, co-authored with

Merrimack College's innovative microscale labs are being copied, not only by other colleges and universities, but by high schools as well.

Merrimack's chemistry professors Zvi Szafran and Mono Singh, soon to be published.

Dr. Pike does not work solely with undergraduates. When in residence at Merrimack, Pike regularly offers courses for working chemists to keep them advised of the latest in technological advancements. However, during the academic year 1990–91, Dr. Pike was not on campus to teach either group; he was on leave to introduce microscale to West Point. The Air Force Academy was already using microscale.

Filtering Down

The success of microscale at the college level has inspired hundreds of high schools across the United States to reconsider the potential abilities of students and to introduce microscale into their curriculums. In an era of tight budgets, the inspired idea of three chemistry professors, plus several years of hard work, may mean that some high schools that might otherwise be forced to close their labs will be able to keep them open.

APPENDIX

NOBEL PRIZE IN PHYSICS

Jerome Friedman, United States   **Henry Kendall**, United States   **Richard Taylor**, Canada

While working at the Stanford Linear Accelerator Center in the late 1960s, the three scientists first detected the existence of quarks. In work that paralleled the discovery of the atomic nuclei, electrons were fired at protons and neutrons. The way that electrons bounced off the particles revealed that they were made of tiny concentrations of matter, which had earlier been dubbed quarks by Murray Gell-Mann, who had laid the intellectual groundwork for the existence of quarks and for the work performed by the three winners.

NOBEL PRIZE IN CHEMISTRY

James Corey, United States

Corey is characterized as an organic chemistry master of the art of making biological molecules one painstaking step at a time. During a long career, he and his students have synthesized some 100 important drugs and chemicals. He was honored for his broad intellectual achievement in pioneering "retrosynthetic analysis," an approach likened to playing a chess game with nature.

NOBEL PRIZE IN PHYSIOLOGY OR MEDICINE

Joseph E. Murray, United States   **E. Donnall Thomas**, United States

Working independently, the two physicians paved the way for now-commonplace organ and tissue transplants. In 1954, Murray performed the first successful kidney transplant, avoiding rejection of the organ by the patient by using the kidney of an identical twin. He subsequently found that radiation would permit the use of organs from unrelated donors. In 1956, Thomas performed the first successful transplant of bone marrow. He initiated the use of drugs rather than radiation to suppress rejection.

NOBEL PRIZE IN ECONOMICS

Harry Markowitz, United States   **William Sharpe**, United States   **Merton Miller**, United States

When Harry Markowitz first proposed, in the 1950s, that investors should diversify their portfolios, he did so on the premise that risks tended to offset one another. Economists scoffed that the idea was not good mathematics, economics, or finance. Markowitz's insight made him the intellectual father of the mutual-fund industry. Sharpe demonstrated that the risks and rewards of holding an asset like a stock were linked to the stock's volatility in relation to the rest of the market. Miller focused on corporate finance and co-wrote a paper with Franco Modigliani that established that the overall value of a company was based on the cash the company generated.

ALBERT LASKER MEDICAL RESEARCH AWARDS

None were awarded in 1990.

APPENDIX

NATIONAL MEDALS OF SCIENCE AND NATIONAL MEDALS OF TECHNOLOGY

The awards are the nation's highest honors in science and technology and are conferred by the President in a White House ceremony. In addition to Medal of Technology awards to 10 individuals, in 1990, President Bush presented an award to one company.

MEDALS OF SCIENCE

Winner	Field	Affiliation
Baruj Benacerraf	Biology	Harvard University
Elkan Blout	Chemistry	Harvard University
Herbert Boyer	Biology	University of California, San Francisco
George Carrier	Mathematics	Harvard University
Allan Cormack	Physics	Tufts University
Mildred Dresselhaus	Engineering	Massachusetts Institute of Technology
Karl Folkers	Chemistry	University of Texas, Austin
Nick Holonyak, Jr.	Engineering	University of Illinois
Leonid Hurwicz	Behavior	University of Minnesota
Stephen Kleene	Mathematics	University of Wisconsin
Daniel Koshland, Jr.	Biology	University of California, Berkeley
Edward Lewis	Biology	California Institute of Technology
John McCarthy	Mathematics	Stanford University
Edwin McMillan	Physics	University of California, Berkeley
David G. Nathan	Biology	Harvard University
Robert Pound	Physics	Harvard University
Roger R.D. Revelle	Physics	Harvard University
John D. Roberts	Chemistry	California Institute of Technology
Patrick Suppes	Behavior	Stanford University
E. Donnall Thomas	Biology	Fred Hutchinson Cancer Research Center

MEDALS OF TECHNOLOGY

Winner	Field	Affiliation
John Atanasoff	Computers	Iowa State University
Marvin Camras	Computers	Illinois Institute of Technology
Du Pont Company	Chemistry	E.I. Du Pont de Nemours & Company
Donald Frey	Engineering	Institute for Illinois
Fred Garry	Engineering	General Electric Company
Wilson Greatbach	Engineering	Wilson Greatbach, Ltd.
Jack St. Clair Kilby	Engineering	Texas Instruments
John S. Mayo	Engineering	AT&T Bell
Gordon Moore	Engineering	Intel
David B. Pall	Engineering	Pall Corporation
Chauncey Starr	Engineering	Electric Research Power Institute

GLOSSARY

actuator a mechanism to activate control equipment by use of pneumatic (operated by air or gas), hydraulic (operated by water or other low-viscosity fluid) or electronic (controlled conduction of electrons) signals. For example, a valve actuator opens or closes a valve to control the rate of fluid flow.

analogue an organ similar in function to that in another organism, but of dissimilar evolutionary origin.

Antarctica Treaty an international treaty ratified in 1961 setting down conditions for research and exploration in Antarctica; the treaty bans military activity, nuclear explosions, radioactive waste disposal, and mandates international cooperation and freedom of scientific inquiry. The participants agreed not to press territorial claims while the treaty remained in force.

antigen a substance foreign to the body, often a protein, that causes the body to form an antibody that reacts in defense against only that antigen.

apnea a pattern of breathing in which an individual typically breathes in for a long time and then fails to breathe out for a long time.

ARPAnet a computer network system developed by a group of computer scientists in the late 1960s, originally built around small computers that handled connections with dial-up terminals and separate message-processing computers, known as interface message processors, or IMPs; the grandfather of all computer networks.

automatic demographic transition, theory of belief that birthrates declined as a consequence of industrial development. The theory ignored the fact that in some countries with little or no industrial development there was a decline in birthrates and in some countries with substantial industrial development fertility failed to decline.

avian pertaining to birds.

barometric pressure atmospheric pressure, as measured by a barometer. Moist air weighs less than dry air, so water vapor exerts less pressure on the barometer and the approach of wet weather is signaled by a drop in the barometer.

bearings any part of a machine in or on which another part revolves or slides.

bit short for binary digit, the smallest unit of information in a binary computer system. A bit can be either 1 or 0, meaning that a switch is either open or closed.

bivalve any mollusk (such as clams, oysters, mussels, snails) having a shell consisting of two parts or valves, hinged together by an elastic ligament, or a shell consisting of two parts that open and shut.

byssuses (or byssi) long, lustrous, silky bunches of filaments secreted by bivalves to attach themselves to hard surfaces.

capercaillie the Scotch wood grouse; the largest grouse of Europe, found in the northern part of the continent; eats pine needles, buries itself in the snow; and is plentiful in the area around Lake Baikal in the U.S.S.R. A grouse is any of a group of game birds that have a round, plump body, firm feathered legs, feather-covered nostrils and mottled feathers.

capture-mark-recapture method an approach to counting a large, elusive population. A scientist captures a large sample of the specie, marks or tags it, and releases it to the pool. Subsequently the scientist takes a second sample and notes the number of newly caught and formerly caught specimens. The ratio of the formerly caught to the total caught provides an estimate of the overall population. For example, if one out of every eight was formerly caught, then the scientist might assume that they represented one-eighth of the total.

Carboniferous period a period approximately 340 million to 280 million years ago that was characterized by swamp formations and the deposit of plant remains that later hardened into coal.

circadian rhythms the waxing and waning of bodily functions during 24-hour intervals.

cirrus clouds   a principal cloud type; filmy, fleecy clouds, found at an average height of 33,000 feet; composed of small particles, mostly ice crystals, which are fairly widely dispersed, usually resulting in relative transparency and whiteness and often producing halo phenomena not observed with other clouds.

chlorophyll   photoreceptors of light energy for photosynthesis (the formation of carbon dioxide and water into carbohydrates).

chorea   a condition of uncontrolled, purposeless, rapid motion. Typical movements involve bending and extending the fingers, raising and lowering shoulders, or grimacing. The causes vary and include bacterial infections and genetic disorders.

climatology   the branch of meteorology that examines the average physical state of the atmosphere and its variations throughout geographic space and over time.

cloud microphysics   analysis of the behavior of tiny particles found in clouds.

Coriolis effect or force   the deflection of a moving body caused by the earth's rotation. It appears as a deflection to the right in the Northern Hemisphere and to the left in the Southern Hemisphere and affects air masses, aircraft, projectiles and falling bodies.

compromised immune system   an immune system, under stress due to the presence of a severe infection, that loses its effectiveness to varying degrees; in other words it is compromised.

crystalline   pertaining to a crystal, which is a homogeneous solid made up of an element, chemical compound or isomorphous mixture (two or more crystalline compounds with different chemical compositions but identical structures) throughout which the atoms or molecules are arranged in a regular repeating pattern.

cumulonimbus cloud   a principal cloud type, exceptionally dense and vertically developed (towering), occurring either as isolated clouds or as a line or wall of clouds with imposing upper portions, often referred to as thunderheads.

delta   a triangular shaped tract of alluvial land (thrown up by the action of waves or currents of water) at the mouth of a river, such as the Mississippi or the Nile.

demographics   analysis of vital statistics, such as birth, death, marriage and migration of populations.

depression   an atmospheric area of low-pressure, usually applied to a particular stage in the development of a tropical cyclone.

determinative   in hieroglyphics, an ideographic (pictorial) sign attached to a word for the purpose of defining its meaning. In the Merenptah Stele in Egypt, determinatives distinguish the symbols for city-states and rural areas.

dimethylsulfide   a substance emitted by plankton; when it reaches the atmosphere, it reacts with oxygen to form ultramicroscopic particles (aerosols); is a flammable, colorless liquid with a disagreeable aroma; insoluble in water; soluble in ether and alcohol; used as a chemical intermediate (a precursor or forerunner to a desired product); also known as methylsulfide.

DNA   deoxyribonucleic acid, agents for the design and assembly of proteins, the building blocks of all life. The double helix coils of DNA contain a genetic code that determines the precise genetic characteristics of the organism.

drainages   geographic areas drained as by a river or groundwater runoff.

doubling rate   the rate at which the human population has been doubling its numbers. From the year 8000 B.C. until A.D. 1650, the population doubled itself every one thousand years or so. The next doubling took 200 years. The following took 80 years. From 1930 to 1990, a period of 60 years, the population more than doubled, increasing from 2 billion to 5.3 billion.

drip irrigation   a technique for preventing salt buildup in plants, that involves dripping water constantly around the roots of plants rather than wetting the field entirely.

drone foundation   a sheet of wax in which a queen bee lays her eggs. The type of egg laid varies in accordance with the size of the cell in the wax.

ecocentric ethic   a philosophy about the environment that assumes a network of mutual obligations between humans and nature.

ecological interaction   the relationship between species that live together in a community, particularly the effect an individual of one species may exert on another.

ecology   the study of the interrelationships between organisms and their environment.

embryogenesis   the formation and development of an embryo, an animal in the earliest stages of development in the uterus; the human organism is called an embryo during the first three months after conception and thereafter is called a fetus.

encephalitis   an inflammation of the brain, usually caused by a virus infection from the bite of an infected mosquito. It may also be caused by lead or other poisoning or by bleeding.

entropy   a measure of the degree of disorder in a system. In a closed system, entropy always increases and available energy decreases.

error bars   the specified range within which a specific finding may fall; also known as a confidence interval. The range indicates the limits within which a finding may be viewed as acceptable, and provides an estimate of the degree of confidence a researcher has in the accuracy of his or her finding.

estuary   an arm of the sea that extends inland to meet the mouth of a river; the waters are tidal.

expert system a computer system that has a high level of information in a particular field and has the capacity to solve problems as a human expert in that area would.

fiber optics the technique of transmitting light through long, thin, flexible fibers of glass, plastic or other transparent materials; bundles of parallel fibers can be used to transmit complete images.

flexible-fuel engines engines under development that will make it possible to burn methanol, ethanol and gasoline interchangeably or at the same time.

fluorometer an instrument that uses a small pulsating light, together with a light meter, to measure chlorophyll in water. The laser strikes the chlorophyll in phytoplankton and the chlorophyll fluoresces briefly. Between bursts of the laser, the light meter registers the level of light. The light registered is carried as a signal back to a transcription device in the lab to make a permanent record.

flyways the concept of funnel-shaped bird migration paths, outlined by ornithologist Frederick Lincoln, which are wide in the areas of nesting and narrow in the route of travel.

forebay an area of a hydroelectric plant where water is drawn in as a coolant. Built of concrete, steel-sheet pilings and steel grates the forebay has proven to be an ideal location for zebra mussels to attach themselves.

Fourier Transform a mathematical tool named for the 19th century mathematician, Jean B.J. Fourier, who discovered that complex functions, such as the vibrations of a musical note, could be broken down into the pure tones that made up the note.

fossil fuels fuels like petroleum, natural gas and coal that were formed early in the earth's geological history. They are nonrenewable resources.

fractal a shape in which the structure of a small area is the same as of the whole.

fractionation distilling columns equipment used in separating volatile components with different boiling points.

generation roughly 30 years, a period equivalent to approximately the time between the birth of one generation and the birth of the next.

geodemography the practice of combining demographic data (information about births, deaths, marital status, incomes, etc.) with the characteristics of actual neighborhoods to classify the neighborhoods into different life-styles, such as single family homes of young marrieds without children or apartment houses for singles.

gerrymandering a term for manipulating the boundaries of an electoral district for political purposes. The term was coined following the drawing in 1812 of Essex County's senatorial election districts to ensure that Massachusetts Governor Elbridge Gerry's party's candidates were elected. The drawn districts resembled salamanders in shape, and were dubbed gerrymanders.

gigabit 1 billion bits (units of information).

Gondwanaland an ancient supercontinent, which, in theory, is supposed to have fragmented and drifted apart to form the present continents.

groundwater tables the level of water found underground in porous rock strata and soils.

halophytes wild plants that thrive in salt water.

helix any spiral, either lying in a single plane, or particularly coiling around a cone or a cylinder, such as the thread of a screw. The structure of DNA is a double helix shape.

hertz a unit of frequency for repeated actions, such as vibrations or wave motions, defined as one cycle per second.

hieroglyphic pictures or symbols representing a word, syllable, or sound, used by ancient Egyptians and other cultures instead of alphabetic letters.

histamine a compound found in all cells, produced by a breakdown of histadine (a basic amino acid). It is released in allergic reactions. The release of histamine causes widening of capillaries, decreased blood pressure, increased release of gastric juices and tightening of smooth muscles of the bronchi and uterus.

homogenization of the planet the transportation of species to new environments where they rapidly take root.

homologue an organ similar in structure to a corresponding organ in a different animal, though differing in function.

hydrogen line a spectral (spectrum) line emitted by neutral hydrogen having a frequency of 1420 megahertz and a wave length of 21 centimeters (8.26 inches); radiation from this line is used in radio astronomy to study the amount and velocity of hydrogen in the Milky Way galaxy.

hydrolab equipment used on research vessels to measure water depth, dissolved oxygen, pH, salinity, and temperature, together with electronic equipment that converts this information into a digital signal and sends it via a cable to a portable computer.

hydrothermal vents openings in the ocean floor where molten rock oozing up from the interior of the earth heats water ladened with minerals, which serve as nutrients for bizarre organisms that live around them.

hyperjump a period of accelerated reproduction.

immunoglobulin E (IgE) one of the five classes of antibodies produced by the body. Concentrated in the lungs, the skin and mucous membranes, it is the main defense against antigens from the environment and is believed to be stimulated by immunoglobulin A, which is the major antibody in all secretions of the body and of the mucous membrane of the intestines, bronchi, saliva and tears, and seeks out foreign microorganisms and starts an antigen-antibody reaction.

incubation   the time elapsed between exposure to an infection and the onset of symptoms.

infrared radiation   the invisible rays just beyond the red area of the color spectrum; their waves are longer than those of the spectrum of colors but shorter than radio waves, and have a penetrating heating effect; the wavelengths lie in the range from 0.75 or 0.8 micrometers (the long wavelength limit of visible red light) to 1,000 micrometers (the shortest microwaves).

infrastructure   a substructure or underlying foundation.

International Geophysical Year (IGY)   a period of intense international cooperative research, involving 67 nations, during an agreed-upon halt in international claim-staking in the Antarctica, extending from July 1957 to December 1958. The time span was one during which scientists predicted there would be a period of peak sunspot activity.

I=PAT   an equation used to explain the impact of populations on the environment. I stands for impact, P for population size, A for the per-person level of consumption (affluence), and T for the environmental disruptiveness of the technologies used to provide the goods consumed (technologies).

iterative process   a procedure for calculating a desired result by means of a repeated cycle of operations, which come closer and closer to the desired result.

jet contrails   condensed water vapor that forms in the wake of an aircraft.

Koplik's spots   small, irregular bright red spots with minute specks in the center, which appear on the inside of the mouth on the cheeks and serve as a diagnostic sign in measles before the typical rash appears.

laser   an electron device that converts input power into a very narrow, intense beam of visible or infrared light; the input power excites atoms of an optical resonator to a higher energy level, and the resonator forces the excited atoms to radiate in phase.

leukotrienes   a group of chemical compounds that occur naturally in white blood cells (leukocytes). They are able to produce allergic and inflammatory reactions, and may take part in the development of asthma and rheumatoid arthritis.

light year   the distance that light travels in a vacuum for the period of a year, approximately 9.46 trillion kilometers or 5.878 trillion miles.

limnologists   scientists who study the life, and conditions for life, in fresh water, i.e., lakes, ponds and streams.

littoral zone   the interval on a seacoast between the high- and low-water mark.

malignancy   diseased tissue.

mammalology   the branch of zoology that deals with the study of Mammalia, a class of vertebrate animals (having a backbone) of more than 15,000 species, including humans; distinguished by self-regulating temperature, hair, and in the females, milk-producing mammae (breasts).

mature river   a river that has undergone maximum development.

Merenptah Stele   a black granite tablet found in Egypt inscribed with the account of the pharaoh Merenptah's military exploits.

micro-arousals   frequent periods of wakefulness lasting less than 10 seconds; common among older people who, as a consequence, are apt to feel unrested when they arise.

mitochondria   slender filaments in cells that are a source of energy. Small threadlike organs, they control cell life and breathing. They occur in varying numbers in most living cells, with exceptions such as bacteria, viruses and blood cells.

molecular paleontologist   a biologist who analyzes the molecular structure of fossils.

mollusks   a large phylum (broad division of the plant or animal kingdom) of invertebrates (without a backbone or spinal column), including oysters, clams, mussels, snails etc.; characterized by having a soft unsegmented body, usually partially or wholly enclosed in a calcerous shell, and a gill (organ for breathing), a foot and a mantle (a membranous flap that contains glands that secrete shell-forming fluids). Also referred to as Mollusca or mollusc.

morphogen   a molecule that helps cells to migrate and form patterns characteristic of mature organs, ensuring that cells arrive in the proper locales where they grow into an appropriate limb, ear, nose or whatever are ultimately supposed to become.

motile   in biology, having an inherent power of motion; exhibiting spontaneous motion.

Multiple Sleep Latency Test   subjects are hooked up to an electroencephalograph machine and allowed to lie down in a dark room for a short period every two hours. A record is kept of whether the subject falls asleep and how long it takes. Those who fall asleep in under five minutes are considered to be pathologically sleep-deprived.

mutagenically skewed   suddenly altered genetically.

nanophase materials   crucibles containing metals or ceramics are placed in a vacuum chamber and heated to temperatures sufficient to reduce them to a gaseous or vapor state. The vaporized material condenses to a powder on a cold rod inside the chamber.

narcolepsy   a disease characterized by sudden sleep attacks, sleep paralysis and sight and hearing hallucinations at the onset of sleep. Patients with narcolepsy have an uncontrollable urge to sleep many times a day. Sleep periods may last from a few minutes to several hours. Often difficult to diagnose because not all patients have all of the symptoms. The cause is unknown.

nonrenewable resources   resources such as ancient forests and their ecosystems that cannot survive or be replaced when exhausted; minerals, such as oil, coal and gas, that cannot be replenished; species that have been hunted or fished until they become extinct.

nucleotide   a single group of the three substances (bases, sugars and phosphates) that are found in repeating sequences in DNA.

oncogene   a gene that may cause cancer to grow. The gene may have a benign role to play in the growth and dispersion of cells but, when exposed to certain conditions, stimulates the growth of cancer.

Operation Highjump   the largest expedition to Antarctica ever mounted, included 13 ships, 50 helicopters and 5,000 personnel. The expedition was one of several launched by the United States that could be used, should the nation ever choose to do so, to make a claim to territory in the Antarctica.

opportunistic disease   a disease that might have resulted in a mild illness or been staved off entirely by a fully functioning immune system but has a serious impact when the immune system has been rendered vulnerable.

orthogonal   pertaining to right angles and perpendicular lines.

ozonation   the process of treating, impregnating or combining with ozone.

ozone   an unstable blue gas with a pungent odor that is used as an oxidant bleach, water purifier and treatment for industrial waste.

ozone layer   the general stratum (layer) of the upper atmosphere where ozone is produced by the interaction of ultraviolet radiation from the sun with oxygen. The ozone layer absorbs most of the ultraviolet radiation from the sun that would otherwise harm living organisms on Earth. The ozone layer has been depleted by the use of chlorofluorocarbons in aerosols and other products. It lies roughly between 10 and 50 kilometers (6.25 to 31.25 miles), with a maximum ozone concentration at about 20 to 25 kilometers (12.5 to 15.62 miles). Also known as the ozonosphere.

paradigm   a pattern, example, or model.

parameterization   in meterology, equations that represent a general "cloudiness" factor, based on physical principles and empirical observations. For example, an equation might indicate that when relative humidity reached a certain level in a box (sector) of the model, the box would begin to reflect sunlight and rain.

pastoralists   shepherds or people who follow a rural life.

PCBs   polychlorinated biphenyls, substances once widely used in inks, oils and insulating fluids that were linked with birth defects, cancer and other disorders. Banned from use in the United States in 1977.

penstocks   a valve or sluice gate for regulating water flow into a hydroelectric plant.

pH   a measure of the acidity of water. As measured by a specific scale, water with a pH below 7 is considered acidic, with a pH of 7 is considered neutral, and above 7 is considered basic.

pheromone   a chemical substance that stimulates physiological or social responses, most often from the opposite sex. Many pheromones have a strong odor.

photovoltaic cell   a device that becomes capable of generating electricity as a result of exposure to visible light or other forms of radiation; makes electricity directly from sunlight. When energy in the form of light hits the silicon of the cell, it shakes lose an electron, which creates an electric current.

phytoplankton   microscopic animal and plant life that float in the ocean or in bodies of fresh water and serve as food for fish; also known as plankton.

polarized light   electromagnetic radiation whose frequency is in the optical (visible or near visible) range. Polarization in optics refers to a condition of light and radiant heat in which the transverse vibrations (from side to side) of rays assume different forms in different planes.

Ponar grab   a scoop that takes samples from the bottom of a lake or river.

prosthesis   an artificial replacement of a missing part of the body, such as a limb, eye, tooth or facial part.

quantum gravity   a yet-unrealized theory that is the quantum-mechanical version of the general theory of relativity. (Quantum mechanics refers to a mathematical theory that begins with the assumption that energy is not infinitely divisible and deals with atomic structure and phenomena by the methods of quantum theory, which assumes that energy is not radiated continuously but instead is radiated discontinuously in definite units called quanta.)

quantum theory   an explanation of the energy and movement in molecules, atoms and subatomic particles. All the motions of particles—spin, revolution, vibration—occur in quantum jumps, or leaps.

radiation generator   equipment designed to deliver therapeutic radiation when positioned sequentially at different locations around a patient in order to deliver a lethal dosage to a tumor and not to other tissue.

radio astronomy   the study of galaxies, stars and other celestial bodies by means of the radio waves they emit. All objects in the universe (except black holes) emit radiant energy at various wavelengths that can be detected with appropriate instruments. Celestial radio waves have wavelengths in the same range as short waves, FM and radar waves but carry no coded message.

radionuclides   nuclides (atoms characterized by the number of protons, neutrons and energy content in the nucleus) that exhibit radioactivity.

relativity   a theory devised by Albert Einstein stating that the laws governing the wave motion of light and other physical laws operate throughout the universe and formulating the relationship between such concepts as mass, energy, space and time.

reagent a substance, chemical or solution used in the laboratory to detect, measure or otherwise examine other substances, chemicals or solutions.

REM (rapid eye movement) sleep intervals during the four sleep cycles in the course of a typical night's sleep in which the eyes twitch beneath the closed eyelids and the sleeper reports having dreams if awakened.

replacement reproduction the number of children needed to maintain a population. To keep the population stable, the number needs to be slightly more than two (to replace the parents) in order to take into account children who die before reaching reproductive age. In countries with high infant mortality rates, the replacement rates require slightly more births per family, but the actual birthrate in most such countries is actually substantially higher than the replacement rate.

resource economics the use, distribution, and consumption of a nation's natural resources, such as water, rivers and minerals.

resistance the degree of inhibition which a material exhibits to the passage of electricity.

retinoblastoma a cancer growing from eye (retinal) cells. The rapidly growing tumor may invade the brain and spread to distant sites. Treatment includes removal of the eye and as much of the optic nerve as possible, followed by radiation and chemical treatment.

retrofitting making modifications to already existing facilities.

rift valley an opening in the earth caused by cracking.

rookery a breeding place or colony of gregarious birds or animals, such as penguins or seals.

salinity the amount of saline (salt) in a solution or material.

scrubber a device for the removal or washing out of entrapped liquid droplets or dust, or for the removal of an undesired gas component from process gas streams. Coal, for example, includes 3.5% sulfur, which when burned makes sulfur dioxide, the main ingredient in acid rain. Scrubbers run the smoke through lime or limestone, usually mixed with water to bind it chemically. The scrubbers can remove about 95% of sulfur dioxide, but produce hundreds of thousands of tons of waste each year per plant.

secchi disc a flat circle painted in alternating quadrants of black and white, which is lowered into the water until it disappears; used to measure the clarity of the water.

secretariat a department administered by a governmental secretary, especially for an international organization.

sedimentary strata horizontal layers of rock in and below the earth's crust that contain the compressed remains of former life that provide a record of the area's environmental history.

sensor a device that senses either an absolute value or a change in a physical quantity, such as temperature, pressure, flow rate, or the intensity of light, sound or radio waves, and converts that change into an input signal to an information gathering system.

septicemia any infection of the whole body caused by germs that spread from an infected part of the body through the bloodstream; usually results in fever, chill, prostration, pain, headache, nausea or diarrhea.

sequential hot deck imputation a method used during the tabulation of the census. During the process of running forms through the computer, the machine keeps track of the last 16 plausible responses to each question. When the computer encounters a record with an implausible answer or no answer, it substitutes a plausible one from its stack of 16.

set theory a method of the organization of objects according to a specific characteristic. For example, a person is either left-handed or he or she is not. A number is either even or it is not.

sinter to heat without melting.

sleep inertia a stunned, drowsy feeling that many people experience when they awake from a daytime nap. Researchers believe that the inertia is due to their having awakened from the deepest level of sleep, the "slow wave sleep."

smart cards plastic cards, similar to credit cards, that can be coded with varying amounts of information. For example, a smart card might simply carry vital statistics, such as name, address, date of birth or it might carry a complex medical history, including vaccinations, childhood illnesses and allergies to medications. Smart cards have been suggested as an inexpensive, fast way to do a substantial portion of the U.S. decennial census.

smelting the heating of ore mixtures accompanied by a chemical change, resulting in a liquid metal.

spirometry a measurement of the air capacity of the lungs, typically used to determine whether an individual has asthma. A spirometer, consisting of a cylindrical bell immersed in water and equipped with tubes, measures the volume of air inhaled or exhaled.

statistician a scientist who specializes in the collection, assembly, tabulation and classification of data. Analysis is typically made using statistical techniques that permit inferences to be drawn from the data.

Stratocumulus clouds a principal cloud type; dark, low-lying clouds with fluffy contours that appear to be mounds piled on top of each other; predominantly stratiform (layered) in the form of grayish or whitish patches, which nearly always have dark parts.

streptococcal infection an infection caused by bacteria of one of several types of disease-causing streptococcus bacteria or their poisons; almost any organ of the body may be involved and the infections take many forms.

Super Cockpit the Visually Coupled Airborne Systems Simulator, a model which projects a virtual reality system on the inside of the face shield of the pilot's helmet. It was developed to train pilots to fly the enormously complex F-16 fighter jet and similar high-speed aircraft.

supercomputer a computer that is among those with the highest speed, largest functional size, biggest physical dimensions or greatest monetary costs in any given period of time.

superconductivity a property of many metals, alloys and chemical compounds at temperatures near absolute zero that involves the disappearance of their resistance to the passage of electricity. A great deal of research has gone into finding materials whose superconductivity takes place at warmer temperatures.

surface evolver a computer program in use at the University of Minnesota's Supercomputer Project that takes a geometric figure and changes it into a new shape with the smallest possible surface area containing the same volume.

thermals rising currents of air that develop when the ground is warmed by the sun.

topology the study of properties of geometric figures that remain unchanged, even when under distortion, so long as no surfaces are torn.

torque the combination of forces that produce a twisting motion.

transformations a basic tool in engineering, science and mathematics used to analyze a wide range of complex phenomena, such as sound, which can be plotted on a graph as wavy lines to represent the changing position of the function over time; used to make data easier to analyze, free of distracting "noise" and capable of being transmitted or stored.

transgression a rise in the sea level that submerges a previously exposed area under water for a lengthy period. Evidence of a transgression can be found in fossil remains (traces of organisms of a past geologic age embedded in the earth's crust). Also known as an invasion or a marine transgression.

troposphere the lowest layer of the earth's atmosphere where clouds and air currents form and the earth's weather originates.

tubercle a small rounded nodule caused by an infection with *Mycobacterium tuberculosis*, made up of a gray translucent mass of small round cells surrounded by connective tissue.

turbines motors driven by the pressure of steam, water or air against curved vanes of a wheel.

universal joint a joint or a coupling, such as a ball and socket, that permits a swing at any angle within certain limits.

veliger a mollusk larva during a stage when it is equipped with a vellum or ciliated membrane (clusters of small hairlike projections) that allows it to hang suspended in the water to be carried swiftly by the current.

vital signs the measurements of pulse rate, breathing rate, and body temperature. Although not strictly considered a vital sign, the blood pressure is usually included. Abnormalities of vital signs are clues to the presence of disease or injury, and vital signs are used to monitor a patient's progress.

wadi Arabic term for valley, river or dry riverbed.

wavelets mathematical tools for eliminating distortion from visual images; they are used in a technical formula called the "wavelet transform" or "wavelet transformation."

Wellington Convention an agreement among Antarctica Treaty nations, which allows mineral exploration or development provided that all treaty participants agree. If proposed mining were deemed to have no "significant adverse effect," the treaty would allow even large-scale extractions. After six years of negotiations, the agreement was accepted by the treaty nations in June 1988 and submitted for signature. Controversy about the convention continued in 1989 and 1990, with the possibility that one or more of the treaty nations might refuse to sign.

INDEX